Newton

A SOURCE BOOK

in

MATHEMATICS

By

DAVID EUGENE SMITH

VOLUME ONE

DOVER PUBLICATIONS, INC.

NEW YORK

Library of Congress Catalog Card Number: 59-14227

Manufactured in the United States of America

Dover Publications, Inc.
180 Varick Street
New York 14, N. Y.

A SOURCE BOOK IN MATHEMATICS

Author's Preface

The purpose of a source book is to supply teachers and students with a selection of excerpts from the works of the makers of the subject considered. The purpose of supplying such excerpts is to stimulate the study of the various branches of this subject—in the present case, the subject of mathematics. By knowing the beginnings of these branches, the reader is encouraged to follow the growth of the science, to see how it has developed, to appreciate more clearly its present status, and thus to see its future possibilities.

It need hardly be said that the preparation of a source book has many difficulties. In this particular case, one of these lies in the fact that the general plan allows for no sources before the advent of printing or after the close of the nineteenth century. On the one hand, this eliminates most of mathematics before the invention of the calculus and modern geometry; while on the other hand, it excludes all recent activities in this field. The latter fact is not of great consequence for the large majority of readers, but the former is more serious for all who seek the sources of elementary mathematics. It is to be hoped that the success of the series will permit of a volume devoted to this important phase of the development of the science.

In the selection of material in the four and a half centuries closing with the year 1900, it is desirable to touch upon a wide range of interests. In no other way can any source book be made to meet the needs, the interests, and the tastes of a wide range of readers. To make selections from the field, however, is to neglect many more sources than can possibly be selected. It would be an easy thing for anyone to name a hundred excerpts that he would wish to see, and to eliminate selections in which he has no special interest. Some may naturally seek for more light on our symbols, but Professor Cajori's recent work furnishes this with a satisfactory approach to completeness. Others may wish for a worthy treatment of algebraic equations, but Matthiessen's *Grundzüge* contains such a wealth of material as to render the undertaking unnecessary. The extensive field of number theory will appeal to many readers, but the monumental work of Professor Dickson, while not a source book in the ordinary sense of the term, satisfies most of the needs in this respect. Consideration must always be given to the demands of readers, and naturally these demands change as the literature of the history of mathematics becomes more extensive. Furthermore, the possibility of finding source material that is stated succinctly enough for purposes of quotation has to be considered, and also that of finding material that is not so ultra-technical as to serve no useful purpose for any considerable number of readers. Such are a few of the many difficulties which will naturally occur to everyone and which will explain some of the reasons which compel all source books to be matters of legitimate compromise.

Although no single department of "the science venerable" can or should be distinct from any other, and although the general trend is strongly in the direction of unity of both purpose and method, it will still serve to assist the reader if his attention is called to the rough classification set forth in the Contents.

The selections in the field of Number vary in content from the first steps in printed arithmetic, through the development of a few selected number systems, to the early phases of number theory. It seems proper, also, to consider the mechanics of computation in the early stages of the subject, extending the topic to include even as late a theory as nomography. There remains, of course, a large field that is untouched, but this is a necessary condition in each branch.

The field of Algebra is arbitrarily bounded. Part of the articles classified under Number might have been included here, but such questions of classification are of little moment in a work of this nature. In general the articles relate to equations, symbolism, and series, and include such topics as imaginary roots, the early methods of solving the cubic and biquadratic algebraic equations and numerical equations of higher degree, and the Fundamental Theorem of Algebra. Trigonometry, which is partly algebraic, has been considered briefly under Geometry. Probability, which is even more algebraic, is treated by itself, and is given somewhat more space than would have been allowed were it not for the present interest in the subject in connection with statistics.

The field of Geometry is naturally concerned chiefly with the rise of the modern branches. The amount of available material is such that in some cases merely a single important theorem or statement of purpose has been all that could be included. The topics range from the contributions of such sixteenth-century writers as Fermat, Desargues, Pascal, and Descartes, to a few of those who, in the nineteenth century, revived the study of the subject and developed various forms of modern geometry.

The majority of the selections thus far mentioned have been as non-technical as possible. In the field of Probability, however, it has been found necessary to take a step beyond the elementary bounds if the selections are to serve the purposes of those who have a special interest in the subject.

The fields of the Calculus, Function Theory, Quaternions, and the general range of Mathematics belong to a region so extensive as to permit of relatively limited attention. It is essential that certain early sources of the Calculus should be considered, and that some attention should be given to such important advances as relate to the commutative law in Quaternions and Ausdehnungs-lehre, but most readers in such special branches as are now the subject of research in our universities will have at hand the material relating to the origins of their particular subjects. The limits of this work would not, in any case, permit of an extensive offering of extracts from such sources.

It should be stated that all the translations in this work have been contributed without other reward than the satisfaction of assisting students and teachers in knowing the sources of certain phases of mathematics. Like the editor and the advisory committee, those who have prepared the articles have given their services gratuitously. Special mention should, however, be made of the unusual interest taken by a few who have devoted much time to assisting the editor and committee in the somewhat difficult labor of securing and assembling the material. Those to whom they are particularly indebted for assistance beyond the preparation of special articles are Professor Lao G. Simons, head of the department of mathematics in Hunter College, Professor Jekuthiel Ginsburg, of the Yeshiva College, Professor Vera Sanford of Western Reserve University, and Professor Helen M.

Walker, of Teachers College, Columbia University. To Professor Sanford special thanks are due for her generous sacrifice of time and effort in the reading of the proofs during the editor's prolonged absence abroad.

The advisory committee, consisting of Professors Raymond Clare Archibald of Brown University, Professor Florian Cajori of the University of California, and Professor Leonard Eugene Dickson of the University of Chicago, have all contributed of their time and knowledge in the selection of topics and in the securing of competent translators. Without their aid the labor of preparing this work would have been too great a burden to have been assumed by the editor.

In the text and the accompanying notes, the remarks of the translators, elucidating the text or supplying historical notes of value to the reader, are inclosed in brackets [ ]. To these contributors, also, are due slight variations in symbolism and in the spelling of proper names, it being felt that they should give the final decision in such relatively unimportant matters.

DAVID EUGENE SMITH.

NEW YORK,
September, 1929.

Contents for Volume One and Volume Two

III. THE FIELD OF GEOMETRY

A SOURCE BOOK IN MATHEMATICS

SOURCE BOOK IN MATHEMATICS

I. FIELD OF NUMBER

THE FIRST PRINTED ARITHMETIC

TREVISO, ITALY, 1478

(Translated from the Italian by Professor David Eugene Smith, Teachers College, Columbia University, New York City.)

Although it may justly be said that mere computation and its simple applications in the lives of most people are not a part of the science of mathematics, it seems proper that, in a source book of this kind, some little attention should be given to its status in the early days of printing. For this reason, these extracts are selected from the first book on arithmetic to appear from the newly established presses of the Renaissance period.[1] The author of the work is unknown, and there is even some question as to the publisher, although he seems to have been one Manzolo or Manzolino. It is a source in the chronological rather than the material sense, since the matter which it contains had apparently but little influence upon the other early writers on arithmetic. The work is in the Venetian dialect and is exceedingly rare.[2] The copy from which this translation was made is in the library of George A. Plimpton of New York City. As with many other *incunabula*, the book has no title. It simply begins with the words, *Incommincia vna practica molto bona et vtilez a ciaschaduno chi vuole vxare larte dela merchadantia. chiamata vulgarmente larte de labbacho.* It was published at Treviso, a city not far to the north of Venice, and the colophon has the words "At Treviso, on the 10th day of December, 1478."

Here beginneth a Practica, very helpful to all who have to do with that commercial art commonly known as the abacus.

I have often been asked by certain youths in whom I have much interest, and who look forward to mercantile pursuits, to put into writing the fundamental principles of arithmetic, commonly

---

[1] For the most part, these selections are taken from an article by this translator which appeared in *Isis*, Vol. VI (3), pp. 311–331, 1924, and are here published by permission of the editor. For a more extended account of the book, the reader is referred to this periodical.

[2] A critical study of it from the bibliographical standpoint was made by Prince Boncompagni in the *Atti dell' Accademia Pontificia de' Nuovi Lincei*, tomo XVI, 1862–1863.

called the abacus.   Therefore, being impelled by my affection for them, and by the value of the subject, I have to the best of my small ability undertaken to satisfy them in some slight degree, to the end that their laudable desires may bear useful fruit.   Therefore in the name of God I take for my subject this work in algorism, and proceed as follows:

All things which have existed since the beginning of time have owed their origin to number.   Furthermore, such as now exist are subject to its laws, and therefore in all domains of knowledge this Practica is necessary.   To enter into the subject, the reader must first know the basis of our science. Number is a multitude brought together or assembled from several units, and always from two at least, as in the case of 2, which is the first and the smallest number.   Unity is that by virtue of which anything is said to be one.   Furthermore be it known that there are three kinds of numbers, of which the first is called a simple number, the second an article, and the third a composite or mixed number.   A simple number is one that contains no tens, and it is represented by a single figure, like i, 2, 3, etc.   An article is a number that is exactly divisible by ten, like i0, 20, 30 and similar numbers.   A mixed number is one that exceeds ten but that cannot be divided by ten without a remainder, such as ii, i2, i3, etc.   Furthermore be it known that there are five fundamental operations which must be understood in the Practica, viz., numeration, addition, subtraction, multiplication, and division. Of these we shall first treat of numeration, and then of the others in order.

Numeration is the representation of numbers by figures.   This is done by means of ten letters or figures, as here shown.   .i., .2.,

.3., .4., .5., .6., .7., .8., .9., .0.. Of these the first figure, i, is not called a number but the source of number. The tenth figure, 0, is called cipher or "nulla," *i. e.*, the figure of nothing, since by itself it has no value, although when joined with others it increases their value. Furthermore you should note that when you find a figure by itself its value cannot exceed nine, *i. e.*, 9; and from that figure on, if you wish to express a number you must use at least two figures, thus: ten is expressed by i0, eleven by ii, and so on. And this can be understood from the following figures.[1]

Thousands of millions	Hundreds of millions	Tens of millions	Millions	Hundreds of thousands	Tens of thousands	Thousands	Hundreds	Tens	Units
									i
									2
									3
									4
									5
									6
									7
									8
									9
								i	0
							i	2	0
						i	2	3	0
					i	2	3	4	0
				i	2	3	4	5	0
			i	2	3	4	5	6	0
		i	2	3	4	5	6	7	0
	i	2	3	4	5	6	7	8	0
i	2	3	4	5	6	7	8	9	0
2	3	4	5	6	7	8	9	0	0
3	4	5	6	7	8	9	0	0	0
4	5	6	7	8	9	0	0	0	0
5	6	7	8	9	0	0	0	0	0
6	7	8	9	0	0	0	0	0	0
7	8	9	0	0	0	0	0	0	0
8	9	0	0	0	0	0	0	0	0
9	0	0	0	0	0	0	0	0	0

---

[1] The figure 1 was not always in the early fonts of type, the letter "i" being then used in its stead.

To understand the figures it is necessary to have well in mind the following table:[1]

i times i makes i	i times i0 makes i0
i times 2 makes 2	2 times i0 makes 20
i times 3 makes 3	3 times i0 makes 30
i times 4 makes 4	4 times i0 makes 40
i times 5 makes 5	5 times i0 makes 50
i times 6 makes 6	6 times i0 makes 60
i times 7 makes 7	7 times i0 makes 70
i times 8 makes 8	8 times i0 makes 80
i times 9 makes 9	9 times i0 makes 90
i times 0 makes 0	0 times i0 makes 0

And to understand the preceding table it is necessary to observe that the words written at the top[2] give the names of the places occupied by the figures beneath. For example, below 'units' are the figures designating units, below 'tens' are the tens, below 'hundreds' are the hundreds, and so on. Hence if we take each figure by its own name, and multiply this by its place value, we shall have its true value. For instance, if we multiply i, which is beneath the word 'units,' by its place,—that is, by units,—we shall have 'i time i gives i,' meaning that we have one unit. Again, if we take the 2 which is found in the same column, and multiply by its place, we shall have 'i time 2 gives 2,' meaning that we have two units,...and so on for the other figures found in this column... This rule applies to the various other figures, each of which is to be multiplied by its place value.

And this suffices for a statement concerning the 'act'[3] of numeration.

Having now considered the first operation, viz. numeration, let us proceed to the other four, which are addition, subtraction, multiplication, and division. To differentiate between these operations it is well to note that each has a characteristic word, as follows:

---

[1] [The table continues from "i times i00 makes i00" to "0 times i00 makes 0."]

[2] [That is, the numeration table shown on p. 3.]

[3] [The fundamental operations, which the author calls "acts" (atti) went by various names. The medieval Latin writers called them "species," a word that appears in *The Crafte of Nombryng*, the oldest English manuscript on arithmetic, where the author speaks of "7 spices or partes of this craft." This word, in one form or another, is also found in various languages. The Italians used both 'atti' and 'passioni.']

Addition has the word   *and,*
Subtraction has the word   *from,*
Multiplication has the word *times,*
Division has the word   *in.*

It should also be noticed that in taking two numbers, since at least two are necessary in each operation, there may be determined by these numbers any one of the above named operations. Furthermore each operation gives rise to a different number, with the exception that 2 times 2 gives the same result as 2 and 2, since each is 4. Taking, then, 3 and 9 we have:

Addition:	3 and	9 make	i2
Subtraction:	3 from	9 leaves	6
Multiplication:	3 times	9 makes	27
Division:	3 in	9 gives	3

We thus see how the different operations with their distinctive words lead to different results.

In order to understand the second operation, addition, it is necessary to know that this is the union of several numbers, at least of two, in a single one, to the end that we may know the sum arising from this increase. It is also to be understood that, in the operation of adding, two numbers at least are necessary, namely the number to which we add the other, which should be the larger, and the number which is to be added, which should be the smaller. Thus we always add the smaller number to the larger, a more convenient plan than to follow the contrary order, although the latter is possible, the result being the same in either case. For example, if we add 2 to 8 the sum is i0, and the same result is obtained by adding 8 to 2. Therefore if we wish to add one number to another we write the larger one above and the smaller one below, placing the figures in convenient order, *i. e.*, the units under units, tens under tens, hundreds under hundreds, etc. We always begin to add with the lowest order, which is of least value. Therefore if we wish to add 38 and 59 we write the numbers thus:

59
38
Sum 97

We then say, '8 and 9 make i7,' writing 7 in the column which was added, and carrying the i (for when there are two figures in one place we always write the one of the lower order and carry the other to the next higher place). This i we now add to 3, making 4, and this to the 5, making 9, which is written in the column from which it is derived. The two together make 97.

The proof of this work consists in subtracting either addend from the sum, the remainder being the other. Since subtraction proves addition, and addition proves subtraction, I leave the method of proof until the latter topic is studied, when the proof of each operation by the other will be understood.

Besides this proof there is another. If you wish to check the sum by casting out nines, add the units, paying no attention to 9 or 0, but always considering each as nothing. And whenever the sum exceeds 9, subtract 9, and consider the remainder as the sum. Then the number arising from the sum will equal the sum of the numbers arising from the addends. For example, suppose that you wish to prove the following sum:

.59.

.38.

Sum   .97. | 7

The excess of nines in 59 is 5; 5 and 3 are 8; 8 and 8 are 16; subtract 9 and 7 remains. Write this after the sum, separated by a bar. The excess of nines in 97 is 7, and the excess of nines in 7 equals 7, since neither contains 9. In this way it is possible to prove the result of any addition of abstract numbers or of those having no reference to money, measure, or weight. I shall show you another plan of proof according to the nature of the case. If you have to add 816 and 1916,[1] arrange the numbers as follows:

1916

816

Sum   2732

Since the sum of 6 and 6 is 12, write the 2 and carry the 1. Then add this 1 to that which follows to the left, saying, '1 and 1 are 2, and the other 1 makes 3.' Write this 3 in the proper place, and add 8 and 9. The sum of this 8 and 9 is 17, the 7 being written and the 1 carried to the other 1, making 2, which is written in the proper place, the sum being now complete. If you wish to prove by 9 arrange the work thus:

1916

816

The sum   2732 | 5

---

[1] [From now on, the figure 1 will be used in the translation instead of the letter 'i' which appears always in the original.]

You may now effect the proof by beginning with the upper number, saying '1 and 1 are 2, and 6 are 8, and 8 are 16. Subtract 9, and 7 remains. The 7 and 1 are 8, and 6 are 14. Subtract 9, and 5 remains,' which should be written after the sum, separated by a bar. Look now for the excess of nines in the sum: 2 and 7 are 9, the excess being 0; 3 and 2 are 5, so that the result is correct.[1]

Having now considered the second operation of the Practica of arithmetic, namely the operation of addition, the reader should give attention to the third, namely the operation of subtraction. Therefore I say that the operation of subtraction is nothing else than this: that of two numbers we are to find how much difference there is from the less to the greater, to the end that we may know this difference. For example, take 3 from 9 and there remains 6. It is necessary that there should be two numbers in subtraction, the number from which we subtract and the number which is subtracted from it.

The number from which the other is subtracted is written above, and the number which is subtracted below, in convenient order, viz., units under units and tens under tens, and so on. If we then wish to subtract one number of any order from another we shall find that the number from which we are to subtract is equal to it, or greater, or less. If it is equal, as in the case of 8 and 8, the remainder is 0, which 0 we write underneath in the proper column. If the number from which we subtract is greater, then take away the number of units in the smaller number, writing the remainder below, as in the case of 3 from 9, where the remainder is 6. If, however, the number is less, since we cannot take a greater number from a less one, take the complement of the larger number with respect to 10, and to this add the other, but with this condition: that you add one to the next left-hand figure. And be very careful that whenever you take a larger number from a smaller, using the complement, you remember the condition above mentioned. Take now an example: Subtract 348 from 452, arranging the work thus:

$$452$$
$$348$$

Remainder 104

First we have to take a greater number from a less, and then an equal from an equal, and third, a less from a greater. We proceed

---

[1] [The addition of larger numbers and of the compound numbers like 916 lire 14 soldi plus 1945 lire 15 soldi are now considered.]

as follows: We cannot take 8 from 2, but 2 is the complement of 8 with respect to 10, and this we add to the other 2 which is above the 8, thus: 2 and 2 make 4, which we write beneath the 8 for the remainder. There is, however, this condition, that to the figure following the 8 (viz., to 4), we add 1, making it 5. Then 5 from 5, which is an equal, leaves 0, which 0 we write beneath.

Then 3 from 4, which is a less from a greater, is 1, which 1 we write under the 3, so that the remainder is 104.

If we wish to prove this result, add the number subtracted to the remainder, and the result will be the number from which we subtracted. We may arrange the work as follows:

$$
\begin{array}{r|l}
452 & 2 \\
348 & 6 \\
\hline
104 & 5 \\
\hline
452 &
\end{array}
$$

Now add, 4 and 8 are 12; write 2 under the 4 and carry 1; then 1 and 4 are 5; write this 5 under the 0; then add 1 and 3, making 4, and write this 4 under the 1, and the work checks. Thus is found that which was promised you, as you can see[1]...

Having now explained the third operation, namely that of subtraction, the reader should give attention to the fourth, namely that of multiplication. To understand this it is necessary to know that to multiply one number by itself or by another is to find from two given numbers a third number which contains one of these numbers as many times as there are units in the other. For example, 2 times 4 are 8, and 8 contains 4 as many times as there are units in 2, so that 8 contains 4 in itself twice. Also the 8 contains 2 as many times as there are units in 4, and 4 has in itself four units, so that 8 contains 2 four times. It should be well understood that in multiplication two numbers are necessary, namely the multiplying number and the number multiplied, and also that the multiplying number may itself be the number multiplied, and vice versa, the result being the same in both cases. Nevertheless usage and practice demand that the smaller number shall be taken as the multiplying number, and not the larger. Thus we should say, 2 times 4 makes 8, and not 4 times 2 makes 8,

---

[1] [The author now gives a further proof of subtraction by the casting out of nines, after which he devotes about six or seven pages to checks on subtraction and to the subtraction of lire, soldi, grossi, pizoli, and the like.]

although the results are the same. Now not to speak at too great length I say in brief, but sufficiently for the purposes of a Practica, that there are three methods of multiplication, viz., by the tables, cross multiplication, and the chess-board plan. These three methods I will explain to you as briefly as I am able. But before I give you a rule or any method, it is necessary that you commit to memory the following state-ments, without which no one can understand all of this oper-ation of multiplication[1]...

I have now given you to learn by heart all the statements needed in the Practica of arith-metic, without which no one is able to master the Art. We should not complain, however, at having to learn these things by heart in order to acquire readiness; for I assure you that these things which I have set forth are necessary to any one who would be proficient in this art, and no one can get along with less. Those facts which are to be learned besides these are valuable, but they are not necessary.

Having learned by heart all of the above facts, the pupil

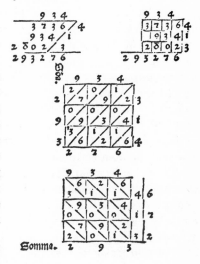

may with zeal begin to multiply by the table. This operation arises when the multiplier is a simple number, and the number multiplied has at least two figures, but as many more as we wish. And that we may more easily understand this operation we shall call the first figure toward the right, units; the second toward the left, tens, and the third shall be called hundreds. This being under-stood, attend to the rule of working by the table, which is as follows: First multiply together the units of the multiplier and

---

[1] [The author now gives the multiplication table, omitting all duplications like 3 × 2 after 2 × 3 has been given, but extending for "those who are of scholarly tastes" the table to include multiples of 12, 20, 24, 32 and 36, as needed in the monetary systems used by merchants of the time.]

the number multiplied. If from this multiplication you get a simple number, write it under its proper place; if an article, write a 0 and reserve the tens to add to the product of the tens; but if a mixed number is found, write its units in the proper place, and save the tens to add to the product of the tens, proceeding in the same way with all the other orders. Then multiply together the units of the multiplier with the tens; then with the hundreds, and so on in regular order[1]. . .

In order to understand the fourth operation, viz., division, three things are to be observed, viz., what is meant by division; second, how many numbers are necessary in division; third, which of these numbers is the greater. As to the first I say that division is the operation of finding, from two given numbers, a third number, which is contained as many times in the greater number as unity is contained in the less number. You will find this number when you see how many times the less number is contained in the greater. Suppose, for example, that we have to divide 8 by 2; here 2 is contained 4 times in 8, so we say that 4 is the quotient demanded. Also, divide 8 by 4. Here the 4 is contained 2 times in 8, so that 2 is the quotient demanded.

Second, it is to be noticed that three numbers are necessary in division,—the number to be divided, the divisor, and the quotient, as you have understood from the example above given, where 2 is the divisor, 8 the number to be divided, and 4 the quotient. From this is derived the knowledge of the third thing which is to be noted, that the number which is to be divided is always greater than, or at least is equal to, the divisor. When the numbers are equal the quotient is always 1.

Now to speak briefly, it is sufficient in practice to say that there are two ways of dividing,—by the table and the galley method. In this operation you should begin with the figure of highest value, that is by the one which is found at the left, proceeding thence to the right. If you can divide by the table you will be able to divide by the galley method, and it is well, for brevity, to avoid the latter when you can. Therefore this is the method of dividing by the table: See how many times your divisor is found in the first

---

[1] [The author now gives an example in multiplying by a one-figure number, proving the work by casting out nines. He then gives a proof by casting out sevens, after which he sets forth various methods of multiplication, such as that of the chessboard, that of the quadrilateral, or the one known by the name of gelosia, all of which were in common use at the time.]

left-hand figure, if it is contained in it, and write the quotient beneath it. If it is not so contained, consider this figure as tens and take together with it the following figure; then, finding the quotient write it beneath the smaller of the two figures. If there is any remainder, consider this as tens, and add it to the next number to the right, and see how many times your divisor is found in these two figures, writing the quotient under the units. In this same way proceed with the rest of the figures to the right. And when you have exhausted them all, having set down the quotient, write the remainder at the right, separated by a bar; and if the remainder is 0, place it where I have said. In the name of God I propose the first example, so attend well.

Divide 7624 ducats into two parts, viz. by 2, arranging your work as follows:

The divisor .2. 7624 | 0 the remainder[1]
The quotient   3812 |

The operations which I have set forth above being understood, it is necessary to take up the method and the rules of using them. The rule you must now study is the rule of the three things. Therefore that you may have occasion to sharpen your understanding in the four operations above mentioned,—addition, subtraction, multiplication, and division,—I shall compare them. As a carpenter (wishing to do well in his profession) needs to have his tools very sharp, and to know what tools to use first, and what next to use, &c., to the end that he may have honor from his work, so it is in the work of this Practica. Before you take the rule of the three things it is necessary that you should be very skilled in the operations which have been set forth in addition, subtraction, multiplication, and division, so that you may enter enthusiastically into your work. Furthermore, that the rule of the three things, which is of utmost importance in this art, may be at your command, you must have at hand this tool of the operations, so that you can begin your labors without spoiling your instruments and without failing. Thus will your labors command high praise.

---

[1] [The author now devotes twelve quarto pages to completing the explanation of division, which shows the degree of difficulty which the subject then offered. The rest of the text is devoted largely to the solution of mercantile problems by the Rule of Three. The preliminary statement and four problems will suffice to show the nature of the work. The subject is treated much more fully in *Isis*, Vol. VI (3), pp. 311–331, 1924.]

The rule of the three things is this: that you should multiply the thing which you wish to know, by that which is not like it, and divide by the other. And the quotient which arises will be of the nature of the thing which has no term like it. And the divisor will always be dissimilar (in weight, in measure, or in other difference) to the thing which we wish to know.

In setting forth this rule, note first that in every case which comes under it there are only two things of different nature, of which one is named twice,—by two different numbers,—and the other thing is named once, by one number alone. For example:

If 1 lira of saffron is worth 7 lire of pizoli, what will 25 lire of this same saffron be worth? Here are not mentioned together both saffron and money, but the saffron is mentioned twice by two different numbers, 1 and 25; and the money is mentioned once, by the one number 7. So this is not called the rule of three things because there are three things of different nature, for one thing is mentioned twice.

. . . .

Three merchants have invested their money in a partnership, whom to make the problem clearer I will mention by name. The first was called Piero, the second Polo, and the third Zuanne. Piero put in 112 ducats, Polo 200 ducats, and Zuanne 142 ducats. At the end of a certain period they found that they had gained 563 ducàts. Required to know how much falls to each man so that no one shall be cheated.

. . . .

There are two merchants of whom the one has cloth worth 22 soldi a yard, but who holds it in barter at 27 soldi. The other has wool which is worth in the country 19 lire per hundredweight. Required to know how much he must ask per hundredweight in barter so that he may not be cheated.

. . . .

The Holy Father sent a courier from Rome to Venice, commanding him that he should reach Venice in 7 days. And the most illustrious Signoria of Venice also sent another courier to Rome, who should reach Rome in 9 days. And from Rome to Venice is 250 miles. It happened that by order of these lords the couriers started on their journeys at the same time. It is required to find in how many days they will meet.

. . . .

What availeth virtue to him who does not labor? Nothing. At Treviso, on the 10th day of December, 1478.

RECORDE

On "The Declaration of the Profit of Arithmeticke"

(Selected by Professor David Eugene Smith, Teachers College, Columbia University, New York City.)

Robert Recorde (c. 1510–1558), a student and later a private teacher at both Oxford and Cambridge, wrote several works on mathematics. His arithmetic, *The Grovnd of Artes*, was not the first one published in England, but it was by far the most influential of the early books upon the subject as far as the English-speaking peoples are concerned. This is not because of its catechetic style, although it doubtless influenced other writers to adopt this form of textbook instruction, but rather because through its subject matter and style of problems it set a standard that has been followed until comparatively recent times. On the principle that a source book should touch at least lightly upon the elementary branches, "The declaration of the profit of Arithmeticke" is here set forth. The exact date of the first edition is uncertain, but it was about 1540 to 1542. Although a number of the early editions are available in the library of George A. Plimpton of New York City, it has been thought best to select one which represents the results of Recorde's influence for a full century,—that of 1646. As the title page says, this was "afterward augmented by M. John Dee," the promoter of the first English edition of Euclid; "enlarged—By John Mellis," and "diligently perused, corrected, illustrated and enlarged by R. C.", and its tables "diligently calculated by Rv: Hartwell, Philomathemat." It therefore represents the best efforts of the teaching profession for a hundred years.

The following is an extract from Recorde's preface:

TO THE LOVING Readers,
The Preface of Mr. *Robert Record*

Sore oft times have I lamented with my self the unfortunate condition of England, seeing so many great Clerks to arise in sundry other parts of the world, and so few to appear in this our Nation: whereas for pregnancy of naturall wit (I think) few Nations do excell Englishmen: But I cannot impute the cause to any other thing, then to be contempt, or misregard of learning. For as Englishmen are inferiour to no men in mother wit, so they passe all men in vain pleasures, to which they may attain with great pain and labour: and are as slack to any never so great

commodity; if there hang of it any painfull study or travelsome
labour.

Howbeit, yet all men are not of that sort, though the most part
be, the more pity it is: but of them that are so glad, not onely with
painfull study, and studious pain to attain learning, but also with
as great study and pain to communicate their learning to other,
and make all England (if it might be) partakers of the same; the
most part are such, that unneath they can support their own
necessary charges, so that they are not able to bear any charges
in doing of that good, that else they desire to do.

But a greater cause of lamentation is this, that when learned
men have taken pains to do things for the aid of the unlearned,
scarce they shall be allowed for their wel-doing, but derided and
scorned, and so utterly discouraged to take in hand any like
enterprise again.

The following is "The declaration of the profit of Arithmeticke" and constitutes the first ten pages of the text.   It may be said to represent the influence of this text upon establishing for a long period what educators at present
speak of as "the objectives" of elementary arithmetic.

A Dialogue between the Master and the Scholar: *teaching the* Art
and use of Arithmetick with Pen.
The Scholar speaketh.

*SIR, such is your authority in mine estimation, that I am content
to consent to your saying, and to receive it as truth, though I see none
other reason that doth lead me thereunto: whereas else in mine own
conceit it appeareth but vain, to bestow any time privately in learning
of that thing, that every childe may, and doth learn at all times and
hours, when he doth any thing himself alone, and much more when
he talketh or reasoneth with others.*

Master.   Lo, this is the fashion and chance of all them that seek
to defend their blinde ignorance, that when they think they have
made strong reason for themselves, then have they proved quite
contrary.   For if numbring be so common (as you grant it to be)
that no man can do anything alone, and much lesse talk or bargain
with other, but he shall still have to do with number: this proveth
not number to be contemptible and vile, but rather right excellent
and of high reputation, sith it is the ground of all mens affairs, in
that without it no tale can be told, no communication without it
can be continued, no bargaining without it can duely be ended, or
no businesse that man hath, justly completed.   These commodi-

ties, if there were none other, are sufficient to approve the worthinesse of number. But there are other innumerable, farre passing all these, which declare number to exceed all praise. Wherefore in all great works are Clerks so much desired? Wherefore are Auditors so richly fed? What causeth Geometricians so highly to be enhaunsed? Why are Astronomers so greatly advanced? Because that by number such things they finde, which else would farre excell mans minde.

Scholar. Verily, sir, if it bee so, that these men by numbring, their cunning do attain, at whose great works most men do wonder, then I see well I was much deceived, and numbring is a more cunning thing then I took it to be.

Master. If number were so vile a thing as you did esteem it, then need it not to be used so much in mens communication. Exclude number, and answer to this question: How many years old are you?

Scholar. Mum.

Master. How many dayes in a weeke? How many weeks in a year? What lands hath your Father? How many men doth hee keep? How long is it since you came from him to me?

Scholar. Mum.

Master. So that if number want, you answer all by Mummes: How many miles to London?

Scholar. A poak full of plums.

Master. Why, thus you may see, what rule number beareth, and that if number bee lacking it maketh men dumb, so that to most questions they must answer Mum.

Scholar. This is the cause, sir, that I judged it so vile, because it is so common in talking every while: Nor plenty is not dainty, as the common saying is.

Master. No, nor store is no sore, perceive you this? The more common that the thing is, being needfully required, the better is the thing, and the more to be desired. But in numbring, as some of it is light and plain, so the most part is difficult, and not easie to attain. The easier part serveth all men in common, and the other requireth some learning. Wherefore as without numbring a man can do almost nothing, so with the help of it, you may attain to all things.

Scholar. Yes, sir, why then it were best to learn the Art of numbring, first of all other learning, and then a man need learn no more, if all other come with it.

Master.   Nay not so: but if it be first learned, then shall a man be able (I mean) to learn, perceive, and attain to other Sciences; which without it he could never get.

Scholar.   I perceive by your former words, that Astronomy and Geometry depend much on the help of numbring: but that other Sciences, as Musick, Physick, Law, Grammer, and such like, have any help of Arithmetick, I perceive not.

Master.   I may perceive your great Clerk-linesse by the ordering of your Sciences: but I will let that passe now, because it toucheth not the matter that I intend, and I will shew you how Arithmetick doth profit in all these somewhat grosly, according to your small understanding, omitting other reasons more substantiall.

First (as you reckon them) Musick hath not onely great help of Arithmetick, but is made, and hath his perfectnesse of it: for all Musick standeth by number and proportion: And in Physick, beside the calculation of criticall dayes, with other things, which I omit, how can any man judge the pulse rightly, that is ignorant of the proportion of numbers?

And so for the Law, it is plain, that the man that is ignorant of Arithmetick, is neither meet to be a Judge, neither an Advocate, nor yet a Proctor.   For how can hee well understand another mans cause, appertaining to distribution of goods, or other debts, or of summes of money, if he be ignorant of Arithmetick?   This oftentimes causeth right to bee hindered, when the Judge either delighteth not to hear of a matter that hee perceiveth not, or cannot judge for lack of understanding: this commeth by ignorance of Arithmetick.

Now, as for Grammer, me thinketh you would not doubt in what it needeth number, sith you have learned that Nouns of all sorts, Pronouns, Verbs, and Participles are distinct diversly by numbers: besides the variety of Nouns of Numbers, and Adverbs. And if you take away number from Grammer, then is all the quantity of Syllables lost.   And many other ways doth number help Grammer.   Whereby were all kindes of Meeters found and made? was it not by number?

But how needfull Arithmetick is to all parts of Philosophy, they may soon see, that do read either Aristotle, Plato, or any other Philosophers writings.   For all their examples almost, and their probations, depend of Arithmetick.   It is the saying of Aristotle, that hee that is ignorant of Arithmetick, is meet for no Science.

And Plato his Master wrote a little sentence over his Schoolhouse door, Let none enter in hither (quoth he) that is ignorant of Geometry. Seeing hee would have all his Scholars expert in Geometry, much rather he would the same in Arithmetick, without which Geometry cannot stand.

And how needfull Arithmetick is to Divinity, it appeareth, seeing so many Doctors gather so great mysteries out of number, and so much do write of it. And if I should go about to write all the commodities of Arithmetick in civill acts, as in governance of Common-weales in time of peace, and in due provision & order of Armies, in time of war, for numbering of the Host, summing of their wages, provision of victuals, viewing of Artillery, with other Armour; beside the cunningest point of all, for casting of ground, for encamping of men, with such other like: And how many wayes also Arithmetick is conducible for all private Weales, of Lords and all Possessioners, of Merchants, and all other occupiers, and generally for all estates of men, besides Auditors, Treasurers, Receivers, Stewards, Bailiffes, and such like, whose Offices without Arithmetick are nothing: If I should (I say) particularly repeat all such commodities of the noble Science of Arithmetick, it were enough to make a very great book.

Scholar. No, no sir, you shall not need: For I doubt not, but this, that you have said, were enough to perswade any man to think this Art to be right excellent and good, and so necessary for man, that (as I think now) so much as a man lacketh of it, so much hee lacketh of his sense and wit.

Master. What, are you so farre changed since, by hearing these few commodities in generall: by likelihood you would be farre changed if you knew all the particular Commodities.

Scholar. I beseech you Sir, reserve those Commodities that rest yet behinde unto their place more convenient: and if yee will bee so good as to utter at this time this excellent treasure, so that I may be somewhat inriched thereby, if ever I shall be able, I will requite your pain.

Master. I am very glad of your request, and will do it speedily, sith that to learn it you bee so ready.

Scholar. And I to your authority my wit do subdue; whatsoever you say, I take it for true.

Master. That is too much; and meet for no man to bee beleeved in all things, without shewing of reason. Though I might of my Scholar some credence require, yet except I shew reason, I do it not desire. But now sith you are so earnestly set this Art to attaine, best it is to omit no time, lest some other passion coole this great heat, and then you leave off before you see the end.

Scholar. Though many there bee so unconstant of mind, that flitter and turn with every winde, which often begin, and never come to the end, I am none of this sort, as I trust you partly know. For by my good will what I once begin, till I have it fully ended, I would never blin.

Master. So have I found you hitherto indeed, and I trust you will increase rather then go back. For, better it were never to assay, then to shrink and flie in the mid way: But I trust you will not do so; therefore tell mee briefly: What call you the Science that you desire so greatly.

Scholar. Why sir, you know.

Master. That maketh no matter, I would hear whether you know, and therefore I ask you. For great rebuke it were to have studied a Science, and yet cannot tell how it is named.

Scholar. Some call it Arsemetrick, and some Augrime.

Master. And what do these names betoken?

Scholar. That, if it please you, of you would I learn.

Master. Both names are corruptly written: Arsemetrick for Arithmetick, as the Greeks call it, and Augrime for Algorisme, as the Arabians found it: which both betoken the Science of Numbring: for Arithmos in Greek is called Number: and of it commeth Arithmetick, the Art of Numbring. So that Arithmetick is a Science or Art teaching the manner and use of Numbring: This Art may be wrought diversly, with Pen or with Counters. But I will first shew you the working with the Pen, and then the other in order.

Scholar. This I will remember. But how many things are to bee learned to attain this Art fully?

Master. There are reckoned commonly seven parts or works of it.

Numeration, Addition, Subtraction, Multiplication, Division, Progression, and Extraction of roots: to these some men adde Duplication, Triplation, and Mediation. But as for these three last they are contained under the other seven. For Duplication, and Triplation are contained under Multiplication; as it shall appear in their place: And Mediation is contained under Division, as I will declare in his place also.

Scholar. Yet then there remain the first seven kinds of Numbring.

Master. So there doth: Howbeit if I shall speak exactly of the
parts of Numbring, I must make but five of them: for Progression
is a compound operation of Addition, Multiplication and Division.
And so is the Extractions of roots. But it is no harme to name
them as kindes severall, seeing they appear to have some severall
working. For it forceth not so much to contend for the number
of them, as for the due knowledge and practising of them.

Scholar. Then you will that I shall name them as seven kindes
distinct. But now I desire you to instruct mee in the use of each
of them.

Master. So I will, but it must be done in order: for you may
not learn the last so soon as the first, but you must learn them in
that order, as I did rehearse them, if you will learn them speedily,
and well.

Scholar. Even as you please. Then to begin; Numeration is
the first in order: what shall I do with it?

Master. First, you must know what the thing is, and then after
learn the use of the same.

STEVIN

ON DECIMAL FRACTIONS

(Translated from the French by Professor Vera Sanford, Western Reserve University, Cleveland, Ohio.)

The invention of the decimal fraction cannot be assigned to any single individual. Pellos (1492) used a decimal point to set off one, two, or three places in the dividend when the divisor was a multiple of 10, 100, or 1000. Adam Reise (1522) printed a table of square roots in which values to three places were computed for the irrationals. Most important of all, Rudolff (1530) used the symbol as a decimal point in a compound interest table.[1]

The first person to discuss the theory of decimal fractions and their arithmetic was Simon Stevin (c.1548–c.1620), a native of Bruges and a firm supporter of William the Silent in the struggle of the Low Countries against Spain. Stevin was tutor to Maurice of Nassau, served as quartermaster general in the Dutch army, and acted as commissioner of certain public works, especially of the dikes. He is reported to have been the first to adapt the principles of commercial bookkeeping to national accounts, and his studies in hydraulics resulted in theorems which foreshadowed the integral calculus.

Stevin's work on decimal fractions was published in 1585, two editions appearing in that year—one in Flemish with the title *La Thiende*, the other in French with the title *La Disme*.

The translation that follows was made from *Les Oeuvres Mathematiques de Simon Stevin*, edited by Girard and published in Leyden in 1634.[2]

LA DISME

Teaching how all Computations that are met in Business may be performed by Integers alone without the aid of Fractions
Written first in Flemish and now done into French
by
Simon Stevin of Bruges

To Astrologers, Surveyors, Measurers of Tapestry, Gaugers, Stereometers in General, Mint-masters, and to All Merchants Simon Stevin Sends Greeting

A person who contrasts the small size of this book with your greatness, my most honorable sirs to whom it is dedicated, will

---

[1] These instances are discussed with facsimiles of the cases in point in "The Invention of the Decimal Fraction," by David Eugene Smith, *Teachers College Bulletin*, First Series. No. 5.

[2] A facsimile of the original edition with an introduction by the late Father Bosmans was printed by the Société des Bibliophiles Anversois in Antwerp, in 1924, with the title *La "Thiende" de Simon Stevin.*

think my idea absurd, especially if he imagines that the size of this volume bears the same ratio to human ignorance that its usefulness has to men of your outstanding ability; but, in so doing, he will have compared the extreme terms of the proportion which may not be done. Let him rather compare the third term with the fourth. What is it that is here propounded? Some wonderful invention? Hardly that, but a thing so simple that it scarce deserves the name invention; for it is as if some stupid country lout chanced upon great treasure without using any skill in the finding. If anyone thinks that, in expounding the usefulness of decimal numbers, I am boasting of my cleverness in devising them, he shows without doubt that he has neither the judgment nor the intelligence to distinguish simple things from difficult, or else that he is jealous of a thing that is for the common good. However this may be, I shall not fail to mention the usefulness of these numbers even in the face of this man's empty calumny. But, just as the mariner who has found by chance an unknown isle, may declare all its riches to the king, as, for instance, its having beautiful fruits, pleasant plains, precious minerals, etc., without its being imputed to him as conceit; so may I speak freely of the great usefulness of this invention, a usefulness greater than I think any of you anticipates, without constantly priding myself on my achievements.

As your daily experience, Messieurs, makes you sufficiently aware of the usefulness of number, which is the subject of *La Disme*, it will not be necessary to say many words with reference to this. The astrologer[1] knows that, by computation, using tables of declinations, the pilot may describe the true latitude and longitude of a place and that by such means every point upon the earth's surface may be located. But as the sweet is never without the bitter, the labor of such computations cannot be disguised, for they involve tedious multiplications and divisions of sexagesimal fractions,[2] degrees, minutes, seconds, thirds, etc. The surveyor

---

[1] [This is used for "astrologer" and for "astronomer" as well.]

[2] [Fractions whose denominators were the powers of sixty. They were not restricted to the measurement of time or angles but were used by scientists and mathematicians in all sorts of computations. They afforded a convenient way of expressing the approximate root of an equation,—in one case, for instance a root is given to the tenth sexagesimal,—but although their use facilitated the comparing of one number with another and although they were well suited to addition and subtraction, multiplication, division, and square root were difficult and were frequently performed by tables.]

knows the great benefit which the world receives from his science by which it avoids many disputes concerning the unknown areas of land. And he who deals in large matters, cannot be ignorant of the tiresome multiplications of rods, feet, and inches[1] the one by the other, which often give rise to error tending to the injury of one of the parties, and to the ruin of the reputation of the surveyor. So too, with mint-masters, merchants, etc., each in his own business. The more important these calculations are, and the more laborious their execution, so much the greater is this discovery of decimal numbers which does away with all these difficulties. To speak briefly, *La Disme* teaches how all computations of the type of the four principles of arithmetic—addition, subtraction, multiplication and division—may be performed by whole numbers with as much ease as in counter-reckoning.[2]

If by these means, time may be saved which would otherwise be lost, if work may be avoided, as well as disputes, mistakes, lawsuits, and other mischances commonly joined thereto, I willingly submit *La Disme* to your consideration. Someone may raise the point that many inventions which seem good at first sight are of no effect when one wishes to use them, and as often happens, new methods good in a few minor cases are worthless in more important ones. No such doubt exists in this instance, for we have shown this method to expert surveyors in Holland and they have abandoned the devices which they have invented to lighten the work of their computations and now use this one to their great satisfaction. The same satisfaction will come to each of you, my most honorable sirs, who will do as they have done.

Argument

La Disme consists of two parts,—definitions and operations. In the first part, the first definition explains what decimal numbers[3] are, the second, third, and fourth explain the meaning of the terms unit,[4] prime, second, etc., and the other decimal numbers.

---

[1] [Here Stevin uses the units *verge, pied, doigt.*]

[2] [That is, reckoning with jetons or counters, a method of reckoning that was still in vogue in Stevin's time.]

[3] [In this translation, the words "decimal numbers" are used where the literal translation would be "the numbers of *La Disme.*"]

[4] [In the Flemish version, Stevin uses the word *Begbin* and in the French one, *Commencement.*]

In the operations, four propositions show the addition, subtraction, multiplication, and division of decimal numbers. The order of these topics may be succinctly represented in a table.

La Disme has two divisions........

Definitions....... {
Decimals
Unit
Prime, Second, etc.
Decimal Numbers
}

Operations....... {
Addition
Subtraction
Multiplication
Division
}

At the end of this discussion, there will be added an appendix setting forth the use of decimal numbers in real problems.

THE FIRST DIVISION OF LA DISME
OF DEFINITIONS
Definition I

Decimal numbers[1] are a kind of arithmetic based on the idea of the progression by tens, making use of the ordinary Arabic numerals, in which any number may be written and by which all computations that are met in business may be performed by integers alone without the aid of fractions.

Explanation

Let the number one thousand one hundred eleven be written in Arabic numerals 1111, in which form it appears that each 1 is the tenth part of the next higher figure. Similarly, in the number 2378, each unit of the 8 is the tenth part of each unit of the 7, and so for all the others. But since it is convenient that the things which we study have names, and since this type of computation is based solely upon the idea of the progression by tens[2] as will be seen in our later discussion, we may properly speak of this treatise as *La Disme* and we shall see that by it we may perform all the computations we meet in business without the aid of fractions.

---

[1] [Disme est une espece d'arithmetique.]

[2] [Disme: "tithe," later the word was contracted into dîme. Earlier forms in English use are *dyme* and *dessime*. Disme came into the language when Stevin's work was translated in 1608. It was used as a noun meaning a tenth and as a synonym for decimal arithmetic; also as a verb, to divide into tenths.]

Definition II

Any given number is called the *unit* and has the sign ⓪.

Explanation

In the number three hundred sixty four, for example, we call the three hundred sixty four units and write the number 364⓪. Similarly for other cases.

Definition III

The tenth part of a unit is called a *Prime*, and has the sign ①, and the tenth of a prime is called a *Second*, and has the sign ②. Similarly for each tenth part of the unit of the next higher figure.

Explanation

Thus 3①7②5③9④ is 3 primes, 7 seconds, 3 thirds, 9 fourths, and we might continue this indefinitely.   It is evident from the definition that the latter numbers are $\frac{3}{10}$, $\frac{7}{100}$, $\frac{5}{1000}$, $\frac{9}{10,000}$, and that this number is $3759\frac{3}{10,000}$.   Likewise 8⓪9①3②7③ has the value $8\frac{9}{10}$, $\frac{3}{100}$, $\frac{7}{1000}$, or $893\frac{7}{1000}$.   And so for other numbers. We must also realize that in these numbers we use no fractions and that the number under each sign except the "unit" never exceeds the 9.   For instance, we do not write 7①12② but 8①2② instead, for it has the same value.

Definition IV

The numbers of the 2nd and 3d definitions are called *Decimal Numbers*.

The End of the Definitions[1]

---

[1] [These same names and symbols are given a more general application in Stevin's other works. The following discussion is from his work on the subject in *l'Arithmétique* where geometric progressions, or geometric numbers play a prominent part.

He says, "When the ancients realized the value of progressions of the sort where the first term multiplied by itself gives the second term..., they saw that it would be necessary to choose meaningful names for these numbers so that they might the more readily distinguish them.   Thus they called the first term *Prime* which we denote by ①, the next *Second* which we write as ② etc. "For example,

①2②4③ 8④16...
①3②9③27④81...
. . . .

"We intend that the *Unit* of a quantity shall mean something distinct from the first quantity or prime.   Any arithmetic number or radical which one uses in algebraic computation as 6 or $\sqrt{3}$ or $2 + \sqrt{3}$..., we will call

The Second Division of La Disme
Of Operations

Proposition I.—To add decimal numbers. Given three decimal numbers, 27⓪8①4②7③, 37⓪6①7②5③, 875⓪7①8②2③. Required to find their sum.

Construction.—Arrange the numbers as in the accompanying figure, adding them in the usual manner of adding integers. This (by the first problem of *l'Arithmétique*[1]) gives the sum 941304,[1] which, as the signs above the numbers show[2] is 941⓪3①0②4③. And this is the sum required.

	⓪	①	②	③
	2	7	8	4	7
	3	7	6	7	5
8	7	5	7	8	2
9	4	1	3	0	4

Proof.—By the third definition of this book, the given number 27⓪8①4②7③ is 27⅞₀, ⁴⁄₁₀₀, ⁷⁄₁₀₀₀, or 27847⁄₁₀₀₀. Similarly, the 37⓪6①7②5③ is 37675⁄₁₀₀₀, and the 875⓪7①8②3③ is 875783⁄₁₀₀₀. These three numbers 27847⁄₁₀₀₀, 37675⁄₁₀₀₀, 875783⁄₁₀₀₀ added, according to the 10th problem of *l'Arithmétique*, make 941304⁄₁₀₀₀, but 941⓪3①0②4③ has this same value, and is therefore the true sum which was to be shown.

Conclusion.—Having been given decimal numbers to add, we have found their sum which was to be done.

Note.—If, in the numbers in question, some figure of the natural order be lacking, fill its place with a zero. For example, in the numbers 8⓪5①6② and 5⓪7② where the second lacks a figure of order prime, insert 0① and take 5⓪0①7② as the given number and add as before. This note applies to the three following propositions also.

	⓪	①	②
	8	5	6
	5	0	7
1	3	6	3

the *Unit* and we will give it the symbol ⓪: but this symbol shall be used only when the arithmetic number or radical is not denominate. (quand les nombres Arithmetiques ou radicaux ne sont pas absoluement descripts)."

Stevin writes denominate numbers as 1 hour 3①5②, 5 degrees 4①18②, 2790 verges 5①9②. He later notes (*l'Arithmétique*, p. 8) that Bombelli has used this symbolism also except for the ⓪. In Bombelli's *Algebra* (1572) the symbols ⊍, ⊌, ⊍... are used for the powers of the unknown quantity just as Stevin used his ①, ②, ③,..., *i. e.*, a specialized form of the geometric progression.

The names for these quantities except that of the unit, are easily traced to the *pars minuta prima*, etc., of the sexagesimals.]

[1] [*La Pratiqve D'Arithmétiqve De Simon Stevin De Brvges, Leyden,* 1585.]

[2] [Stevin has three ways of writing these numbers, depending upon the exigencies of the case: 27⓪8①4②7③, ⓪①②③, 27 8 4 7. / 27 8 4 7. ⓪①②③]

Proposition II.—To subtract decimal numbers.

Given the number 237⓪5①7②8③ from which the number 59⓪7①4②9③ is to be subtracted.

Required to find the remainder.

Construction.—Place the numbers in order as in the adjoining figure, subtracting after the usual manner of subtracting integers (by the 2nd problem of *l'Arithmétique*). There remains 177829 which, as indicated by the signs above the numbers, is 177⓪8①2②9③; and this is the remainder required.

$$
\begin{array}{r}
⓪①②③ \\
2\ 3\ 7\ 5\ 7\ 8 \\
5\ 9\ 7\ 4\ 9 \\
\hline
1\ 7\ 7\ 8\ 2\ 9
\end{array}
$$

Proof.—By the third definition of *la Disme*, the 237⓪ 5①7②8③ is 2375⁵/₁₀, ⁷/₁₀₀, ⁸/₁₀₀₀ or 237⁵⁷⁸/₁₀₀₀. And, by the same reasoning, the 59⓪7①4②9③ is 59⁷⁴⁹/₁₀₀₀; subtracting this from 237⁵⁷⁸/₁₀₀₀, according to the tenth problem of *l'Arithmétique*, leaves 178²⁹/₁₀₀₀. But the aforesaid 177⓪8①2②9③ has this same value and is, therefore, the true remainder, which was to be proved.

Conclusion.—Having been given a decimal number and a similar number which is to be subtracted from it, we have found the remainder which was to be done.

Proposition III.—To multiply decimal numbers.

Given the number 32⓪5①7② and the multiplier 89⓪4①6②.

Required to find their product.

Construction.—Place the numbers in order and multiply in the ordinary way of multiplying whole numbers (by the third problem of *l'Arithmétique*). This gives the product 29137122. To find what this is, add the last two signs of the given numbers, the one ② and the other ② also, which together are ④. We say, then, that the sign of the last figure of the product will be ④. Once this is established, all the signs are known on account of their continuous order. Therefore, 2913⓪7①1②2③2④ is the required product.

$$
\begin{array}{r}
⓪①② \\
3\ 2\ 5\ 7 \\
8\ 9\ 4\ 6 \\
\hline
1\ 9\ 5\ 4\ 2 \\
1\ 3\ 0\ 2\ 8 \\
2\ 9\ 3\ 1\ 3 \\
2\ 6\ 0\ 5\ 6 \\
\hline
2\ 9\ 1\ 3\ 7\ 1\ 2\ 2 \\
⓪①②③④
\end{array}
$$

Proof.—As appears by the third definition of *La Disme*, the given number 32⓪5①7② is 32⁵/₁₀, ⁷/₁₀₀, or 325⁷/₁₀₀, and likewise the multiplier 89⓪4①6② is 894⁶/₁₀₀. Multiplying the aforesaid 325⁷/₁₀₀ by this number gives the product 291371²²/₁₀,₀₀₀ (by the twelfth problem of *l'Arithmétique*). But the aforesaid product 2913⓪7①1②2③2④ has this value and is, therefore, the true

product which we were required to prove. We will now explain
why second multiplied by second gives the product fourths, which
is the sum of their signs, and why fourth by fifth gives the product
ninth and why unit by third gives the product third and so forth.

Let us take for example ²⁄₁₀ and ³⁄₁₀₀ which, by the definitions
of *La Disme*, are the values of 2① and 3②. Their product is
⁶⁄₁₀₀₀, which by the third defintion given above is 6③. Hence,
multiplying prime by second gives a product in thirds, that is,
a number whose sign is the sum of the given signs.

Conclusion.—Having been given a decimal number to multiply
and the multiplier we have found the product, which was to be done.

NOTE.—If the last sign of the multiplicand is not equal to the
last sign of the multiplier, for example, 3④7⑤6⑥   ④⑤⑥
and 5①4②, proceed as above.   The placing of the   3 7 8
figures will appear as here shown.   5 4②

                                                    ─────────────
                                                      1 5 1 2
                                                      1 8 9 0
                                                    ─────────────
                                                      2 0 4 1 2
                                                      ④⑤⑥⑦⑧

Proposition IV.—To divide decimal numbers.
Given 3⓪4①4②3③5④2⑤ to be divided by 9①6②.
Required to find their quotient.

Construction.—Omitting their signs, divide   1
the given numbers in the ordinary way of   18
dividing whole numbers by the fourth problem   5184
of *l'Arithmétique*. This gives the quotient   7687   ⓪①②③
3587. To determine the signs, subtract the   344352 (3 5 8 7
last sign of the divisor ② from the last sign of   96666
the dividend ⑤, leaving ③ as the sign of the   999
last digit of the quotient. Once this is determined, all the other
signs are known because of their continuous order. 3⓪5①8②7③
is, therefore, the quotient required.

Proof.—By the third definition of *La Disme* the dividend
3⓪4①4②3③5④2⑤ is 3 ⁴⁄₁₀, ⁴⁄₁₀₀, ³⁄₁₀₀₀, ⁵⁄₁₀,₀₀₀ ²⁄₁₀₀,₀₀₀ or
344,352⁄₁₀₀,₀₀₀. The divisor 9①6② is ⁹⁄₁₀, ⁶⁄₁₀₀ or ⁹⁶⁄₁₀₀. By
the thirteenth problem of *l'Arithmétique*, the quotient of these
numbers is 3587⁄₁₀₀₀. The aforesaid 3⓪5①8②7③ is therefore
the true quotient which was to be shown.

Conclusion.—Having been given a decimal number to be divided
and the divisor, we have found the quotient, which was to be done.

NOTE I.—If the signs of the divisor be higher than the signs of the dividend, add to the dividend as many zeros as may be necessary. For example, in dividing 7② by 4⑤, I place zeros after the 7 and divide as above getting the quotient 1750.

It sometimes happens that the quotient cannot be expressed by whole numbers as in the case of 4② divided by 3④. Here. it appears that the quotient will be infinitely many threes with always one third in addition. In such a case, we may approach as near to the real quotient as the problem requires and omit the remainder. It is true indeed that 13⓪3①3② or 13⓪3①3②3⅓③ is the exact result, but in this work we propose to use whole numbers only, and, moreover, we notice that in business one does not take account of the thousandth part of a maille[1] or of a grain. Omissions such as these are made by the principal Geometricians and Arithmeticians even in computations of great consequence. Ptolemy and Jehan de Montroyal, for instance, did not make up their tables with the utmost accuracy that could be reached with mixed numbers, for in view of the purpose of these tables, approximation is more useful than perfection.

$$
\begin{array}{r}
3\!\!\not{2} \qquad ⓪ \\
4②\quad7\!\!\not{0}\!\!\not{0}\!\!\not{0}\ (175\ 0 \\
3④ \\
4\!\!\not{4}\!\!\not{4}\!\!\not{4}
\end{array}
$$

$$
\begin{array}{r}
1\!\!\not{1}\!\!\not{1} \qquad ⓪①② \\
4\!\!\not{0}\!\!\not{0}\!\!\not{0}000\ (1\ 3\ 3\ 3 \\
3\!\!\not{3}\!\!\not{3}\!\!\not{3}
\end{array}
$$

NOTE II.—Decimal numbers may be used in the extraction of roots. For example, to find the square root of 5②2③9④, work according to the ordinary method of extracting square root and the root will be 2①3②. The last sign of the root is always one half the last sign of the given number. If, however, the last sign is odd, add (a zero in place of) the next sign and extract the root of the resulting number as above. By a similar method with cube root, the third of the last sign of the given number will be the sign of ther oot—similarly for all other roots.

$$
\begin{array}{r}
\not{1} \\
5\!\!\not{2}\!\!\not{9} \\
2,\ 3 \\
\hline
\overline{4\!\!\not{2}\!\!\not{9}}
\end{array}
$$

THE END OF LA DISME

Appendix

Decimal numbers have been described above. We now come to their applications and in the following six articles we shall show how all computations which arise in business may be performed by them. We shall begin with the computations of surveying as this subject was the first one mentioned in the introduction.

---

[1] [¼ ounce.]

Article One

Of the Computations of Surveying

When decimal numbers are used in surveying, the verge[1] is called the unit, and it is divided into ten equal parts or primes, each prime is divided into seconds and, if smaller units are required, the seconds into thirds and so on so far as may be necessary. For the purposes of surveying the divisions into seconds are sufficiently small but in matters that require greater accuracy as in the measuring of lead roofs, thicknesses etc., one may need to use the thirds. Many surveyors, however, do not use the verge, but a chain three, four, or five verges long, and a cross-staff[2] with its shaft marked in five or six feet divided into inches. These men may follow the same practise here substituting five or six primes with their seconds. They should use these markings of the cross-staff without regard to the number of feet and inches that the verge contains in that locality, and add, subtract, multiply, and divide the resulting numbers as in the preceding examples. Suppose, for instance, four areas[3] are to be added: 345⓪7①8②, and 872⓪-5①3②, 615⓪4①8②, and 956⓪8①6②. Add these as in the first proposition of *La Disme*. This gives the sum 2790 verges 5 primes, 9 seconds. This number, divided by the number of verges in an arpent[4] gives the number of arpents required. To find the number of small divisions in 5 primes 9 seconds, look on the other side of the verge to see how many feet and inches match with them; but this is a thing which the surveyor must do but once, *i. e.*, at the end of the account which he

	⓪	①	②
3	4	5	7	2
8	7	2	5	3
6	1	5	4	8
9	5	6	8	6
2 7	9	0	5	0

---

[1] [The word verge was used for a measuring rod of that length.]

[2] [The cross-staff was a piece of wood mounted at its mid-point perpendicular to a shaft and free to move along this shaft to positions parallel to the first one. To use this instrument, the observer adjusts it so the lines of sight from the ends of the staff to the tip of the cross-piece coincide with the end-points of the line to be measured, and the distances are computed from one measurement and similar triangles. When neither point of the required line is accessible, the distance is computed from two observations at known distances from each other.]

[3] [Stevin's area units evidently proceed directly from his decimal scheme. Thus the prime of the area unit is one tenth of the unit itself, not a square whose side is the prime of the linear unit.]

[4] [The arpent was the common unit of area. It varied from about 3000 to 5100 square meters, according to the locality.]

gives to the proprietaries, and often not then, as the majority think it useless to mention the smaller units.

Secondly, to subtract 32⓪5①7② from 57⓪3①2②, work according to the second proposition of *La Disme*, and there remains 24 verges, 7 primes, 5 seconds.

⓪①②
5 7 3 2
―――――
3 2 5 7
―――――
2 4 7 5

Thirdly, to multiply 8⓪7①3② by 7⓪5①4② (these might be the sides of a rectangle or quadrangle), proceed as above according to the third proposition of *La Disme*, getting the product, or area, 65 verges 8 primes etc.

⓪①②
8 7 3
7 5 4
―――――
3 4 9 2
4 3 6 5
6 1 1 1
―――――
6 5 8 2 4 2
⓪①②③ ④

Fourthly, suppose that the rectangle *ABCD* has the side *AD* 26⓪3①. From what point on *AB* should a line be drawn parallel to *AD* to cut off a rectangle of area 367⓪6①? Divide 367⓪6① by 26⓪3① according to the fourth proposition of *La Disme* getting the quotient 13⓪9①7② which is the required distance *AE*. If greater accuracy is desired, this division may be carried further, although such accuracy does not seem necessary. The proofs of these problems are given above in the propositions to which we have referred.

1
2̸2̸
7̸6̸
2̸5̸0̸8
4̸6̸3̸1̸
1̸0̸4̸7̸3̸9   ⓪①②
3̸6̸7̸6̸0̸0̸ (13 9 7
2̸6̸3̸3̸3̸3̸
2̸6̸6̸6̸
2̸2̸

Article Two

Of the Computations of the Measuring of Tapestry

The aûne[1] is the unit of the measurer of tapestry. The blank side of the aûne should be divided into ten equal parts each of which is 1 prime, just as is done in the case of the verge of the surveyor. Then each prime is divided into ten equal parts, each 1 second etc. It is not necessary to discuss the use of this measure as examples of it would be similar in every respect to those given in the article on surveying.

―――――――――――

[1] [About 46 inches.]

Article Three
Of Computations Used in Gauging and in the Measuring of all Casks

· · · · · · · · · ·

Article Four
Of Computations of Volume Measurement in General

It is true, indeed, that gauging is stereometry that is the science of measuring volumes, but all stereometry is not gauging. We therefore distinguish them in this treatise. The stereometer who uses the method of *La Disme*, should mark the customary measure of his town, whether this be the verge or the aûne, with the decimal divisions described in the first and second articles above.

Let us suppose that he is to find the volume of a rectangular column whose length is 3①2②, breadth 2①4②, 2⓪3①5②. He should multiply the length by the breadth (according to the 4th proposition of *La Disme*) and this product by the height, getting as his result 1①8②4④8⑤.

```
        3 2
        2 4
      1 2 8
      6 4
      7 6 8
      2 3 5
    3 8 4 0
    2 3 0 4
  1 5 3 6
  1 8 0 4 8 0
  ①②③④⑤⑥
```

NOTE.—Someone who is ignorant of the fundamentals of stereometry—for it is such a man that we are addressing now—may wonder why we say that the volume of the above column is but 1① etc., for it contains more than 180 cubes of side 1 prime. He should realize that a cubic verge is not 10 but 1000 cubes of side 1 prime. Similarly, 1 prime of the volume unit is 100 cubes each of side 1 prime. The like is well known to surveyors for when one says 2 verges 3 feet of earth, he does not mean 2 verges 3 feet square, but 2 verges and (counting 12 feet to the verge) 36 feet square.

If however the question had been how many cubes of side 1 prime are in the above column, the result would have been changed to conform to this requirement, bearing in mind that each prime of volume units is 100 cubes of side 1 prime, and each second is 10 such cubes. If the tenth part of the verge is the greatest measure that the stereometer intends using, he should call it the unit and proceed as above.

Article Five

Of Astronomical Computations

The ancient astronomers who divided the circle into 360 degrees, saw that computations with these and their fractional parts were too laborious. They divided the degree, therefore, into submultiples and these again into the same number of equal parts, and in order to always work with integers, they chose for this division the sexagesimal progression for sixty is a number commensurate with many whole numbers, to wit with 1, 2, 3, 4, 5, 6, 10, 12, 15, 20, 30. If we may trust to experience, however, and we say this with all reverence for the past, the decimal and not the sexagesimal is the most convenient of all the progressions that exist potentially in nature. Thus, we would call the 360 degrees the unit and we would divide the degree into ten equal parts, or primes, and the prime in turn into ten parts and so forth, as has been done several times above. Having once agreed upon this division, we might describe the easy methods of adding, subtracting, multiplying, and dividing these numbers, but as this does not differ from the preceding propositions such a recital would be but a waste of time. We therefore let those examples illustrate this article. Moreover we would use this division of the degree in all astronomical tables and we hope to publish one such[1] in our own Flemish language which is the richest, the most ornate, and the most perfect of all languages. Of its exquisite uniqueness, we contemplate a fuller proof than the brief one which Pierre and Jehan made in the *Bewysconst* or *Dialectique*[2] which was recently published.

---

[1] [Stevin did not make this promise good, however, for in his work on astronomy, the *Wiscontige Gedachtenissen* (1608), he keeps to the old partition of the degree. Father Bosmans is of the opinion that this was due to the tremendous labor involved, but he also points out that the errors incident to converting readings to the decimal system for computation and then shifting back again would be greater than those involved in the mere computation with sexagesimals.]

[2] [*Dialectike Ofte Bewysconst. Leerende van allen saeken recht ende constelick Oirdeelen; Oock openende den wech tot de alderiepste verborgentheden der Natureren. Beschreven int Neerdytach door Simon Stevin van Brugghe. Tot Leyden by Christoffel Plantijn* M.D.LXXXV.

In this book, which was an imitation of Cicero's *Tusculan Disputations*, Pierre and Jehan discuss the beauties of the Flemish tongue. (First edition, pp. 141–166.)

The more complete proof comes as a digression at the end of the preface of Stevin's *Beghinselen der Weeghconst*, 1596.]

Article Six
Of the Computations of Mint-masters, Merchants, and in General of All States

To summarize this article, we might say that all measures—linear, liquid, dry, and monetary—may be divided decimally, and that each large unit may be called the unit. Thus the marc is the unit of weight for gold and silver; the livre, for other common weights; and the livre gros in Flanders, the livre esterlain in England, and the ducat in Spain, are the units of money in those countries. In the case of the money, the highest symbol (and the lowest denomination) of the marc would be the fourth, for the prime weighs half the Es of Antwerp. The third suffices for the highest symbol of the livre gros, for the third is less than the fourth of a penny.

Instead of the demi-livre, once, demi-once, esterlain, grain etc. the subdivisions of the weights should be the 5, 3, 2, 1 of each sign, that is to say, after a livre would follow a weight of 5 primes (or ½ lb.) then 3 primes, then 2, then 1. Similar parts of other weights would have the 5 and the other multiples of the division following.

We think it essential that each subdivision should be named prime, second, third etc., whatever sort of measure it may be, for it is evident to us that second multiplied by third gives the product fifth (2 & 3 make 5 as was said above), and third divided by second gives the quotient prime, facts which cannot be shown so neatly by other names. But when one wishes to name them so as to distinguish the systems of measure, as we say demi-aûne, demi-livre, demi-pinte, etc., we may call them prime of marc, second of marc, second of livre, second of aûne, etc.

As examples of this, let us suppose that 1 marc of gold is worth 36 lb. 5①3②, how much is 8 marcs 3①5②4③ worth? Multiply 3653 by 8354 getting the product 305 lb. 1①7②1③ which is the required solution.[1] As for the 6④2⑤, these are of no account here.

Again, take the case of 2 aûnes 3① (of cloth) which cost 3 lb. 2①5②, what would be the cost of 7 aûnes 5①3②? To find this, multiply the last of the given numbers by the second and divide this product by the third according to the usual custom, that is to

---

[1] [Stevin is not consistent in his approximation of results. When he computes his interest tables, he says he considers $10\%_{01}$ an extra unit 'for it is more than one half.']

say 753 by 325 which gives 244725.   This divided by 23 gives the
quotient and solution 10 lb. 6①4②.

We might give examples of all the common rules of arithmetic
that pertain to business, as the rules of partnership, interest,
exchange etc., and show how they may be carried out by integers
alone and also how they may be performed by easy operations
with counters, but as these may be deduced from the preceding,
we shall not elaborate them here.   We might also show by comparison with vexing problems with fractions the great difference
in ease between working with ordinary numbers and with decimal
numbers, but we omit this in the interest of brevity.

Finally, we must speak of one difference between the sixth
article and the five preceding articles, namely that any individual
may make the divisions set forth in the five articles, but this is not
the case in the last article where the results must be accepted by
every one as being good and lawful.   In view of the great usefulness of the decimal division, it would be a praiseworthy thing if
the people would urge having this put into effect so that in addition
to the common divisions of measures, weights, and money that
now exist, the state would declare the decimal division of the large
units legitimate to the end that he who wished might use them.
It would further this cause also, if all new money should be based
on this system of primes, seconds, thirds, etc.   If this is not put
into operation so soon as we might wish, we have the consolation
that it will be of use to posterity, for it is certain that if men of
the future are like men of the past, they will not always be neglect-
ful of a thing of such great value.

Secondly, it is not the most discouraging thing to know that
men may free themselves from great labor at any hour they wish.

Lastly, though the sixth article may not go into effect for some
time, individuals may always use the five preceding articles indeed
it is evident that some are already in operation.

The End of the Appendix

DEDEKIND

On Irrational Numbers

(Translated from the German by the Late Professor Wooster Woodruff Beman, University of Michigan, Ann Arbor, Michigan. Selection made and edited by Professor Vera Sanford, Western Reserve University, Cleveland, Ohio)

Julius Wilhelm Richard Dedekind (1831–1916) studied at Göttingen and later taught in Zürich and Braunschweig. His essay *Stetigkeit und irra-tionale Zahlen* published in 1872 was the outcome of researches begun in Zürich in 1858 when Dedekind, teaching differential calculus for the first time, became increasingly conscious of the need for a scientific discussion of the concept of continuity.

This work is included in *Essays on the Theory of Numbers*, by Richard Dedekind, translated by the late Professor Wooster Woodruff Beman (Open Court Publishing Company, Chicago, 1901). The extract here given is on pages 6 to 24 of this translation and is reproduced by the consent of the publishers.

The author begins with a statement of three properties of rational numbers and of the three corresponding properties of the points on a straight line. These properties are as follows:

For Numbers

I. If $a > b$, and $b > c$, then $a > c$.

II. If a, c are two different numbers, there are infinitely many different numbers lying between a, c.

III. If a is any definite number, then all numbers of the system R fall into two classes, A_1 and A_2, each of which contains infinitely many individuals; the first class A_1 comprises all numbers a_1 that are $< a$, the second class A_2 comprises all numbers a_2 that are $> a$; the number a itself may be assigned at pleasure to the first or second class, being respectively the greatest number of the first class or the least of the second.

For the Points on a Line

I. If p lies to the right of q, and q to the right of r, then p lies to the right of r; and we say that q lies between the points p and r.

II. If p, r are two different points, then there always exist infinitely many points that lie between p and r.

III. If p is a definite point in L, then all points in L fall into two classes, P_1 and P_2 each of which contains infinitely many individuals; the first class P_1 contains all the points p_1 that lie to the left of p, and the second class P_2 contains all the points p_2 that lie to the right of p; the point p itself may be assigned at pleasure to the first or second class. In every case, the separation of the straight line L into the two classes or portions P_1, P_2 is of such a character that every point of the first class P_1 lies to the left of every point of the second class P_2.

III.

CONTINUITY OF THE STRAIGHT LINE.

Of the greatest importance, however, is the fact that in the straight line L there are infinitely many points which correspond to no rational number. If the point p corresponds to the rational number a, then, as is well known, the length op is commensurable with the invariable unit of measure used in the construction, i. e., there exists a third length, a so-called common measure, of which these two lengths are integral multiples. But the ancient Greeks already knew and had demonstrated that there are lengths incommensurable with a given unit of length, e. g., the diagonal of the square whose side is the unit of length. If we lay off such a length from the point o upon the line we obtain an end-point which corresponds to no rational number. Since further it can be easily shown that there are infinitely many lengths which are incommensurable with the unit of length, we may affirm: The straight line L is infinitely richer in point-individuals than the domain R of rational numbers in number individuals.

If now, as is our desire, we try to follow up arithmetically all phenomena in the straight line, the domain of rational numbers is insufficient and it becomes absolutely necessary that the instrument R constructed by the creation of the rational numbers be essentially improved by the creation of new numbers such that the domain of numbers shall gain the same completeness, or as we may say at once, the same *continuity*, as the straight line.

The previous considerations are so familiar and well known to all that many will regard their repetition quite superfluous. Still I regarded this recapitulation as necessary to prepare properly for the main question. For, the way in which the irrational numbers are usually introduced is based directly upon the conception of extensive magnitudes—which itself is nowhere carefully defined—and explains number as the result of measuring such a magnitude by another of the same kind.[1] Instead of this I demand that arithmetic shall be developed out of itself.

---

[1] The apparent advantage of the generality of this definition of number disappears as soon as we consider complex numbers. According to my view, on the other hand, the notion of the ratio between two numbers of the same kind can be clearly developed only after the introduction of irrational numbers.

That such comparisons with non-arithmetic notions have furnished the immediate occasion for the extension of the number-concept may, in a general way, be granted (though this was certainly not the case in the introduction of complex numbers); but this surely is no sufficient ground for introducing these foreign notions into arithmetic, the science of numbers. Just as negative and fractional rational numbers are formed by a new creation, and as the laws of operating with these numbers must and can be reduced to the laws of operating with positive integers, so we must endeavor completely to define irrational numbers by means of the rational numbers alone. The question only remains how to do this.

The above comparison of the domain R of rational numbers with a straight line has led to the recognition of the existence of gaps, of a certain incompleteness or discontinuity of the former, while we ascribe to the straight line completeness, absence of gaps, or continuity. In what then does this continuity consist? Everything must depend on the answer to this question, and only through it shall we obtain a scientific basis for the investigation of *all* continuous domains. By vague remarks upon the unbroken connection in the smallest parts obviously nothing is gained; the problem is to indicate a precise characteristic of continuity that can serve as the basis for valid deductions. For a long time I pondered over this in vain, but finally I found what I was seeking. This discovery will, perhaps, be differently estimated by different people; the majority may find its substance very commonplace. It consists of the following. In the preceding section attention was called to the fact that every point p of the straight line produces a separation of the same into two portions such that every point of one portion lies to the left of every point of the other. I find the essence of continuity in the converse, i. e., in the following principle:

"If all points of the straight line fall into two classes such that every point of the first class lies to the left of every point of the second class, then there exists one and only one point which produces this division of all points into two classes, this severing of the straight line into two portions."

As already said I think I shall not err in assuming that every one will at once grant the truth of this statement; the majority of my readers will be very much disappointed in learning that by this commonplace remark the secret of continuity is to be revealed. To this I may say that I am glad if every one finds the above principle so obvious and so in harmony with his own ideas of a line; for I am utterly unable to adduce any proof of its correctness, nor has any one the power. The assumption of this property of the line is nothing else than an axiom by which we attribute to the line its continuity, by which we find continuity in the line. If space has at all a real existence it is *not* necessary for it to be continuous; many of its properties would remain the same even were it discontinuous. And if we knew for certain that space was discontinuous there would be nothing to prevent us, in case we so desired, from filling up its gaps, in thought, and thus making it continuous; this filling up would consist in a creation of new point-individuals and would have to be effected in accordance with the above principle.

IV.

CREATION OF IRRATIONAL NUMBERS.

From the last remarks it is sufficiently obvious how the discontinuous domain R of rational numbers may be rendered complete so as to form a continuous domain. In Section I it was pointed out that every rational number a effects a separation of the system R into two classes such that every number a_1 of the first class A_1 is less than every number a_2 of the second class A_2; the number a is either the greatest number of the class A_1 or the least number of the class A_2. If now any separation of the system R into two classes A_1, A_2, is given which possesses only *this* characteristic property that every number a_1 in A_1 is less than every number a_2 in A_2, then for brevity we shall call such a separation a *cut* [Schnitt] and designate it by (A_1, A_2). We can then say that every rational number a produces one cut or, strictly speaking, two cuts, which, however, we shall not look upon as essentially different; this cut possesses, *besides*, the property that either among the numbers of the first class there exists a greatest or among the numbers of the second class a least number. And conversely, if a cut possesses this property, then it is produced by this greatest or least rational number.

But it is easy to show that there exist infinitely many cuts not produced by rational numbers. The following example suggests itself most readily.

Let D be a positive integer but not the square of an integer, then there exists a positive integer λ such that

$$\lambda^2 < D < (\lambda + 1)^2.$$

If we assign to the second class A_2, every positive rational number a_2 whose square is $>D$, to the first class A_1 all other rational numbers a_1, this separation forms a cut (A_1, A_2), i. e., every number a_1 is less than every number a_2. For if $a_1 = 0$, or is negative, then on that ground a_1 is less than any number a_2, because, by definition, this last is positive; if a_1 is positive, then is its square $\leqq D$, and hence a_1 is less than any positive number a_2 whose square is $>D$.

But this cut is produced by no rational number. To demonstrate this it must be shown first of all that there exists no rational number whose square $= D$. Although this is known from the first elements of the theory of numbers, still the following indirect proof may find place here. If there exist a rational number whose square $= D$, then there exist two positive integers t, u, that satisfy the equation

$$t^2 - Du^2 = 0,$$

and we may assume that u is the *least* positive integer possessing the property that its square, by multiplication by D, may be converted into the square of an integer t. Since evidently

$$\lambda u < t < (\lambda + 1)u,$$

the number $u' = t - \lambda u$ is a positive integer certainly *less* than u. If further we put

$$t' = Du - \lambda t,$$

t' is likewise a positive integer, and we have

$$t'^2 - Du'^2 = (\lambda^2 - D)(t^2 - Du^2) = 0,$$

which is contrary to the assumption respecting u.

Hence the square of every rational number x is either $<D$ or $>D$. From this it easily follows that there is neither in the class A_1 a greatest, nor in the class A_2 a least number. For if we put

$$y = \frac{x(x^2 + 3D)}{3x^2 + D},$$

we have

$$y - x = \frac{2x(D - x^2)}{3x^2 + D}$$

and

$$y^2 - D = \frac{(x^2 - D)^3}{(3x^2 + D)^2}.$$

If in this we assume x to be a positive number from the class A_1, then $x^2 < D$, and hence $y > x$ and $y^2 < D$. Therefore y likewise belongs to the class A_1. But if we assume x to be a number from the class A_2, then $x^2 > D$, and hence $y < x$, $y > 0$, and $y^2 > D$. Therefore y likewise belongs to the class A_2. This cut is therefore produced by no rational number.

In this property that not all cuts are produced by rational numbers consists the incompleteness or discontinuity of the domain R of all rational numbers.

Whenever, then, we have to do with a cut (A_1, A_2) produced by no rational number, we create a new, an *irrational* number a, which we regard as completely defined by this cut (A_1, A_2); we shall say that the number a corresponds to this cut, or that it produces this cut. From now on, therefore, to every definite cut there corresponds a definite rational or irrational number, and we regard two numbers as *different* or *unequal* always and only when they correspond to essentially different cuts.

In order to obtain a basis for the orderly arrangement of all *real*, i. e., of all rational and irrational numbers we must investigate the relation between any two cuts (A_1, A_2) and (B_1, B_2) produced by any two numbers a and β. Obviously a cut (A_1, A_2) is given completely when one of the two classes, e. g., the first A_1 is known, because the second A_2 consists of all rational numbers not contained in A_1, and the characteristic property of such a first class lies in this that if the number a_1 is contained in it, it also contains all numbers less than a_1. If now we compare two such first classes A_1, B_1 with each other, it may happen

1. That they are perfectly identical, i. e., that every number contained in A_1 is also contained in B_1, and that every number contained in B_1 is also contained in A_1. In this case A_2 is necessarily identical with B_2, and the two cuts are perfectly identical, which we denote in symbols by $a = \beta$ or $\beta = a$.

But if the two classes A_1, B_1 are not identical, then there exists in the one, e. g., in A_1, a number $a'_1 = b'_2$ not contained in the other B_1 and consequently found in B_2; hence all numbers b_1 contained in B_1 are certainly less than this number $a'_1 = b'_2$ and therefore all numbers b_1 are contained in A_1.

2. If now this number a'_1 is the only one in A_1 that is not contained in B_1, then is every other number a_1 contained in A_1 also contained in B_1 and is consequently $< a'_1$, i. e., a'_1 is the greatest among all the numbers a_1, hence the cut (A_1, A_2) is produced by the rational number $a = a'_1 = b'_2$. Concerning the other cut (B_1, B_2) we know already that all numbers b_1 in B_1 are also contained in A_1 and are less than the number $a'_1 = b'_2$ which is

contained in B_2; every other number b_2 contained in B_2 must, however, be greater than b'_2, for otherwise it would be less than a'_1, therefore contained in A_1 and hence in B_1; hence b'_2 is the least among all numbers contained in B_2, and consequently the cut (B_1, B_2) is produced by the same rational number $\beta = b'_2 = a'_1 = \alpha$. The two cuts are then only unessentially different.

3. If, however, there exist in A_1 at least two different numbers $a'_1 = b'_2$ and $a''_1 = b''_2$, which are not contained in B_1, then there exist infinitely many of them, because all the infinitely many numbers lying between a'_1 and a''_1 are obviously contained in A_1 (Section I, II) but not in B_1. In this case we say that the numbers α and β corresponding to these two essentially different cuts (A_1, A_2) and (B_1, B_2) are *different*, and further that α is *greater* than β, that β is *less* than α, which we express in symbols by $\alpha > \beta$ as well as $\beta < \alpha$. It is to be noticed that this definition coincides completely with the one given earlier, when α, β are rational.

The remaining possible cases are these:

4. If there exists in B_1 one and only one number $b'_1 = a'_2$, that is not contained in A_1 then the two cuts (A_1, A_2) and (B_1, B_2) are only unessentially different and they are produced by one and the same rational number $\alpha = a'_2 = b'_1 = \beta$.

5. But if there are in B_1 at least two numbers which are not contained in A_1, then $\beta > \alpha$, $\alpha < \beta$.

As this exhausts the possible cases, it follows that of two different numbers one is necessarily the greater, the other the less, which gives two possibilities. A third case is impossible. This was indeed involved in the use of the *comparative* (greater, less) to designate the relation between α, β; but this use has only now been justified. In just such investigations one needs to exercise the greatest care so that even with the best intention to be honest he shall not, through a hasty choice of expressions borrowed from other notions already developed, allow himself to be led into the use of inadmissible transfers from one domain to the other.

If now we consider again somewhat carefully the case $\alpha > \beta$ it is obvious that the less number β, if rational, certainly belongs to the class A_1; for since there is in A_1 a number $a'_1 = b'_2$ which belongs to the class B_2, it follows that the number β, whether the greatest number in B_1 or the least in B_2 is certainly $\leqq a'_1$ and hence contained in A_1. Likewise it is obvious from $\alpha > \beta$ that the greater number α, if rational, certainly belongs to the class B_2, because $\alpha \geqq a'_1$. Combining these two considerations we get the following result: If a cut is produced by the number a then any rational number belongs to the class A_1 or to the class A_2 according as it is less or greater than a; if the number a is itself rational it may belong to either class.

From this we obtain finally the following: If $a > \beta$, i. e., if there are infinitely many numbers in A_1 not contained in B_1 then there are infinitely many such numbers that at the same time are different from a and from β; every such rational number c is $<a$, because it is contained in A_1 and at the same time it is $>\beta$ because contained in β_2.

V.

CONTINUITY OF THE DOMAIN OF REAL NUMBERS.

In consequence of the distinctions just established the system $\Re$ of all real numbers forms a well-arranged domain of one dimension; this is to mean merely that the following laws prevail:

I. If $a > \beta$, and $\beta > \gamma$, then is also $a > \gamma$. We shall say that the number β lies between a and γ.

II. If a, γ are any two different numbers, then there exist infinitely many different numbers β lying between a, γ.

III. If a is any definite number then all numbers of the system $\Re$ fall into two classes $\mathfrak{U}_1$ and $\mathfrak{U}_2$ each of which contains infinitely many individuals; the first class $\mathfrak{U}_1$ comprises all the numbers a_1 that are less than a, the second $\mathfrak{U}_2$ comprises all the numbers a_2 that are greater than a; the number a itself may be assigned at pleasure to the first class or to the second, and it is respectively the greatest of the first or the least of the second class. In each case the separation of the system $\Re$ into the two classes $\mathfrak{U}_1$, $\mathfrak{U}_2$ is such that every number of the first class $\mathfrak{U}_1$ is smaller than every number of the second class $\mathfrak{U}_2$ and we say that this separation is produced by the number a.

For brevity and in order not to weary the reader I suppress the proofs of these theorems which follow immediately from the definitions of the previous section.

Beside these properties, however, the domain $\Re$ possesses also *continuity;* i. e., the following theorem is true:

IV. If the system $\Re$ of all real numbers breaks up into two classes $\mathfrak{U}_1$, $\mathfrak{U}_2$ such that every number a_1 of the class $\mathfrak{U}_1$ is less than every number a_2 of the class $\mathfrak{U}_2$ then there exists one and only one number a by which this separation is produced.

Proof. By the separation or the cut of $\mathfrak{R}$ into $\mathfrak{U}_1$ and $\mathfrak{U}_2$ we obtain at the same time a cut (A_1, A_2) of the system R of all rational numbers which is defined by this that A_1 contains all rational numbers of the class $\mathfrak{U}_1$ and A_2 all other rational numbers, i. e., all rational numbers of the class $\mathfrak{U}_2$. Let a be the perfectly definite number which produces this cut (A_1, A_2). If β is any number different from a, there are always infinitely many rational numbers c lying between a and β. If $\beta < a$, then $c < a$; hence c belongs to the class A_1 and consequently also to the class $\mathfrak{U}_1$, and since at the same time $\beta < c$ then β also belongs to the same class $\mathfrak{U}_1$, because every number in $\mathfrak{U}_2$ is greater than every number c in $\mathfrak{U}_1$. But if $\beta > a$, then is $c > a$; hence c belongs to the class A_2 and consequently also to the class $\mathfrak{U}_2$, and since at the same time $\beta > c$, then β also belongs to the same class $\mathfrak{U}_2$, because every number in $\mathfrak{U}_1$ is less than every number c in $\mathfrak{U}_2$. Hence every number β different from a belongs to the class $\mathfrak{U}_1$ or to the class $\mathfrak{U}_2$ according as $\beta < a$ or $\beta > a$; consequently a itself is either the greatest number in $\mathfrak{U}_1$ or the least number in $\mathfrak{U}_2$, i. e., a is one and obviously the only number by which the separation of $\mathfrak{R}$ into the classes $\mathfrak{U}_1$, $\mathfrak{U}_2$ is produced. Which was to be proved.

VI.

OPERATIONS WITH REAL NUMBERS.

To reduce any operation with two real numbers a, β to operations with rational numbers, it is only necessary from the cuts (A_1, A_2), (B_1, B_2) produced by the numbers a and β in the system R to define the cut (C_1, C_2) which is to correspond to the result of the operation, γ. I confine myself here to the discussion of the simplest case, that of addition.

If c is any rational number, we put it into the class C_1, provided there are two numbers one a_1 in A_1 and one b_1 in B_1 such that their sum $a_1 + b_1 \geqq c$; all other rational numbers shall be put into the class C_2. This separation of all rational numbers into the two classes C_1, C_2 evidently forms a cut, since every number c_1 in C_1 is less than every number c_2 in C_2. If both a and β are rational, then every number c_1 contained in C_1 is $\leqq a + \beta$, because $a_1 \leqq a$, $b_1 \leqq \beta$, and therefore $a_1 + b_1 \leqq a + \beta$; further, if there were contained in C_2 a number $c_2 < a + \beta$, hence $a + \beta = c_2 + p$, where p is a positive rational number, then we should have

$$c_2 = (a - \tfrac{1}{2}p) + (\beta - \tfrac{1}{2}p),$$

which contradicts the definition of the number c_2, because $a-\frac{1}{2}p$ is a number in A_1, and $\beta-\frac{1}{2}p$ a number in B_1; consequently every number c_2 contained in C_2 is $\geqq a+\beta$. Therefore in this case the cut (C_1, C_2) is produced by the sum $a+\beta$. Thus we shall not violate the definition which holds in the arithmetic of rational numbers if in all cases we understand by the sum $a+\beta$ of any two real numbers a, β that number γ by which the cut (C_1, C_2) is produced. Further, if only one of the two numbers a, β is rational, e. g., a, it is easy to see that it makes no difference with the sum $\gamma = a+\beta$ whether the number a is put into the class A_1 or into the class A_2.

Just as addition is defined, so can the other operations of the so-called elementary arithmetic be defined, viz., the formation of differences, products, quotients, powers, roots, logarithms, and in this way we arrive at real proofs of theorems (as, e. g., $\sqrt{2}\cdot\sqrt{3} = \sqrt{6}$), which to the best of my knowledge have never been established before. The excessive length that is to be feared in the definitions of the more complicated operations is partly inherent in the nature of the subject but can for the most part be avoided. Very useful in this connection is the notion of an *interval*, i. e., a system A of rational numbers possessing the following characteristic property: if a and a' are numbers of the system A, then are all rational numbers lying between a and a' contained in A. The system R of all rational numbers, and also the two classes of any cut are intervals. If there exist a rational number a_1 which is less and a rational number a_2 which is greater than every number of the interval A, then A is called a finite interval; there then exist infinitely many numbers in the same condition as a_1 and infinitely many in the same condition as a_2; the whole domain R breaks up into three parts A_1, A, A_2 and there enter two perfectly definite rational or irrational numbers a_1, a_2 which may be called respectively the lower and upper (or the less and greater) *limits* of the interval; the lower limit a_1 is determined by the cut for which the system A_1 forms the first class and the upper a_2 by the cut for which the system A_2 forms the second class. Of every rational or irrational number a lying between a_1 and a_2 it may be said that it lies *within* the interval A. If all numbers of an interval A are also numbers of an interval B, then A is called a portion of B.

Still lengthier considerations seem to loom up when we attempt to adapt the numerous theorems of the arithmetic of rational numbers (as, e. g., the theorem $(a+b)c=ac+bc$) to any real numbers. This, however, is not the case. It is easy to see that it all reduces to showing that the arithmetic operations possess a certain continuity. What I mean by this statement may be expressed in the form of a general theorem:

"If the number λ is the result of an operation performed on the numbers $a, \beta, \gamma, \ldots$ and λ lies within the interval L, then intervals $A, B, C, \ldots$ can be taken within which lie the numbers $a, \beta, \gamma, \ldots$ such that the result of the same operation in which the numbers $a, \beta, \gamma, \ldots$ are replaced by arbitrary numbers of the intervals $A, B, C, \ldots$ is always a number lying within the interval L." The forbidding clumsiness, however, which marks the statement of such a theorem convinces us that something must be brought in as an aid to expression; this is, in fact, attained in the most satisfactory way by introducing the ideas of *variable magnitudes, functions, limiting values,* and it would be best to base the definitions of even the simplest arithmetic operations upon these ideas, a matter which, however, cannot be carried further here.

WALLIS

On Imaginary Numbers

(Selected from the English Version, by Professor David Eugene Smith, Teachers College, Columbia University, New York City)

John Wallis (1616–1703), Savilian professor of geometry at Oxford (1649–1703), contemporary of Newton (see also p. 217), was the first to make any considerable contribution to the geometric treatment of imaginary numbers. This appeared in his *Algebra* (1673), cap. LXVI (Vol. II, p. 286), of the Latin edition. The following extract is from his English translation:

CHAP. LXVI.[1]

Of Negative Squares, *and their* Imaginary Roots *in Algebra.*

We have before had occasion (in the Solution of some Quadratick and Cubick Equations) to make mention of Negative Squares, and Imaginary Roots, (as contradistinguished to what they call Real Roots, whether Affirmative or Negative:) But referred the fuller consideration of them to this place.

These *Imaginary* Quantities (as they are commonly called) arising from the *Supposed* Root of a Negative Square, (when they happen,) are reputed to imply that the Case proposed is Impossible.

And so indeed it is, as to the first and strict notion of what is proposed. For it is not possible, that any Number (Negative or Affirmative) Multiplied into itself, can produce (for instance) −4. Since that Like Signs (whether + or −) will produce +; and therefore not −4.

But it is also Impossible, that any Quantity (though not a Supposed Square) can be *Negative.* Since that it is not possible that any *Magnitude* can be *Less than Nothing*, or any *Number Fewer than None.*

Yet[2] is not that Supposition (of Negative Quantities,) either Unuseful or Absurd; when rightly understood. And though, as to the bare Algebraick Notation, it import a Quantity less than nothing: Yet, when it comes to a Physical Application, it denotes as Real a Quantity as if the Sign were +; but to be interpreted in a contrary sense.

---

[1] [Page 264.] [2] [Page 265.]

As for instance: Supposing a man to have advanced or moved forward, (from A to B,) 5 Yards; and then to retreat (from B to C) 2 Yards: If it be asked, how much he had Advanced (upon the whole march) when at C? or how many Yards he is now Forwarder than when he was at A? I find (by Subducting 2 from 5,) that he is Advanced 3 Yards. (Because $+5-2 = +3$.)

But if, having Advanced 5 Yards to B, he thence Retreat 8 Yards to D; and it be then asked, How much he is Advanced when at D, or how much Forwarder than when he was at A: I say -3 Yards. (Because $+5-8 = -3$.) That is to say, he is advanced 3 Yards less than nothing.

Which in propriety of Speech, cannot be, (since there cannot be less than nothing.) And therefore as to the Line AB *Forward*, the case is Impossible.

But if (contrary to the Supposition,) the Line from A, be continued *Backward*, we shall find D, 3 Yards *Behind* A. (Which was presumed to be *Before* it.)

And thus to say, he is *Advanced* — 3 Yards; is but what we should say (in ordinary form of Speech), he is *Retreated* 3 Yards; or he wants 3 Yards of being so Forward as he was at A.

Which doth not only answer Negatively to the Question asked. That he is not (as was supposed,) Advanced at all: But tells moreover, he is so far from being advanced, (as was supposed) that he is Retreated 3 Yards; or that he is at D, more Backward by 3 Yards, than he was at A.

And consequently — 3, doth as truly design the Point D; as + 3 designed the Point C. Not Forward, as was supposed; but Backward, from A.

So that + 3, signifies 3 Yards Forward; and — 3, signifies 3 Yards Backward: But still in the same Streight Line. And each designs (at least in the same Infinite Line,) one Single Point: And but one. And thus it is in all Lateral Equations; as having but one Single Root.

Now what is admitted in Lines, must on the same Reason, be allowed in Plains also.

As for instance: Supposing that in one Place, we Gain from the Sea, 30 Acres, but Lose in another Place, 20 Acres: If it be now asked, How many Acres we have gained upon the whole: The

Answer is, 10 Acres, or $+$ 10. (Because of $30-20=10$.) Or, which is all one 1600 Square Perches. (For the *English* Acre being Equal to a Plain of 40 Perches in length, and 4 in breadth, whose Area is 160; 10 Acres will be 1600 Square Perches.) Which if it lye in a Square Form, the Side of that Square will be 40 Perches in length; or (admitting of a Negative Root,) $-$ 40.

But if then in a Third place, we lose 20 Acres more; and the same Question be again asked, How much we have gained in the whole; the Answer must be $-$ 10 Acres. (Because $30-20-20=-10$.) That is to say, The Gain is 10 Acres less than nothing. Which is the same as to say, there is a Loss of 10 Acres: or of 1600 Square Perches.

And hitherto, there is no new Difficulty arising, nor any other Impossibility than what we met with before, (in supposing a Negative Quantity, or somewhat Less than nothing:) Save only that $\sqrt{1600}$ is ambiguous; and may be $+$ 40, or $-$ 40. And from such Ambiguity it is, that Quadratick Equations admit of Two Roots.

But now (supposing this Negative Plain, $-$ 1600 Perches, to be in the form of a Square;) must not this Supposed Square be supposed to have a Side? And if so, What shall this Side be?

We[1] cannot say it is 40, nor that it is -40. (Because either of these Multiplyed into itself, will make $+$ 1600; not -1600).

But thus rather, that it is $\sqrt{-1600}$, (the Supposed Root of a Negative Square;) or (which is Equivalent thereunto) $10\sqrt{-16}$, or $20\sqrt{-4}$, or $40\sqrt{-1}$.

Where $\sqrt{}$ implies a Mean Proportional between a Positive and a Negative Quantity. For like as $\sqrt{}\ b\ c$ signifies a Mean Proportional between $+b$ and $+c$; or between $-b$, and $-c$; (either of which, by Multiplication, makes $+bc$:) So doth $\sqrt{-bc}$ signify a Mean Proportional between $+\ b$ and $-\ c$, or between $-\ b$ and $+\ c$; either of which being Multiplied, makes $-bc$. And this as to Algebraick consideration, is the true notion of such Imaginary Root, $\sqrt{-bc}$.

CHAP. LXVII.

The same Exemplified in Geometry.

What hath been already said of $\sqrt{-}\ bc$ in Algebra, (as a Mean Proportional between a Positive and a Negative Quantity:) may be thus Exemplified in Geometry.

---

[1] [Page 266].

If (for instance,) Forward from A, I take A B $= +b$; and Forward from thence, BC $= +c$; (making AC $= +$AB$+$BC$= +b+c$, the Diameter of a Circle:) Then is the Sine, or Mean Proportional BP$=\sqrt{+bc}$.

But if Backward from A, I take AB $= -b$; and then Forward from that B, BC$= +c$; (making AC $= -$AB$+$BC$= -b+c$, the Diameter of the Circle:) Then is the Tangent or Mean Proportional BP$=\sqrt{-bc}$.

So that where $\sqrt{+b}\ c$ signifies a Sine; $\sqrt{-b}\ c$ shall signify a Tangent, to the same Arch (of the same Circle,) AP, from the same Point P, to the same Diameter AC.

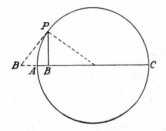
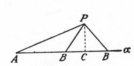

Suppose now (for further Illustration,) A Triangle standing on the Line AC (of indefinite length;) whose one Leg AP$=20$ is given; together with (the Angle PAB, and consequently) the Height PC$=12$; and the length of the other Leg PB$=15$: By which we are to find the length of the Base AB.

'Tis manifest that the Square of AP being 400; and of PC, 144; their Difference 256 ($= 400-144$) is the Square of AC.

And therefore AC($= \sqrt{256}$) $= +16$, or -16; Forward or Backward according as we please to take the Affirmative or Negative Root. But we will here take the Affirmative.

Then, because the Square of PB is 225; and of PC, 144; their Difference 81, is the Square of CB. And therefore CB $= \sqrt{81}$; which is indifferently, $+9$ or -9: And may therefore be taken Forward or Backward from C. Which gives a Double value for the length of AB; to wit, AB$=16+9=25$, or AB$=16-9=7$. Both Affirmative. (But if we should take, Backward from A, AC$=-16$; AB$=-16+9=-7$, and AB$=-16-9=-25$. Both Negative.)

Suppose[1] again, AP$=15$, PC$=12$, (and therefore AC$=\sqrt{}$: 225 -144 : $=\sqrt{81}=9$,) PB$=20$ (and therefore BC$=\sqrt{}$:400-144:

---

[1] [Part 267.]

$=\sqrt{256}=+16$, or -16:) Then is $AB=9+16=25$, or AB $=9-16=-7$. The one Affirmative, the other Negative. (The same values would be, but with contrary Signs, if we take $AC=\sqrt{81}=-9$: That is, $AB=-9+16=+7$, $AB=-9-16=-25$.)

In all which cases, the Point B is found, (if not Forward, at least Backward,) in the Line AC, as the Question supposeth.

And of this nature, are those Quadratick Equations, whose Roots are Real, (whether Affirmative or Negative, or partly the one, partly the other;) without any other Impossibility than (what is incident also to Lateral Equations,) that the Roots (one or both) may be Negative Quantities.

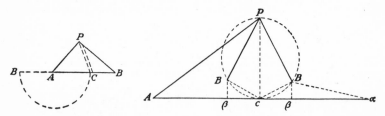

But if we shall Suppose, $AP=20$, $PB=12$, $PC=15$, (and there-fore $AC=\sqrt{175}$:) When we come to Subtract as before, the Square of PC (225,) out of the Square PB (144,) to find the Square of BC, we find that cannot be done without a Negative Remainder, $144-225=-81$.

So that the Square of BC is (indeed) the Difference of the Squares of PB, PC; but a defective Deference; (that of PC proving the greater, which was supposed the Lesser; and the Triangle PBC, Rectangled, not as was supposed at C, but at B:) And therefore $BC=\sqrt{-81}$.

Which gives indeed (as before) a double value of AB, $\sqrt{175}$, $+\sqrt{-81}$, and $\sqrt{175}$, $-\sqrt{-81}$: But such as requires a new Impossibility in Algebra, (which in Lateral Equations doth not happen;) not that of a Negative Root, or a Quantity less than nothing; (as before,) but the Root of a Negative Square. Which in strictness of speech, cannot be: since that no Real Root (Affirma-tive or Negative,) being Multiplied into itself, will make a Nega-tive Square.

This Impossibility in *Algebra*, argues an Impossibility of the case proposed in Geometry; and that the Point B cannot be had, (as was supposed,) in the Line AC, however produced (forward or backward,) from A.

Yet are there Two Points designed (out of that Line, but) in the same Plain; to either of which, if we draw the Lines AB, BP, we have a Triangle; whose Sides AP, PB, are such as were required: And the Angle PAC, and Altitude PC, (above AC, though not above AB,) such as was proposed; And the Difference of Squares of PB, PC, is that of CB.

And like as in the first case, the Two values of AB (which are both Affirmative,) make the double of AC, $(16+9, +16-9, =16+16=32:)$ So here, $\sqrt{175}+\sqrt{-81}, +\sqrt{175}-\sqrt{-81}, =2\sqrt{175}$.

And (in the Figure,) though not the Two Lines themselves, AB, AB, (as in the First case, where they lay in the Line AC;) yet the Ground-lines on which they stand, Aβ, Aβ, are Equal to the Double of AC: That is, if to either of those AB, we join Ba, equal to the other of them, and with the fame Declivity; ACa (the Distance of Aa) will be a Streight Line equal to the double of AC; as is AC a in the First case.

The greatest difference is this; That in the first Case, the Points B, B, lying in the Line AC, the Lines AB, AB, are the fame with their Ground-Lines, but not so in this last case, where BB are so raised above β β (the respective Points in their Ground-Lines, over which they stand,) as to make the case feasible; (that is, so much as is the versed Sine of CB to the Diameter PC:) But in both ACa (the Ground-Line of ABa) is Equal to the Double of AC.

So that, whereas in case of Negative Roots, we are to say, The Point B cannot be found, so as is supposed in AC Forward, but Backward from A it may in the same Line: We must here say, in case of a Negative Square, the Point B cannot be found so as was supposed, in the Line AC; but Above that Line it may in the same Plain.

This I have the more largely insisted on, because the Notion (I think) is new; and this, the plainest Declaration that at present I can think of, to explicate what we commonly call the *Imaginary Roots* of Quadratick Equations. For such are these.

For instance; The Two Roots of this Equation, $aa-2a\sqrt{175} +256=0$; are $a=\sqrt{175}+\sqrt{-81}$, and $a=\sqrt{175}-\sqrt{-81}$. (Which are the values of AB in the last case.) For if from 175 (the Square of half the Coefficient,) we Subduct the Absolute Quantity 256, the Remainder is -81; the Root of which, Added to, and Subducted from, the half Coefficient,) makes $\sqrt{175}\pm\sqrt{-81}$: Which are therefore the Two Roots of that Equation. In the same manner as in the Equation $a^2 - 32\ a + 175 = 0$; if from 256 (the Square of Half 32,) we Subduct 175, the Remainder is $+81$; whose Root $\sqrt{81} = 9$, Added to and Subducted from, 16 (the half Coefficient,) makes 16 ± 9; which are the values of A B in the First case.

CHAP. LXVIII.

The Geometrical Construction accommodated hereunto.

In the former Chapter, we have shewed what in Geometry answers to the Root of a Negative Square in *Algebra.*

I shall now shew some Geometrical Effections, answering to the Resolution of such Quadratick Equations whose Roots may have (what we call) *Imaginary* values, arising from such Negative Squares.

The natural Construction of this Equation $aa \mp ba + a = 0$; is this. The Coefficient b being the Sum of Two Quantities, whose Rectangle is a, the Absolute Quantity: This cannot be more naturally expressed, in Magnitudes, than by making b ($=Aa$) the Diameter of a Circle, and $\sqrt{a}$ ($=BS$) a Right Sine or Ordinate thereunto. (For it is one of the most known Properties of a Circle, that the Sine or Ordinate is a mean Proportional between the Two Segments of the Diameter.) And because BS (of the same length,) may be taken indifferently on either side of CT, we have therefore, in the Diameter, two Points B, B, (answering to SS in the Semicircumference,) either of which divide the Diameter into AB, Ba, the Two Roots desired. (Both Affirmative, or both Negative, according as in the Equation we have $-ba$, or $+ba$.) And as BS increaseth, so B approacheth (on either Side) to C; and CB (the Co-Sine, or Semi-difference of Roots,) decreaseth.

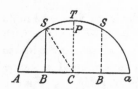

But because the Sine BS can never be greater than CT the Semidiameter: Therefore, whenever $\sqrt{a}$ is greater than $\frac{1}{2}b$; the Case according to this construction is Impossible.

1. The Geometrical Effection, therefore answering to this Equation, $a\ a \mp b\ a + a = 0$, (so as to take in both cases at once, Possible and Impossible; that is, whether $\frac{1}{4}b\ b$ be or be not less than a;) may be this.

On[1] AC$a = b$, bisected in C, erect a Perpendicular CP $= \sqrt{a}$. And taking PB $= \frac{1}{2}b$, make (on whether Side you please of CP,)

---

[1] [Page 269 on this p. 52, a has been used for the æ of Wallis.]

PBC, a Rectangled Triangle. Whose Right Angle will therefore be at C or B, according as PB or PC is bigger; and accordingly, BC a Sine or a Tangent, (to the Radius PB,) terminated in PC.

The Streight Lines AB, B α, are the two values of α. Both Affirmative if (in the Equation,) it be − ba: Both Negative, if +b a. Which values be (what we call) *Real*, if the Right-Angle be at C: But *Imaginary* if at B.

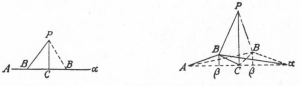

In both cases (whether the Right Angle be at C or B,) the Point B may indifferently be taken on either side of PC, in a like Position. And the Two Points B, B, are those which the Equation designs.

In the former case; ABα is a Streight Line, and the same with ACα.

In the latter; ABα makes at B, such an Angle, as that ACα is the distance cɩ Aα; and is the Ground-line, on which if ABα be Ichnographically projected, B falls on β, the point just under it.

And therefore, if (in the Problem which produceth this Equation) ABα were supposed to be a Streight Line; or the Point B, in the Line ACα; or the same with β; or that ACα be Equal to the Aggregate of AB+Bα; or any thing which doth imply any of these: This Construction shews that Case (so understood) to be Impossible; but how it may be qualified, so as to become possible.

The difference between this Impossibility, and that incident to a Lateral Equation, is this. When in a Lateral Equation, we are reduced to a Negative value; it is as much as to say the Point B demanded, cannot be had (in the Line AC proposed,) Forward from A, as is presumed: But backward from A it may, at such a distance Behind it. But when in a Quadratick Equation, we be reduced, (not to a Negative value; wherein it communicates with the Lateral; but) to (what is wont to be called) an Imaginary value; it is as much as to say, The Point B cannot be had in the Line AC, as was presumed; but, out of that Line it may (in the same Plain;) at such a distance Above it.

The other form of Quadratick Equations, $aa \mp ba - \mathit{x} = 0$; is naturally thus Effected. Taking CA, or CP, $= \frac{1}{2}b$; and PB

$= \sqrt{æ}$; containing a Right Angle at P. The Hypothenuse, BC continued, will cut the Circle PAa, in Aa. And the two Roots 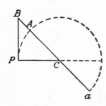 desired, are AB, Ba; between which the Tangent PB is a mean Proportional, and Aa their Difference. But one of them is to be understood Affirmative, the other Negative. (Because if AB be Forward, Ba is Backward; if that be Backward, this Forward.) To wit, $+$AB, $-$Ba, if we have (in the Equation) $+ba$; or $-$AB, $+$Ba, if $-ba$.

But this Construction belongs not properly to this place: Because in this form of Equation, we are never reduced to these Imaginary values. For PB, of whatever length, may be a Tangent to that Circle.

WESSEL

On Complex Numbers

(Translated from the Danish by Professor Martin A. Nordgaard, St. Olaf College, Northfield, Minnesota.)

Caspar Wessel (1745–1818) was a Norwegian surveyor. In 1797, he read a paper upon the graphic representation of complex numbers. The paper was printed in 1798 and appeared in the memoirs of the Royal Academy of Denmark in 1799. This paper may be said to have been the first noteworthy attempt at the modern method. Within a few years thereafter, numerous other attempts were made, all leading to similar results (see Smith, *History of Mathematics*, Vol. II, pp. 263–267). Wessel's work attracted little attention at the time and was almost unknown until the French translation appeared in 1897. The present translation of certain essential passages is made from the original Danish.

On the Analytical Representation of Direction; an Attempt,[1]

Applied Chiefly to the Solution of Plane and Spherical Polygons (By Caspar Wessel, Surveyor.)

This present attempt deals with the question, how may we represent direction analytically; that is, how shall we express right lines so that in a single equation involving one unknown line and others known, both the length and the direction of the unknown line may be expressed.

To help answer this question I base my work on two propositions which to me seem undeniable. The first one is: changes in direction which can be effected by algebraic operations shall be indicated by their signs. And the second: direction is not a subject for algebra except in so far as it can be changed by algebraic operations. But since these cannot change direction (at least, as

---

[1] [In recent histories of mathematics, there have come about very misleading translations into English of Wessel's title word "forsög" as "essay on, etc." This possibility comes from the word "essai" used in the French translation of Wessel's memoir, the French word meaning both an attempt or endeavor, and a treatise (essay.) Wessel's word "forsög" can only mean *attempt* or *endeavor*.]

commonly explained) except to its opposite, that is, from positive to negative, or *vice versa*, these two are the only directions it should be possible to designate, by present methods; for the other directions the problem should be unsolvable. And I suppose this is the reason no one has taken up the matter.[1] It has undoubtedly been considered impermissible to change anything in the accepted explanation of these operations.

And to this we do not object so long as the explanation deals only with quantities in general. But when in certain cases the nature of the quantities dealt with seems to call for more precise definitions of these operations and these can be used to advantage, it ought not to be considered impermissible to offer modifications. For as we pass from arithmetic to geometric analysis, or from operations with abstract numbers to those with right lines, we meet with quantities that have the same relations to one another as numbers, surely; but they also have many more. If we now give these operations a wider meaning, and do not as hitherto limit their use to right lines of the same or opposite direction; but if we extend somewhat our hitherto narrow concept of them so that it becomes applicable not only to the same cases as before, but also to infinitely many more; I say, if we take this liberty, but do not violate the accepted rules of operations, we shall not contravene the first law of numbers. We only extend it, adapt it to the nature of the quantities considered, and observe the rule of method which demands that we by degrees make a difficult principle intelligible.

It is not an unreasonable demand that operations used in geometry be taken in a wider meaning than that given to them in arithmetic. And one will readily admit that in this way it should be possible to produce an infinite number of variations in the directions of lines. Doing this we shall accomplish, as will be proved later, not only that all impossible operations can be avoided —and we shall have light on the paradoxical statement that at times the possible must be tried by impossible means—, but also that the direction of all lines in the same plane can be expressed as analytically as their lengths without burdening the mind with new signs or new rules. There is no question that the general validity of geometric propositions is frequently seen with greater ease if direction can be indicated analytically and governed by alge-

---

[1] Unless it be Magister Gilbert, in Halle, whose prize memoir on *Calculus Situs* possibly contains an explanation of this subject.

braic rules than when it is represented by a figure, and that only in certain cases. Therefore it seems not only permissible, but actually profitable, to make use of operations that apply to other lines than the equal (those of the same direction) and the opposite. On that account my aim in the following chapters will be:

I. First, to define the rules for such operations;
II. Next, to demonstrate their application when the lines are in the same plane, by two examples;
III. To define the direction of lines lying in different planes by a new method of operation, which is not algebraic;
IV. By means of this method to solve plane and spherical polygons;
V. Finally, to derive in the same manner the ordinary formulas of spherical trigonometry.

These will be the chief topics of this treatise. The occasion for its being was my seeking a method whereby I could avoid the impossible operations; and when I had found this, I applied it to convince myself of the universality of certain well-known formulas. The Honorable Mr. Tetens, Councillor-of-state, was kind enough to read through these first investigations. It is due to the encouragement, counsel, and guidance of this distinguished savant that this paper is minus some of its first imperfections and that it has been deemed worthy to be included among the publications of the Royal Academy.

A Method Whereby from Given Right Lines to Form Other Right Lines by Algebraic Operations; and How to Designate Their Directions and Signs

Certain homogeneous quantities have the property that if they are placed together, they increase or diminish one another only as increments or decrements.

There are others which in the same situation effect changes in one another in innumerable other ways. To this class belong right lines.

Thus the distance of a point from a plane may be changed in innumerable ways by the point describing a more or less inclined right line outside the plane.

For, if this line is perpendicular to the axis of the plane, that is, if the path of the point makes a right angle with the axis, the point remains in a plane parallel to the given plane, and its path has no effect on its distance from the plane.

If the described line is indirect, that is, if it makes an oblique angle with the axis of the plane, it will add to or subtract from the distance by a length less than its own; it can increase or diminish the distance in innumerable ways.

If it is direct, that is, in line with the distance, it will increase or diminish the same by its whole length; in the first case it is positive, in the second, negative.

Thus, all the right lines which can be described by a point are, in respect to their effects upon the distance of a given point from a plane outside the point, either direct or indirect or perpendicular[1] according as they add to or subtract from the distance the whole, a part, or nothing, of their own lengths.

Since a quantity is called absolute if its value is given as immediate and not in relation to another quantity, we may in the preceding definitions call the distance the absolute line; and the share of the relative line in lengthening or shortening the absolute line may be called the "effect" of the relative line.

There are other quantities besides right lines among which such relations exist. It would therefore not be a valueless task to explain these relations in general, and to incorporate their general concept in an explanation on operations. But I have accepted the advice of men of judgment, that in this paper both the nature of the contents and plainness of exposition demand that the reader be not burdened here with concepts so abstract. I shall consequently make use of geometric explanation only. These follow.

§1

Two right lines are added if we unite them in such a way that the second line begins where the first one ends, and then pass a right line from the first to the last point of the united lines. This line is the sum of the united lines.

For example, if a point moves forward three feet and backward two feet, the sum of these two paths is not the first three and the last two feet combined; the sum is one foot forward. For this path, described by the same point, gives the same effect as both the other paths.

---

[1] "Indifferent" would be a more fitting name were it not so unfamiliar to our ears.

Similarly, if one side of a triangle extends from *a* to *b* and the other from *b* to *c*, the third one from *a* to *c* shall be called the sum. We shall represent it by *ab* + *bc*, so that *ac* and *ab* + *bc* have the same meaning; or *ac* = *ab* + *bc* = −*ba* + *bc*, if *ba* is the opposite of *ab*. If the added lines are direct, this definition is in complete agreement with the one ordinarily given. If they are indirect, we do not contravene the analogy by calling a right line the sum of two other right lines united, as it gives the same effect as these. Nor is the meaning I have attached to the symbol + so very unusual; for in the expression $ab + \dfrac{ba}{2} = \dfrac{1}{2}ab$ it is seen that $\dfrac{ba}{2}$ is not a part of the sum. We may therefore set *ab* + *bc* = *ac* without, on that account, thinking of *bc* as a part of *ac*; *ab* + *bc* is only the symbol representing *ac*.

§2

If we wish to add more than two right lines we follow the same procedure. They are united by attaching the terminal point of the first to the initial point of the second and the terminal point of this one to the initial point of the third, etc. Then we pass a right line from the point where the first one begins to the point where the last one ends; and this we call their sum.

The order in which these lines are taken is immaterial; for no matter where a point describes a right line within three planes at right angles to one another, this line has the same effect on the distances of the point from each of the planes. Consequently any one of the added lines contributes equally much to the determination of the position of the last point of the sum whether it have first, last, or any other place in the sequence. Consequently, too, the order in the addition of right lines is immaterial. The sum will always be the same; for the first point is supposed to be given and the last point always assumes the same position.

So that in this case, too, the sum may be represented by the added lines connected with one another by the symbol +. In a quadrilateral, for example, if the first side is drawn from *a* to *b*, the second from *b* to *c*, the third from *c* to *d*, but the fourth from *a* to *d*, then we may write: *ad* = *ab* + *bc* + *cd*.

§3

If the sum of several lengths, breadths and heights is equal to zero, then is the sum of the lengths, the sum of the breadths, and the sum of the heights each equal to zero.

§4

It shall be possible in every case to form the product of two right lines from one of its factors in the same manner as the other factor is formed from the positive or absolute line set equal to unity. That is:

Firstly, the factors shall have such a direction that they both can be placed in the same plane with the positive unit.

Secondly, as regards length, the product shall be to one factor as the other factor is to the unit. And,

Finally, if we give the positive unit, the factors, and the product a common origin, the product shall, as regards its direction, lie in the plane of the unit and the factors and diverge from the one factor as many degrees, and on the same side, as the other factor diverges from the unit, so that the direction angle of the product, or its divergence from the positive unit, becomes equal to the sum of the direction angles of the factors.

§5

Let $+1$ designate the positive rectilinear unit and $+\epsilon$ a certain other unit perpendicular to the positive unit and having the same origin; then the direction angle of $+1$ will be equal to $0°$, that of -1 to $180°$, that of $+\epsilon$ to $90°$, and that of $-\epsilon$ to $-90°$ or $270°$. By the rule that the direction angle of the product shall equal the sum of the angles of the factors, we have: $(+1)(+1) = +1$; $(+1)(-1) = -1$; $(-1)(-1) = +1$; $(+1)(+\epsilon) = +\epsilon$; $(+1)(-\epsilon) = -\epsilon$; $(-1)(+\epsilon) = -\epsilon$; $(-1)(-\epsilon) = +\epsilon$; $(+\epsilon)(+\epsilon) = -1$; $(+\epsilon)(-\epsilon) = +1$; $(-\epsilon)(-\epsilon) = -1$.

From this it is seen that ϵ is equal to $\sqrt{-1}$; and the divergence of the product is determined such that not any of the common rules of operation are contravened.

§6

The cosine of a circle arc beginning at the terminal point of the radius $+1$ is that part of the radius, or of its opposite, which begins at the center and ends in the perpendicular dropped from the terminal point of the arc. The sine of the arc is drawn perpendicular to the cosine from its end point to the end point of the arc.

Thus, according to §5, the sine of a right angle is equal to $\sqrt{-1}$. Set $\sqrt{-1} = \epsilon$. Let v be any angle, and let $\sin v$ represent a right line of the same length as the sine of the angle v, positive, if the measure of the angle terminates in the first semi-circumference, but negative, if in the second. Then it follows from §§4 and 5 that $\epsilon \sin v$ expresses the sine of the angle v in respect to both direction and extent. . . .

§7

In agreement with §§1 and 6, the radius which begins at the center and diverges from the absolute or positive unit by angle v is equal to $\cos v + \epsilon \sin v$. But, according to §4, the product of the two factors, of which one diverges from the unit by angle v and the other by angle u, shall diverge from the unit by angle $v + u$. So that if the right line $\cos v + \epsilon \sin v$ is multiplied by the right line $\cos u + \epsilon \sin u$, the product is a right line whose direction angle is $v + u$. Therefore, by §§1 and 6, we may represent the product by $\cos (v + u) + \epsilon \sin (v + u)$.

§8

The product $(\cos v + \epsilon \sin v)(\cos u + \epsilon \sin u)$, or $\cos (v + u) + \epsilon \sin (v + u)$, can be expressed in still another way, namely, by adding into one sum the partial products that result when each of the added lines whose sum constitutes one factor is multiplied by each of those whose sum constitutes the other. Thus, if we use the known trigonometric formulas

$$\cos (v + u) = \cos v \cos u - \sin v \sin u,$$
$$\sin (v + u) = \cos v \sin u + \cos u \sin v,$$

we shall have this form:

$$(\cos v + \epsilon \sin v)(\cos u + \epsilon \sin u) = \cos v \cos u - \sin u$$
$$+ \epsilon(\cos v \sin u + \cos u \sin v).$$

For the above two formulas can be shown, without great difficulty, to hold good for all cases,—be one or both of the angles acute or obtuse, positive or negative. In consequence, the propositions derived from these two formulas also possess universality.

§9

By §7 $\cos v + \epsilon \sin v$ is the radius of a circle whose length is equal to unity and whose divergence from $\cos 0°$ is the angle v. It follows that $r \cos v + r\epsilon \sin v$ represents a right line whose length is r and whose direction angle is v. For if the sides of a right angled triangle increase in length r times, the hypotenuse increases r times; but the angle remains the same. However, by §1, the sum of the sides is equal to the hypotenuse; hence,

$$r \cos v + r\epsilon \sin v = r(\cos v + \epsilon \sin v).$$

This is therefore a general expression for every right line which lies in the same plane with the lines cos 0° and ϵ sin 90°, has the length r, and diverges from cos 0° by v degrees.

§10

If a, b, c denote direct lines of any length, positive or negative, and the two indirect lines $a + \epsilon b$ and $c + \epsilon d$ lie in the same plane with the absolute unit, their product can be found, even when their divergences from the absolute unit are unknown. For we need only to multiply each of the added lines that constitute one sum by each of the lines of the other and add these products; this sum is the required product both in respect to extent and direction: so that $(a + \epsilon b)(c + \epsilon d) = ac - bd + \epsilon(ad + bc)$.

Proof.—Let the length of the line $a + \epsilon b$ be A, and its divergence from the absolute unit be v degrees; also let the length of $c + \epsilon d$ be C, and its divergence be u. Then, by §9, $a + \epsilon b = A \cos v + B\epsilon \sin v$, and $c + \epsilon d = C \cos u + C\epsilon \sin u$. Thus $a = A \cos v$, $b = A \sin v$, $c = C \cos u$, $d = C \sin u$ (§3). But, by §4, $(a + \epsilon b)(c + \epsilon d) = AC[\cos (v + u) + \epsilon \sin (v + u)] = Ac[\cos v \cos u - \sin v \sin u + \epsilon(\cos v \sin u + \cos u \sin v)]$ (§8). Consequently, if instead of $A C \cos v \cos u$ we write ac, and for $A C \sin v \sin u$ write bd, etc., we shall derive the relation we set out to prove.

It follows that, although the added lines of the sum are not all direct, we need make no exception in the known rule on which the theory of equations and the theory of integral functions and their simple divisors are based, namely, that if two sums are to be multiplied, then must each of the added quantities in one be multiplied by each of the added quantities in the other. It is, therefore, certain that if an equation deals with right lines and its root has the form $a + \epsilon b$, then an indirect line is represented. Now, if we should want to multiply together right lines which do not both lie in the same plane with the absolute unit, this rule would have to be put aside. That is the reason why the multiplication of such lines is omitted here. Another way of representing changes of direction is taken up later, in §§24–35.

The quotient multiplied by the divisor shall equal the dividend. We need no proof that these lines must lie in the same plane with the absolute unit, as that follows directly from the definition in §4. It is easily seen also that the quotient must diverge from the absolute unit by angle $v - u$, if the dividend diverges from the same unit by angle v and the divisor by angle u.

Suppose, for example, that we are to divide $A(\cos v + \epsilon \sin v$ by $B(\cos u + \epsilon \sin u)$. The quotient is

$$\frac{A}{B}[\cos (v - u) + \epsilon \sin (v - u)] \text{ since}$$

$$\frac{A}{B}[\cos (v - u) + \epsilon \sin (v - u)] \times B(\cos u + \epsilon \sin u)$$
$$= A (\cos v + \epsilon \sin v),$$

by §7. That is, since $\frac{A}{B}[\cos (v - u) + \epsilon \sin (v - u)]$ multiplied by the divisor $B(\cos u + \epsilon \sin u)$ equals the dividend $A(\cos v + \epsilon \sin v)$, then $\frac{A}{B}[\cos (v - u) + \epsilon \sin (v - u)]$ must be that required quotient. . . .

§12

If a, b, c, and d are direct lines, and the indirect lines $a + \epsilon b$ and $c + \epsilon d$ are in the same plane with the absolute unit: then

$$\frac{1}{c + \epsilon d} = \frac{c - \epsilon d}{c^2 + d^2}, \text{ and the quotient } \frac{a + \epsilon b}{c + \epsilon d} = (a + \epsilon b).\frac{1}{c + \epsilon d}$$

$$= (a + \epsilon b).\frac{c - \epsilon d}{c^2 + d^2} = [ac + bd + \epsilon(bc - ad)]:(c^2 + d^2).$$

For by §9 we may set $a + \epsilon b = A(\cos v + \epsilon \sin v)$, and

$$c + \epsilon d = C(\cos u + \epsilon \sin u),$$

so that

$$c - \epsilon d = C(\cos u - \epsilon \sin u), \text{ by §3.}$$

Since

$$(c + \epsilon d)(c - \epsilon d) = c^2 + d^2 = C^2, \text{ by §10,}$$

then

$$\frac{c - \epsilon d}{c^2 + d^2} = \frac{1}{C}(\cos u - \epsilon \sin u), \text{ by §10;}$$

or

$$\frac{c - \epsilon d}{c^2 + d^2} = \frac{1}{C}[\cos (-u) + \epsilon \sin (-u)] = \frac{1}{c + \epsilon d}, \text{ by §11.}$$

Multiplying by $a + \epsilon b = A(\cos v + \epsilon \sin v)$, gives

$$(a + \epsilon b).\frac{c - \epsilon d}{c^2 + d^2} = \frac{A}{C}[\cos (v - u) + \epsilon \sin (v - u)] = \frac{a + \epsilon b}{c + \epsilon d} \text{ by §11.}$$

Indirect quantities of this class have also this in common with direct, that if the dividend is a sum of several quantities, then each of these, divided by the divisor, gives a quotient, and the sum of these constitute the required quotient.

§13

If m is an integer, then $\cos \dfrac{v}{m} + \epsilon \sin \dfrac{v}{m}$ multiplied by itself m times gives the power $\cos v + \epsilon \sin v$ (§7); therefore we have:

$$(\cos v + \epsilon \sin v)^{\frac{1}{m}} = \cos \frac{v}{m} + \epsilon \sin \frac{v}{m}.$$

But, according to §11,

$$\cos\left(-\frac{v}{m}\right) + \epsilon \sin\left(-\frac{v}{m}\right) = \frac{1}{\cos \dfrac{v}{m} + \epsilon \sin \dfrac{v}{m}} =$$

$$\frac{1}{(\cos v + \epsilon \sin v)^{\frac{1}{m}}} = (\cos v + \epsilon \sin v)^{-\frac{1}{m}}.$$

Consequently, whether m is positive or negative, it is always true that

$$\cos \frac{v}{m} + \epsilon \sin \frac{v}{m} = (\cos v + \epsilon \sin v)^{\frac{1}{m}}.$$

Therefore, if both m and n are integers, we have;

$$(\cos v + \epsilon \sin v)^{\frac{n}{m}} = \cos \frac{n}{m}v + \epsilon \sin \frac{n}{m}v.$$

In this way we find the value of such expressions as $\sqrt[n]{b + c\sqrt{-1}}$ or $\sqrt[m]{a \sqrt[n]{b + c\sqrt{-1}}}$. For example, $\sqrt[3]{4\sqrt{3} + 4\sqrt{-1}}$ denotes a right line whose length is 2 and whose angle with the absolute unit is 10°.

§14

If two angles have equal sines and equal cosines their difference is 0, or ∓ 4 right angles, or a multiple of ± 4 right angles; and conversely, if the difference between two angles is 0 or ± 4 right angles taken once or several times, then their sines as well as their cosines are equal.

§15

If m is an integer and π is equal to 360°, then $(\cos v + \epsilon \sin v)^{\frac{1}{m}}$ has only the following m different values:

$$\cos v + \epsilon \sin v, \ \cos \frac{\pi + v}{m} + \epsilon \sin \frac{\pi + v}{m}, \ \cos \frac{2\pi + v}{m} + \epsilon \sin \frac{2\pi + v}{m} ...,$$

$$\cos \frac{(m-1)\pi + v}{m} + \epsilon \sin \frac{(m-1)\pi + v}{m};$$

for the numbers by which π is multiplied in the preceding series are in the arithmetical progression 1, 2, 3, 4,...$m - 1$. Consequently the sum of every two of them is m, if the one is as far from 1 as the other is from $m - 1$; and if their number is not even, then the middle one taken two times equals m. Therefore if $\dfrac{(m-n)\pi+v}{m}$ is added to $\dfrac{(m-u)\pi+v}{m}$, and the latter is as far from $\dfrac{\pi+v}{m}$, in the series, as $\dfrac{(m-n)\pi+v}{m}$ is from $\dfrac{(m-1)\pi+v}{m}$, then the sum is equal to $\dfrac{2m-u-n}{m}\pi + \dfrac{2v}{m} = \pi + \dfrac{2v}{m}$. But adding $\dfrac{(m-n)\pi}{m}$ is equivalent to subtracting $\dfrac{(m-n)(-\pi)}{m}$; and since the difference is π, $\dfrac{(m-n)(-\pi)+v}{m}$ has the same cosine and sine as $\dfrac{(m-n)\pi+v}{m}$. Hence $(-\pi)$ gives no values not given by $+\pi$.

However, none of these values are equal; for the difference between any two angles of the series is always less than π and never equal to 0. Nor will any more values result if the series is continued; for then the new angles will be $\pi + \dfrac{v}{m}, \pi + \dfrac{\pi+v}{m}, \pi + \dfrac{2\pi+v}{m}$, etc., and according to §14 the values of the sines and cosines of these will be the same as in the angles we already have. There can be no angle outside of the series; for then π would not be multiplied in the numerator by an integer, and the angles multiplied by m would not produce any angle which subtracted from v gives 0, or $\pm\pi$, or a multiple of $\mp\pi$; consequently the mth power of the cosine and sine of such angles could not equal $\cos v + \epsilon \sin v$.

§16

Without knowing the angle which the indirect line $1 + x$ makes with the absolute, we may find, if the length of x is less than 1, the power $(1 + x)^m = 1 + \dfrac{mx}{1} + \dfrac{m}{1}\cdot\dfrac{m-1}{2}x^2 + \text{etc.}$ If this series is arranged according to the powers of m, it has the same value and is changed into the form

$$1 + \frac{ml}{1} + \frac{m^2 l^2}{1} + \frac{m^3 l^3}{1.2.3} + \text{etc.,}$$

where

$$l = x - \frac{x^2}{2} + \frac{x^3}{3} - \frac{x^4}{4} + \text{etc.,}$$

and is a sum of a direct and a perpendicular line. If we call the direct line a and the perpendicular $b\sqrt{-1}$, then b is the smallest measure of the angle which $1 + x$ makes with $+1$. If we set

$$1 + \frac{1}{1} + \frac{1}{1.2} + \frac{1}{1.2.3} + \text{etc.} = e,$$

then

$$(1 + x)^m, \text{ or } 1 + \frac{ml}{1} + \frac{m^2l^2}{1.2} + \frac{m^3l^3}{1.2.3} + \text{etc.},$$

may be represented by $e^{ma + mb\sqrt{-1}}$; that is, $(1 + x)^m$ has the length e^{m4} and a direction angle whose measure is mb, assuming m to be either positive or negative. Lines lying in the same plane may thus have their direction expressed in still another way, namely, by the aid of the natural logarithms. I shall produce complete proofs for these statements at another time, if privileged to do so. Now, that I have rendered an account of my plan for finding the sums, products, quotients, and powers of right lines, I shall next give a couple of examples illustrating the use of this method.

PASCAL

ON THE ARITHMETIC TRIANGLE

(Translated from the French by Anna Savitsky, A. M., Columbia University, New York City.)

Although Pascal (see p. 165) was not the originator of the arithmetic triangle, such an arrangement of numbers having been anticipated, his name has been linked with the triangle by his development of its properties, and by the applications which he made of these properties. The historical interest of the work is to be found, perhaps, in its bearing on probability discussions and on the early developments of the binomial theorem. Since Pascal's contributions to the theory of probability are considered elsewhere in this Source Book, passages pertinent to that theory are omitted in the present translation. Other omissions, also, are necessarily made with great freedom. The original article is found in the works of Pascal, the latest edition of which was edited by Léon Brunschvicg and Pierre Boutroux (Paris, 1908).

TREATISE ON THE ARITHMETIC TRIANGLE
Definitions

I designate as *an arithmetic triangle* a figure whose construction is as follows:

I draw from any point, G, two lines perpendicular to each other, GV, $G\zeta$,[1] in each of which I take as many equal and[2] continuous parts as I please, beginning at G, which I name 1, 2, 3, 4, etc.; and these numbers are *the indices*[3] of the divisions of the lines.

Then I join the points of the first division in each of the two lines by another line that forms a triangle of which it is *the base*.

I join in this manner the two points of the second division by another line that forms a second triangle of which it is *the base*.

And joining in this manner all the points of division which have the same index I form with them as many *triangles* and *bases*.

I draw through each of the points of division lines parallel to the sides, which by their intersections form small squares that I call *cells*.

---

[1] [The editor of the French edition uses ξ instead of ζ by mistake.]

[2] [Pascal employs the words "continües" and "contigües" interchangeably. In the translation, they have been rendered literally.]

[3] [The term used is "exposans."]

The cells which lie between two parallels going from left to right are called *cells of the same parallel rank*, like the cells G, σ, π, etc., or ϕ, ψ, θ, etc.

And those which lie between two lines going from the top downward are called *cells of the same perpendicular rank*, like the cells G, ϕ, A, D, etc., and also σ, ψ, B, etc.

Those which are crossed diagonally by the same base are called *cells of the same base*, like the following: D, B, θ, λ, or A, ψ, π.

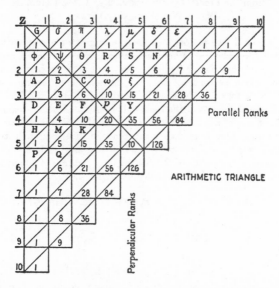

ARITHMETIC TRIANGLE

The cells of the same base equally distant from its ends are called *reciprocals*, as E, R, and B, θ, because the index of the parallel rank of the one is the same as the index of the perpendicular rank of the other, as is apparent in the example where E is in the second perpendicular rank and in the fourth parallel, and its reciprocal R is in the second parallel rank and reciprocally in the fourth perpendicular; and it is quite easy to show that those cells which have their indices reciprocally equal are in the same base and equally distant from its extremities.

It is also quite easy to show that the index of the perpendicular rank of any cell whatsoever, added to the index of its parallel rank, exceeds by unity the index of its base.

For example, cell F is in the third perpendicular rank, and in the fourth parallel rank, and in the sixth base; and the two indices of the ranks $3 + 4$ exceed by unity the index of the base 6, which arises from the fact that the two sides of the triangle are divided into an equal number of parts; but this is rather understood than demonstrated.

The above statement is equivalent to saying that each base contains one cell more than the preceding base, and each as many as the number of units in its index; thus, the second $\phi\sigma$ has two cells, the third $A\psi\pi$ has three of them, etc.

Now the numbers which are placed in each cell are found by this method:

The number of the first cell, which is in the right angle, is arbitrary; but when that has been decided upon, all the others necessarily follow; and for this reason, it is called the *generator* of the triangle. Each of the others is determined by this one rule:

The number of each cell is equal to that of the cell which precedes it in its perpendicular rank, added to that of the cell which precedes it in its parallel rank. Thus, the cell F, that is, the number of the cell F, is equal to the cell C, plus the cell E; and likewise for the others.

From these facts there arise several consequences. Below are the principal ones, in which I consider those triangles whose generator is unity; but what is said of them will apply to all others.

Corollary 1.—In every arithmetic triangle, all the cells of the first parallel rank and of the first perpendicular rank are equal to the generator.

For, by the construction of the triangle, each cell is equal to that of the cell which precedes it in its perpendicular rank, added to that which precedes it in its parallel rank. Now the cells of the first parallel rank have no cells which precede them in their perpendicular ranks, nor those of the first perpendicular rank in their parallel ranks; consequently they are all equal to each other and thus equal to the generating first number.

Thus ϕ equals G + zero, that is, ϕ equals G.

Likewise A equals ϕ + zero, that is, ϕ.

Likewise σ equals G + zero, and π equals σ + zero.

And likewise for the others.

Corollary 2.—In every arithmetic triangle, each cell is equal to the sum of all those of the preceding parallel rank, comprising the cells from its perpendicular rank to the first, inclusively.

Consider any cell ω: I assert that it is equal to $R + \theta + \psi + \phi$, which are cells of the parallel rank above, from the perpendicular rank of ω to the first perpendicular rank.

This is evident by defining the cells, merely, in terms of the cells from which they are formed.

For ω equals $R + C$.

$$\overbrace{\theta + B}$$

$$\overbrace{\psi + A}$$

ϕ, for A and ϕ are equal to each other by the preceding.

Hence ω equals $R + \theta + \psi + \phi$.

Corollary 3.—In every arithmetic triangle, each cell is equal to the sum of all those of the preceding perpendicular rank, comprising the cells from its parallel rank to the first, inclusively.

Consider any cell C: I assert that it is equal to $B + \psi + \sigma$, which are the cells of the preceding perpendicular rank, from the parallel rank of the cell C to the first parallel rank.

This appears likewise by the very definition of the cells.

For C equals $B + \theta$.

$$\overbrace{\psi + \pi}$$

σ, for π equals σ by the first (corollary).

Hence C equals $B + \psi + \sigma$.

Corollary 4.—In every arithmetic triangle, each cell diminished by unity is equal to the sum of all those which are included between its perpendicular rank and its parallel rank, exclusively.

Consider any cell ξ: I assert that $\xi - g$ equals $R + \theta + \psi + \phi + \lambda + \pi + \sigma + G$, which are all the numbers included between the rank $\xi\omega CBA$ and the rank $\xi S\mu$, exclusively.

This appears in like manner from the definition.

For ξ equals $\lambda + R + \omega$.

$$\overbrace{\pi + \theta + C}$$

$$\overbrace{\theta + \psi + B}$$

$$\overbrace{G + \phi + A}$$

$$\overbrace{G.}$$

Hence ξ equals $\lambda + R + \pi + \theta + \sigma + \psi + G + \phi + G$.

NOTE.—I have said in the statement: *each cell diminished by unity*, because unity is the generator; but if it were another number, it would be necessary to say: *each cell diminished by the generating number.*

Corollary 5.—In every arithmetic triangle, each cell is equal to its reciprocal.

For in the second base $\phi\sigma$, it is evident that the two reciprocal cells ϕ, σ, are equal to each other and to G.

In the third $A\psi\pi$, it is likewise seen that the reciprocals π, A, are equal to each other and to G.

In the fourth, it is seen that the extremes D, λ, are again equal to each other and to G.

And those between the two are evidently equal, since B equals $A + \psi$, and θ equals $\psi + \pi$; now $\pi + \psi$ are equal to $A + \psi$, as has been shown; hence, etc.

Likewise it can be shown in all the other bases that the reciprocals are equal, because the extremes are always equal to G, and the rest can always be defined by their equals in the preceding base which are reciprocal to each other.

Corollary 6.—In every arithmetic triangle, a parallel rank and a perpendicular one which have the same index are composed of cells which are respectively equal to each other.

For they are composed of reciprocal cells.

Thus, the second perpendicular rank $\sigma\psi BEMQ$ is exactly equal to the second parallel rank $\phi\psi\theta RSN$.

Corollary 7.—In every arithmetic triangle, the sum of the cells of each base is twice those of the preceding base.

Consider any base $DB\theta\lambda$. I assert that the sum of its cells is double the sum of the cells of the preceding base $A\psi\pi$.

For extremes.......................... $D,$ $\lambda,$

are equal to the extremes................... $A,$ $\pi,$

and each of the others..................... $B,$ $\theta,$

is equal to two of the other base............ $A + \psi,$ $\psi + \pi,$

Hence $D + \lambda + B + \theta$ equal $2A + 2\psi + 2\pi$.

The same thing may be demonstrated for all the others.

Corollary 8.—In every arithmetic triangle, the sum of the cells of each base is a number of the[1] geometric progression which begins with unity, and whose order is the same as the index of the base.

For the first base is unity.

The second is twice the first, hence it is 2.

---

[1] [The term used, "double progression," refers to a geometric progression.]

The third is twice the second, hence it is 4.

And so on to infinity.

NOTE.—If the generator were not unity, but another number like 3, the same thing would be true; however, one should not take the numbers of the geometric progression beginning with unity, that is, 1, 2, 4, 8, 16, etc., but those of another geometric progression beginning with the generator 3, as, 3, 6, 12, 24, 48, etc.

Corollary 9.—In every arithmetic triangle, each base diminished by unity is equal to the sum of all the preceding ones.

For this is a property of the double (geometric) progression.

NOTE.—If the generator were other than unity, it would be necessary to say: *each base diminished by the generator.*

Corollary 10.—In every arithmetic triangle, the sum of a many continuous cells as desired of a base, beginning at one end, is equal to as many cells of the preceding base, taking as many again *less* one.

Let the sum of as many cells as desired of the base $D\lambda$ be taken: for example, the first three $D + B + \theta$.

I assert that it is equal to the sum of the first three cells of the preceding base $A + \psi + \pi$, adding the first two of the same base $A + \psi$.

For D. B. θ.

equals A. $A + \psi$. $\psi + \pi$.

Hence $D + B + \theta$ equals $2A + 2\psi + \pi$.

Definition.—I designate as *cells of the dividend* those which are crossed diagonally by the line which bisects the right angle, as G, ψ, C, ρ, etc.

Corollary 11.—Every cell of the dividend is twice that which precedes it in its parallel or perpendicular rank.

Consider a cell of the dividend C. I assert that it is twice θ, and also twice B.

For C equals $\theta + B$, and θ equals B, by Corollary 5.

NOTE.—All these corollaries are on the subject of the equalities which are encountered in the arithmetic triangle. Now we shall consider those relating to proportions; and for these, the following proposition is fundamental.

Corollary 12.—In every arithmetic triangle, if two cells are contiguous in the same base, the upper is to the lower as the number of cells from the upper to the top of the base is to the number of those from the lower to the bottom, inclusive.

Consider any two contiguous cells of the same base, *E*, *C*: I assert that:

E is to   *C* as 2   is to 3

‾‿‾   ‾‿‾
lower,   upper,   because there are   because there are
                      two cells from *E* to   three cells from *C* to
                      the bottom, that is,   the top, that is, *C*,
                      E, *H*;   *R*, *μ*.

Although this proposition has an infinite number of cases, I will give a rather short demonstration, assuming two lemmas.

Lemma 1: which is self-evident, that this proportion is met with in the second base; for it is apparent that ϕ is to σ as 1 is to 1.

Lemma 2: that if this proportion is found in any base, it will necessarily be found in the following base.

From which it will be seen that this proportion is necessarily in all the bases: for it is in the second base by the first lemma; hence by the second, it is in the third base, hence in the fourth, and so on to infinity.

It is then necessary only to prove the second lemma in this way. If this proportion is met with in any base, as in the fourth *D*λ, that is, if *D* is to *B* as 1 is to 3, and *B* is to *θ* as 2 is to 2, and *θ* is to λ as 3 is to 1, etc., I say that the same proportion will be found in the following base *Hμ*, and that, for example, *E* is to *C* as 2 is to 3.

For *D* is to *B* as 1 is to 3, by the hypothesis.

Hence

$$D + B \text{ is to } B \text{ as } 1 + 3 \text{ is to } 3.$$

‾‿‾   ‾‿‾
E   is to *B* as   4   is to 3.

In the same way *B* is to *θ* as 2 is to 2, by the hypothesis.

Hence

$$B + \theta \text{ is to } B \text{ as } 2 + 2 \text{ is to } 4.$$

‾‿‾   ‾‿‾
C   is to *B* as   4   is to 2.

But

B   is to *E* as   3   is to 4.

Hence by the[1] mixed proportion, *C* is to *E* as 3 is to 2: Which was to be proved.

The same may be demonstrated in all the rest, since this proof is based only on the assumption that the proportion occurs in the

---

[1] [The term used is "proportion troublée."]

preceding base, and that each cell is equal to its preceding plus the one above it, which is true in all cases.

Corollary 13.—In every arithmetic triangle, if two cells are continuous in the same perpendicular rank, the lower is to the upper as the index of the base of the upper is to the index of its parallel rank.

Consider any two cells in the same perpendicular rank, F, C. I assert that F is to C as   5   is to 3
        the lower,   the upper, index of the index of the parallel
                                base of C,   rank of C.

For E is to C as 2 is to 3.
Hence

$$\underbrace{E + C \text{ is to } C \text{ as } \underbrace{2 + 3} \text{ is to } 3.}$$
$$F \quad \text{ is to } C \text{ as } 5 \quad \text{ is to } 3.$$

Corollary 14.—In every arithmetic triangle, if two cells are continuous in the same parallel rank, the greater is to the preceding one as the index of the base of the preceding is to the index of its perpendicular rank.

Consider two cells in the same parallel rank, F, E.   I assert that
      F is to E as   5   is to   2
the greater,   the preceding, index of the index of the per-
                            base of E,   pendicular rank of
                                            E.

For E is to C as 2 is to 3.
Hence

$$\underbrace{E + C \text{ is to } E \text{ as } \underbrace{2 + 3} \text{ is to } 2.}$$
$$F \quad \text{ is to } E \text{ as } 5 \quad \text{ is to } 2.$$

Corollary 15.—In every arithmetic triangle, the sum of the cells of any parallel rank is to the last cell of the rank as the index of the triangle is to the index of the rank.

Consider any triangle, for example, the fourth $GD\lambda$: I assert that for any rank which one takes in it, like the second parallel rank, the sum of its cells, that is $\phi + \psi + \theta$, is to θ as 4 is to 2. For $\phi + \psi + \theta$ equals C, and C is to θ as 4 is to 2, by Corollary 13.

Corollary 16.—In every arithmetic triangle, any parallel rank is to the rank below as the index of the rank below is to the number of its cells.

Consider any triangle, for example the fifth μGH: I assert that, whatever rank one may choose in it, for example the third, the sum of its cells is to the sum of those of the fourth, that is

$A + B + C$ is to $D + E$ as 4, the index of the fourth rank, is to 2, which is the index of the number of its cells, for it contains 2 of them.

For $A + B + C$ equals F, and $D + E$ equals M.

Now F is to M as 4 is to 2, by Corollary 12.

NOTE.—It may also be stated in this manner: *Every parallel rank is to the rank below as the index of the rank below is to the index of the triangle minus the index of the rank above.*

For the index of a triangle, minus the index of one of its ranks, is always equal to the number of cells contained in the rank below.

Corollary 17.—In every arithmetic triangle, any cell whatever added to all those of its perpendicular rank is to the same cell added to all those of its parallel rank as the number of cells taken in each rank.

Consider any cell B: I assert that $B + \psi + \sigma$ is to $B + A$ as 3 is to 2.

I say 3, because there are three cells added in the antecedent, and 2, because there are two of them in the consequent.

For $B + \psi + \sigma$ equals C, by Corollary 3, and $B + A$ equals E, by Corollary 2.

Now C is to E as 3 is to 2, by Corollary 12.

Corollary 18.—In every arithmetic triangle, two parallel ranks equally distant from the ends are to each other as the number of their cells.

Consider any triangle $GV\zeta$, and two of its ranks equally distant from the ends, as the sixth $P + Q$, and the second $\phi + \psi + \theta + R + S + N$: I assert that the sum of the cells of the one is to the sum of the cells of the other as the number of cells of the first is to the number of cells of the second.

For, by Corollary 6, the second parallel rank $\phi\psi\theta RSN$ is the same as the second perpendicular rank $\sigma\psi BEMQ$, for which we have demonstrated this proportion.

NOTE.—It may also be stated: *In every arithmetic triangle, two parallel ranks, whose indices added together exceed by unity the index of the triangle, are to each other inversely as their indices.*

For it is the same thing as that which has just been stated.

Final Corollary.—In every arithmetic triangle, if two cells in the dividend are continuous, the lower is to the upper taken four times as the index of the base of the upper is to a number greater (than the base) by unity.

Consider two cells of the dividend ρ, C: I assert that ρ is to $4C$ as 5, the index of the base of C, is to 6.

For ρ is twice ω, and C twice θ; hence 4θ equal $2C$.

Hence 4θ is to C as 2 is to 1.

Now ρ is to $4C$ as ω is to 4θ,

or by a ratio composed of.................. $\overbrace{\omega \text{ to } C}$ + $\overbrace{C \text{ to } 4\theta}$

by the preceding corollaries............... 5 to 3   1 to 2

                                          or   3 to 6

$$\overline{\quad 5 \qquad \text{to} \qquad 6 \quad}$$

Hence ρ is to $4C$ as 5 is to 6.   Which was to be proved.

NOTE.—Thence many other proportions may be drawn that I have passed over, because they may be easily deduced, and those who would like to apply themselves to it will perhaps find some, more elegant than these which I could present.[1]

APPLICATION OF THE ARITHMETIC TRIANGLE

To Find the Powers of Binomials and[2] Apotomes

If it is proposed to find a certain power, like the fourth degree, of a binomial whose first term is A and the other unity, that is to say, if it is required to find the fourth power of $A + 1$, take the fifth base of the arithmetic triangle, namely, the one whose index 5 is greater by unity than 4, the exponent of the proposed order. The cells of this fifth base are 1, 4, 6, 4, 1; the first number, 1, is to be taken as the coefficient of A to the proposed degree, that is, of A^4; then take the second number of the base, which is 4, as the coefficient of A to the next lower degree, that is to say, of A^3, and take the following number of the base, namely 6, as the coefficient of A to the lower degree, namely, of A^2 and the next number of the base, namely, 4, as the coefficient of A to the lower degree,

---

[1] [At this point, Pascal establishes a theorem which would be stated in modern notations as follows: The cell in the n-th parallel and r-th perpendicular ranks contains the number

$$\frac{n(n+1)\ldots(n+r-2)}{(r-1)!}$$

He then indicates applications of the arithmetic triangle in the theory of combinations, and in the elementary analysis of questions of mathematical probability suggested by games of chance. All of this material is omitted in the present translation.]

[2] [By "apotome," Pascal means a binomial which is the difference between two terms.]

namely, of the root A, and take the last number of the base, 1, as the absolute number; thus we obtain: $1A^4 + 4A^3 + 6A^2 + 4A + 1$, which is the fourth (square-square) power of the binomial $A + 1$. So that if A (which represents any number) is unity, and thus the binomial $A + 1$ becomes 2, this power $1A^4 + 4A^3 + 6A^2 + 4A + 1$, now becomes $1.1^4 + 4.1^3 + 6.1^2 + 4.1 + 1$.

That is, one times the fourth power of A, which is unity 1
> Four times the cube of 1, that is.   4
> Six times the square of 1, that is.   6
> Four times unity, that is.   4
> Plus unity.   1
> Which added together make. . . . . $\overline{16}$

And indeed, the fourth power of 2 is 16.

If A is another number, like 4, and thus the binomial $A + 1$ is 5, then its fourth power will always be, in accordance with this method,

$$1A^4 + 4A^3 + 6A^2 + 4A + 1$$

which now means,

$$1.4^4 + 4.4^3 + 6.4^2 + 4.4 + 1.$$

That is to say, one times the fourth power of 4, namely 256
> Four times the cube of 4, namely. 256
> Six times the square of 4. 96
> Four times the root 4. 16
> Plus unity.   1

whose sum. . . . . $\overline{625}$

produces the fourth power of 5: and indeed, the fourth power of 5 is 625.

Likewise for other examples.

If it is desired to find the same degree of the binomial $A + 2$, take the same expression $1A^4 + 4A^3 + 6A^2 + 4A + 1$, and then write the four numbers, 2, 4, 8, 16, which are the first four degrees of 2, under each of the numbers of the base, omitting the first, in this way

$$1A^4 + 4A^3 + 6A^2 + 4A^1 + 1$$
$$2 \quad\quad 4 \quad\quad 8 \quad\quad 16$$

and multiply the numbers which correspond to each other

$$1A^4 + 4A^3 + \ 6A^2 + \ 4A^1 + \ 1$$
$$2 \quad\quad 4 \quad\quad 8 \quad\quad 16$$

in this way $\overline{1A^4 + 8A^3 + 24A^2 + 32A^1 + 16}$

Thus the fourth power of the binomial $A + 2$ is obtained; if A is unity, the fourth power will be as follows:

One times the fourth power of A, which is unity   1
Eight times the cube of unity................   8
24, 1^2.....................................   24
32, 1.......................................   32
Plus the fourth power of ı..................   16
Whose sum...................................... $\overline{81}$

is the fourth power of 3.   And indeed, 81 is the fourth power of 3.

If A is 2, then $A + 2$ is 4, and its fourth power will be

One times the fourth power of A, or of 2,
        namely................................   16
8, 2^3......................................   64
24, 2^2.....................................   96
32, 2.......................................   64
Plus the fourth power of 2..................   16
whose sum...................................... $\overline{256}$

is the fourth power of 4.

In the same way, the fourth power of $A + 3$ can be found, by writing likewise

$$A^4 + \quad 4A^3 + \quad 6A^2 + \quad 4A + \quad 1$$

and below, the numbers,

$$\frac{3 \qquad 9 \qquad 27 \qquad 81}{1A^4 + 12A^3 + 54A^2 + 108A + 81}$$

which are the first four degrees of 3; and by multiplying the corresponding numbers, we obtain the fourth power of $A + 3$.

And so on to infinity.   If in place of the fourth power, the square-cube, or the fifth degree, is desired, take the sixth base and apply it as I have described in the case of the fifth; and likewise for all the other degrees.

In the same way, the powers of the apotomes $A - 1$, $A - 2$, etc., may be found.   The method is wholly similar, and differs only in the matter of signs, for the signs $+$ and $-$ always alternate, and the sign $+$ is always first.

Thus the fourth power of $A - 1$ may be found in this way. The fourth power of $A + 1$ is, according to the preceding rule, $1A^4 + 4A^3 + 6A^2 + 4A + 1$.   Hence, by changing the signs in the way described, we obtain $1A - 4A^3 + 6A^2 - 4A + 1$. Thus the cube of $A - 2$ is likewise found.   For the cube of $A + 2$, by the preceding rule, is $A^3 + 6A^2 + 12A + 8$.   Hence the cube of $A - 2$ is found by changing the signs, $A^3 - 6A^2 +$ $12A - 8$. And so on to infinity.

I am not giving a demonstration of all this, because others have already treated it, like Hérigogne; besides, the matter is self-evident.

BOMBELLI AND CATALDI

ON CONTINUED FRACTIONS

(Translated from the Italian by Professor Vera Sanford, Western Reserve University, Cleveland, Ohio.)

The study of continued fractions seems to have arisen in connection with the problem of finding the approximate values of the square roots of numbers that are not perfect squares. Various methods of finding such roots had been advanced[1] at an earlier period, but, in general, their operation was difficult and clumsy.

The first mathematician to make use of the concept of continued fractions was Rafael Bombelli (born c. 1530). Little is known of his career, but his contribution to mathematics was the writing of a work which has been characterized as "the most teachable and the most systematic treatment of algebra that had appeared in Italy up to that time."[2] The title was *L'Algebra parte maggiore dell' arimetica divisa in tre libri* and the work was published in Bologna in 1572 and brought out in a second edition in that same city in 1579 under the title *L' Algebra Opera*, the editions being identical except for the title pages and the dedicatory letter. This algebra was noteworthy for its treatment of the cubic and biquadratic equations. The selection here given appears on pages 35 to 37 of the edition of 1579.

Method of Forming Fractions in the Extraction of Roots

Many methods of forming fractions have been given in the works of other authors; the one attacking and accusing another without due cause (in my opinion) for they are all looking to the same end. It is indeed true that one method may be briefer than another, but it is enough that all are at hand and the one that is the most easy will without doubt be accepted by men and be put in use without casting aspersions on another method. Thus it may happen that today I may teach a rule which may be more acceptable than those given in the past, but if another should be discovered later and if one of them should be found to be more vague and if another should be found to be more easy, this [latter] would then be accepted at once and mine would be discarded; for as the saying goes, experience is our master and

---

[1] See SMITH, D. E., *History of Mathematics*, Vol. II, pp. 144, and 253, Boston, Massachusetts, 1925.

[2] *Ibid.*, Vol. I, p. 301.

the result praises the workman. In short, I shall set forth the method which is the most pleasing to me today and it will rest in men's judgment to appraise what they see: mean while I shall continue my discourse going now to the discussion itself.

Let us first assume that if we wish to find the approximate root[1] of 13 that this will be 3 with 4 left over. This remainder should be divided by 6 (double the 3 given above) which gives $\frac{2}{3}$. This is the first fraction which is to be added to the 3, making $3\frac{2}{3}$ which is the approximate root of 13. Since the square of this number is $13\frac{4}{9}$, it is $\frac{4}{9}$ too large, and if one wishes a closer approximation, the 6 which is the double of the 3 should be added to the fraction $\frac{2}{3}$, giving $6\frac{2}{3}$, and this number should be divided into the 4 which is the difference between 13 and 9. The result is $\frac{3}{5}$ which, added to the 3 makes $3\frac{3}{5}$. This is a closer approximation to the root of 13, for its square is $12\frac{24}{25}$, which is closer than that of the $3\frac{2}{3}$.[2] But if I wish a closer approximation, I add this fraction to the 6 making $6\frac{3}{5}$, divide 4 by this, obtaining $\frac{20}{33}$. This should be added to the 3 as was done above, making $3\frac{20}{33}$. This is a closer approximation for its square is $13\frac{4}{1089}$, which is $\frac{4}{4089}$ too large. If I wish a closer approximation, I divide 4 by $6\frac{20}{33}$, obtaining $\frac{109}{180}$, [and] add this to 3, obtaining $3\frac{109}{180}$. This is much closer than before for its square is

---

[1] [Bombelli's term *latus* was a popular one based on the concept of a square root as the side of a square of given area. In this translation, however, the term *root* will be used because of its greater significance.]

[2] [In modern notation, this would, of course be written as: $3 + \cfrac{4}{6 + \cfrac{4}{6}}$.

Bombelli gives no hint as to the reasons for the success of this method, nor does he tell how he discovered it.]

$13\frac{1}{32400}$, which is $\frac{1}{32400}$ too large. If I wish to continue this even further, I divide 4 by $6\frac{109}{180}$ obtaining $\frac{729}{1189}$, which is the root of $13\frac{4}{1413721}$, which is $\frac{4}{1413721}$ too large, and this process may be carried to within an imperceptable difference. Care should be taken, however, in the formation of these fractions in the many cases when the number whose root is to be found falls just short of being a perfect square (as 8, for example). In this case, since 4 is the largest square number, and since 4 is also the remainder, the fraction becomes $\frac{4}{4}$ which is equal to 1.

Adding this to 2 gives 3, whose square is 9. Subtracting the number 8 whose root is required from this number, 1 remains. This should be divided by 6, the double of the 3 giving $\frac{1}{6}$.

Subtracting this from the 3 gives $2\frac{5}{6}$ as the approximate root of 8. The square of this number is $8\frac{1}{36}$[1] which is $\frac{1}{36}$ too large. If a closer approximation is desired, add the $2\frac{5}{6}$ to the 3 getting $5\frac{5}{6}$, and divide 1 by this as was done above, giving $\frac{6}{35}$, which should be subtracted from 3 leaving $2\frac{29}{35}$. This will be a nearer root. If a still closer approximation is desired, divide 1 by $5\frac{29}{35}$. Proceed (as was done above) as close as any one may desire.

. . . .

Pietro Antonio Cataldi[2] (1548–1626) was professor of mathematics and astronomy at Florence, Perugia, and Bologna. He was the author of works on arithmetic, theory of numbers, and geometry and also wrote treatises on topics in algebra. He seems to have been the first to develop a symbolism for continued fractions, and this appears in an essay with the title *Trattato del modo brevissimo Di trouare la Radice quadra delli numeri, Et Regole da approssimarsi di continuo al vero nelle Radici de'numeri non quadrati, con le cause et inuentioni loro, Et anco il modo di pigliarne la Radice cuba, appli-*

---

[1] [Here Bombelli gives $\frac{1}{119}$, evidently a misprint.]

[2] Sometimes given as Cattaldi.

cando il tutto alle Operationi Militari & altre. Bologna, 1613. The selection here given appears on page 70.

Let us now proceed to the consideration of another method of finding roots continuing by adding row on row (*di mano in mano*) to the denominator of the fraction, which finally yields a fraction equal to the fraction of the preceding rule. But for greater convenience, I shall assume a number whose root may be easily taken and I shall assume that the first part of the root is an integer. Then let 18 be the proposed number, and if I assume that the first root is 4. & $\frac{2}{8}$, that is $4\frac{1}{4}$, this will be in excess by $\frac{1}{16}$ which is the square of the fraction $\frac{1}{4}$. The second root will be found by the above mentioned method to be 4. & $\frac{2}{8}$. & $\frac{1}{4}$ which is 4. & $\frac{8}{33}$, which is $\frac{2}{1089}$ too small. This arises from multiplying the entire fraction $\frac{8}{33}$ by $\frac{1}{132}$ in which the whole fraction is less than the $\frac{1}{4}$ which is the added fraction.[1]

Let the root of 18. be

$$4. \,\&\, \frac{2}{8}. \,\&\, \frac{2}{8}. \,\&\, \frac{2}{8}$$

The total fraction added is

makes

$$
\begin{array}{ccc}
 & \dfrac{33}{136} & \dfrac{8}{33} \\[2mm]
2 & 1089 & 1088 \\[2mm]
8\dfrac{1}{4} & \dfrac{1}{136} & \\[2mm]
\dfrac{8}{33} & \dfrac{1}{136 \times 33} \times \dfrac{33 \times 1}{136} &
\end{array}
$$

$$\frac{1}{18,496}$$

That is, 4. & $\frac{2}{8}$. & $\frac{8}{33}$

$$\frac{66}{272}$$

_____

[1] [The work which follows appears in a column at the side of the page, and is rearranged in this translation.]

which is

$$4\frac{33}{136}$$

Squaring, $\frac{1089}{18496}$.

$$17\frac{16}{17} \qquad 1088$$

The square is $18\frac{1}{18496}$, which is too large by $\frac{1}{18496}$.

Be it noted that in the printing when proceeding hurriedly, it is not possible to form fractions and fractions of fractions conveniently in this form, as for instance in the case of

$$4. \& \frac{2}{8}.$$

$$\& \frac{2}{8}.$$

$$\& \frac{2}{8}$$

as we are forcing ourselves to do in this example, but we may denote all of them by adopting this device: 4. $\& \frac{2}{8}. \& \frac{2}{8}. \& \frac{2}{8}.$ letting a period by the 8 in the denominator of each fraction mean that the following fraction is a fraction of the denominator.

. . . .

I shall find the third fraction by the above mentioned method to be 4. $\& \frac{2}{8}. \& \frac{2}{8}. \& \frac{2}{8}.$, or as I might say 4. $\& \frac{2}{8}. \& \frac{2}{8}. \& \frac{1}{4}$, which is 4. $\& \frac{2}{8} \& \frac{8}{33}$, or 4. $\& \dfrac{1}{4 + \dfrac{4}{33}}$, which is 4. $\& \frac{33}{136}$., which will be in excess since $\frac{33}{136}$. the whole fraction is greater than $\frac{8}{33}$. the added fraction. The excess of the square over 18 is $\frac{1}{18496}$ which arises from multiplying $\frac{33}{136}$, the whole fraction by $\frac{1}{136 \times 33}$ in which the whole fraction is greater than the $\frac{8}{33}$ which is the added fraction."[1]

---

[1] [Cataldi continues this work until he reaches the fifteenth fraction.]

JACQUES (I) BERNOULLI

ON THE "BERNOULLI NUMBERS"

(Translated from the Latin by Professor Jekuthiel Ginsburg, Yeshiva College, New York City.)

Of the various special kinds of numbers used in analysis, there is hardly a species that is so important and so generally applicable as the Bernoulli Numbers. Their numerous properties and applications have caused the creation of an extensive literature on the subject which still continues to attract the attention of scholars. The first statement of the properties of these numbers was given to the world by their inventor Jacques (1) Bernoulli (1654–1705) in his posthumously printed work, *Ars Conjectandi* (Basel, 1713), pages 95 to 98. These pages are here translated.

The excerpt is interesting from more than one point of view. First, we witness in it the first stroke of genius that caused ripples in human thought that have not died out even to the present day. Second, the memoir is as fresh and vigorous today as when it was written; in fact, it could be used even now as a popular exposition of the simpler properties of the Bernoulli Numbers. Third, the text reveals the personal touch, the unbounded enthusiasm of the author over the power of the numbers later called by his name. His remark that the results of Bullialdus's enormous treatise could, by means of his numbers, be compressed in less than one page, is both striking and illuminating. Nor is the element of puzzle and mystery lacking. Regardless of the fact that the discovery is more than 200 years old, mathematicians have not been able as yet to find by what process Bernoulli derived the properties of his numbers which he gives in these pages. They can readily be derived by various modern methods, but how did he derive them with the means at his disposal? It is also interesting to compare his criticism of Wallis's use of incomplete induction with his own use of the same imperfect tool. In short, in the compass of three printed pages we get not only information about the invention but also glimpses of the person of the great master.

We will observe here in passing that, many [scholars] engaged in the contemplation of figurate numbers (among them Faulhaber[1]

---

[1] [Johann Faulhaber, a successful teacher of mathematics in Ulm, was born there on May 5, 1580, and died there in 1635 (D. E. Smith, *History of Mathematics*, Vol. I, p. 418). With the help of his friend and protector Johann Remmelin he published a number of mathematical works. In his *Mysterium Arithmeticum*, 1615, he discussed the properties of figurate numbers. Bernoulli possibly refers to this work of his. Faulhaber also developed formulas for Σn^c from $c = 1$ to $c = 17$ (Tropfke, *Geschichte der Elementar Mathematik*, Vol. VI, p. 22).]

and Remmelin of Ulm, Wallis, Mercator,[1] in his *Logarithmo-technia* and others) but I do not know of one who gave a general and scientific proof of this property.[2]

Wallis in his *Arithmetica Infinitorum* investigated by means of induction the ratios that the series of squares, cubes, and other powers of natural numbers have to the series of terms each equal to the greatest term.   This he put in the foundation of his method. His next step was to establish 176 properties of trigonal, pyramidal, and other figurate numbers, but it would have been better and more fitting to the nature of the subject if the process would have been reversed and he would have first given a discussion of figurate numbers, demonstrated in a general and accurate way, and only then have proceeded with the investigation of the sums of powers of the natural numbers.   Even disregarding the fact that the method of induction is not sufficiently scientific and, moreover, requires special work for every new series; it is a method of common judgment that the simpler and more primitive things should precede others.   Such are the figurate numbers as related to the powers, since they are formed by addition, while the others are formed by multiplication; chiefly, however, because the series of figurate numbers, supplied with the corresponding zeros[3] have a submultiple ratio to the series of equals.[4]   In case of powers (when

---

[1] [Nicolaus Mercator was born near Cismar in Holstein, *c.* 1620, and died in Paris in February, 1687.   His *Arithmotechnia sive methodus construendi logarithmos nova accurata et facilis...* was published in London in 1678 (Smith, *l. c.*, I, 434).   Bernoulli fails to mention Oughtred who pointed out the correspondence between the binominal coefficients and the figurate numbers, as did also Nicolo Tartaglia, Pascal, and others.]

[2] [The property refers to the method of finding the nth term and the sum of n terms in a series of figurate numbers.]

[3] [The number of zeros to put in the triangle of figurate numbers to make it look like a square

1	0	0	0	0	0	0
1	1	0	0	0	0	0
1	2	1	0	0	0	0
1	3	3	1	0	0	0
1	4	6	4	1	0	0
1	5	10	10	5	1	0
1	6	15	20	15	6	1
1	7	21	35	35	21	7

Bernoulli counts each zero as a term.   Thus the sum of the terms of the third column is $0 + 0 + 1 + 3 + 6 + 10 + 15 + 21$.]

[4] [That is taking for example column three in the preceding footnote, the ratio of the sum of any number of terms beginning with two zeros to the sum of

the number of terms is finite) this does not hold without some excess or defect no matter how many zeros be added. With the known sums of the figurate numbers it is not difficult to derive the sums of the powers. I will show briefly how it is done.

Let the series of natural numbers 1, 2, 3, 4, 5, etc. up to n be given, and let it be required to find their sum, the sum of the squares, cubes, etc. Since in the table of combinations the general term of the second column is $n - 1$ and the sum of all terms, that is, all $n - 1$, or $\int \overline{n - 1}$ in consequence of above is[2]

$$\frac{n.n - 1}{1.2} = \frac{nn - n}{2}.$$

The sum $\int \overline{n - 1}$ or

$$\int n - \int 1 = \frac{nn - n}{n}.$$

Therefore

$$\int n = \frac{nn - n}{2} + \int 1.$$

But $\int 1$ (the sum of all units) $= n$. Therefore the sum of all n or

$$\int n = \frac{nn - n}{2} + n = \tfrac{1}{2}nn + \tfrac{1}{2}n.$$

A term of the third column is generally taken to be

$$\frac{n - 1.n - 2}{1.2} = \frac{nn - 3n + 2}{2}$$

---

a series of terms each equal to the last term of the first series will be $\frac{1}{3}$. Thus,

$$\frac{0 + 0 + 1 + 3}{3 + 3 + 3 + 3} = \frac{4}{12} = \frac{1}{3}; \quad \frac{0 + 0 + 1 + 3 + 6 + 10}{10 + 10 + 10 + 10 + 10 + 10} = \frac{1}{3};$$

$$\frac{0 + 0 + 1 + 3 + 6 + 10 + 15}{15 + 15 + 15 + 15 + 15 + 15 + 15} = \frac{1}{3}, \text{ etc.}$$

In the fourth column we get $\frac{1}{4}$, and in the fifth we have $\frac{1}{5}$. In every case the first series is a submultiple of the second, which he calls the series of equal terms.]

[2] [*I. e.*, the sum of $0 + 1 + 2 + \ldots + n - 1$ is as was stated above $\frac{1}{2}$ of $(n - 1) + (n - 1) + (n - 1) \ldots (n$ times) since the ratio $\frac{0 + 1 + 2 + \ldots + (n - 1)}{(n - 1) + (n - 1) \ldots + (n - 1)} = \frac{1}{2}$. Hence $\frac{s}{n(n - 1)} = \frac{1}{2} \therefore s = \frac{n(n - 1)}{1.2}$. Throughout the work Bernoulli uses the old form of s, our present integral sign ($\int$) where we would now use Σ. His usage has been followed in the translation. He also writes n.n $-$ 1 where we would write n(n $-$ 1) and he expresses equality by the sign $\propto$ but in this translation the sign $=$ will be used. His use of nn instead of n² should also be noted.]

and the sum of all terms $\left(\text{that is, of all } \dfrac{nn - 3n + 2}{2}\right)$ is

$$\frac{n.\overline{n-1}.\overline{n-2}}{1.2.3} = \frac{n^3 - 3nn + 2n}{6}$$

P A R S   S E C U N D A. 97

$\infty \dfrac{n^4 - 6n^3 + 11nn - 6n}{24}$, erit.utique $\sqrt{\dfrac{n^3 - 6nn + 11n - 6}{6}}$, hoc eft,

$\int \frac{1}{6}n^3 - \int nn + \int \frac{1}{6}n - \int 1 \; \infty \; \dfrac{n^4 - 6n^3 + 11nn - 6n}{24}$, indeque $\int \frac{1}{6}n^3 \; \infty$

$\dfrac{n^4 - 6n^3 + 11nn - 6n}{24} + \int nn - \int \frac{1}{6}n + \int 1$. Et quoniam per modo in-

venta $\int nn \; \infty \; \frac{1}{3}n^3 + \frac{1}{2}nn + \frac{1}{6}n$; nec non $\int \frac{1}{6}n$ five $\frac{1}{6}\int n \; \infty \; \frac{1}{12}nn + \frac{1}{12}n$,

& $\int 1 \; \infty \; n$; hinc factâ horum fubftitutione emerget $\int \frac{1}{6}n^3 \; \infty$

$\dfrac{n^4 - 6n^3 + 11nn - 6n}{24} + \frac{1}{3}n^3 + \frac{1}{2}nn + \frac{1}{6}n - \frac{1}{12}nn - \frac{1}{12}n + n \; \infty$

$\frac{1}{24}n^4 + \frac{1}{12}n^3 + \frac{1}{24}nn$, ejusque proin fextuplum $\int n^3$ (fumma cubo-

rum) $\infty \; \frac{1}{4}n^4 + \frac{1}{2}n^3 + \frac{1}{4}nn$. Atque fic porrò ad altiores gradatim

poteftates pergere, levique negotio fequentem adornare laterculum

licet :

Summæ Poteftatum.

$\int n \; \infty \; \frac{1}{2}nn + \frac{1}{2}n$.

$\int nn \; \infty \; \frac{1}{3}n^3 + \frac{1}{2}nn + \frac{1}{6}n$.

$\int n^3 \; \infty \; \frac{1}{4}n^4 + \frac{1}{2}n^3 + \frac{1}{4}nn$.

$\int n^4 \; \infty \; \frac{1}{5}n^5 + \frac{1}{2}n^4 + \frac{1}{3}n^3 \; * - \frac{1}{30}n$.

$\int n^5 \; \infty \; \frac{1}{6}n^6 + \frac{1}{2}n^5 + \frac{5}{12}n^4 \; * - \frac{1}{12}nn$.

$\int n^6 \; \infty \; \frac{1}{7}n^7 + \frac{1}{2}n^6 + \frac{1}{2}n^5 \; * - \frac{1}{6}n^3 \; * + \frac{1}{42}n$.

$\int n^7 \; \infty \; \frac{1}{8}n^8 + \frac{1}{2}n^7 + \frac{7}{12}n^6 \; * - \frac{7}{24}n^4 \; * + \frac{1}{12}nn$.

$\int n^8 \; \infty \; \frac{1}{9}n^9 + \frac{1}{2}n^8 + \frac{2}{3}n^7 \; * - \frac{7}{15}n^5 \; * + \frac{2}{9}n^3 \; * - \frac{1}{30}n$.

$\int n^9 \; \infty \; \frac{1}{10}n^{10} + \frac{1}{2}n^9 + \frac{3}{4}n^8 \; * - \frac{7}{10}n^6 \; * + \frac{1}{2}n^4 \; * - \frac{3}{20}nn$.

$\int n^{10} \; \infty \; \frac{1}{11}n^{11} + \frac{1}{2}n^{10} + \frac{5}{6}n^9 \; * - 1 \, n^7 \; * + 1 \, n^5 \; * - \frac{1}{2}n^3 \; * + \frac{5}{66}n$.

Quin imò qui legem progreffionis inibi attentius infpexerit, eundem

etiam continuare poterit abfq; his ratiociniorum ambagibus : Sumtâ

enim c pro poteftatis cujuslibet exponente, fit fumma omnium n^c feu

$\int n^c \; \infty \; \dfrac{1}{c+1}n^{c+1} + \frac{1}{2}n^c + \frac{c}{2}An^{c-1} + \dfrac{c.\overline{c-1}.\overline{c-2}}{2.3.4}Bn^{c-3} +$

$\dfrac{c.\overline{c-1}.\overline{c-2}.\overline{c-3}.\overline{c-4}}{2.3.4.5.6}Cn^{c-5} + \dfrac{c.\overline{c-1}.\overline{c-2}.\overline{c-3}.\overline{c-4}.\overline{c-5}.\overline{c-6}}{2.3.4.5.6.7.8}$

$Dn^{c-7} \ldots$ & ita deinceps, exponentem poteftatis ipfius n con-

tinuè minuendo binario, quousque perveniatur ad n vel nn. Literæ

capitales A, B, C, D &c. ordine denotant coëfficientes ultimo-

rum terminorum pro $\int nn$, $\int n^4$, $\int n^6$, $\int n^8$ &c. nempe A $\infty \; \frac{1}{6}$, B

$\infty - \frac{1}{30}$

N

We will have then that

$$\int \frac{n^2 - 3n + 2}{2}$$

or

$$\int \frac{1}{2}{}^2nn - \int \frac{3}{2}n + \int 1 = \frac{n^3 - 3nn + 2n}{6}$$

and

$$\int \tfrac{1}{2}nn = \frac{n^3 - 3nn + 2n}{6} + \int \tfrac{3}{2}n - \int 1;$$

but

$$\int \tfrac{3}{2}n = \tfrac{3}{2}\int n = \tfrac{3}{4}nn + \tfrac{3}{4}n$$

and

$$\int 1 = n.$$

Substituting, we have

$$\int \tfrac{1}{2}nn = \frac{n^3 - 3nn + 2n}{6} + \frac{3nn + 3n}{4} - n = \tfrac{1}{6}n^3 + \tfrac{1}{4}nn + \tfrac{1}{12}n,$$

of which the double $\int nn$ (the sum of the squares of all n) $= \tfrac{1}{3}n^3$ $+ \tfrac{1}{2}nn + \tfrac{1}{6}n$.

A term of the fourth column is generally

$$\frac{n - 1.n - 2.n - 3}{1.2.3} = \frac{n^3 - 6nn + 11n - 6}{6},$$

and the sum of all terms is

$$\frac{n.n - 1.n - 2.n - 3}{1.2.3.4} = \frac{n^4 - 6n^3 + 11nn - 6n}{24}.$$

It must certainly be that

$$\int \frac{n^3 - 6nn + 11n - 6}{6};$$

that is

$$\int \tfrac{1}{6}n^3 - \int nn + \int \tfrac{11}{6}n - \int 1 = \frac{n^4 - 6n^3 + 11nn - 6n}{24}.$$

Hence

$$\int \tfrac{1}{6}n^3 = \frac{n^4 - 6n^3 + 11nn - 6n}{24} + \int nn - \int \tfrac{11}{6}n + \int 1.$$

And before it was found that $\int nn = \tfrac{1}{3}n^3 + \tfrac{1}{2}nn + \tfrac{1}{6}n$, $\int \tfrac{11}{6}n$ or $\tfrac{11}{6}\int n = \tfrac{11}{12}nn + \tfrac{11}{12}n$, and $\int 1 = n$.

When all substitutions are made, the following results:

$$\int \tfrac{1}{6}n^3 = \frac{n^4 - 6n^3 + 11nn - 6n}{24} + \tfrac{1}{3}n^3 + \tfrac{1}{2}nn + \tfrac{1}{6}n - \tfrac{11}{12}nn$$

$$- \tfrac{11}{12}n + n$$

$$= \tfrac{1}{24}n^4 + \tfrac{1}{12}n^3 + \tfrac{1}{24}nn;$$

or, multiplying by 6,

$$\int n^3 = \tfrac{1}{4}n^4 + \tfrac{1}{2}n^3 + \tfrac{1}{4}nn.$$

Thus we can step by step reach higher and higher powers and with slight effort form the following table:[1]

---

[1] [Bernoulli uses ✕ to mean what we now designate by ...]

Sum of Powers

$$\int n = \tfrac{1}{2}nn + \tfrac{1}{2}n,$$

$$\int nn = \tfrac{1}{3}n^3 + \tfrac{1}{2}nn + \tfrac{1}{6}n,$$

$$\int n^3 = \tfrac{1}{4}n^4 + \tfrac{1}{2}n^3 + \tfrac{1}{4}nn,$$

$$\int n^4 = \tfrac{1}{5}n^5 + \tfrac{1}{2}n^4 + \tfrac{1}{3}n^3 \ast -\tfrac{1}{30}n,$$

$$\int n^5 = \tfrac{1}{6}n^6 + \tfrac{1}{2}n^5 + \tfrac{5}{12}n^4 \ast -\tfrac{1}{12}nn,$$

$$\int n^6 = \tfrac{1}{7}n^7 + \tfrac{1}{2}n^6 + \tfrac{1}{2}n^5 \ast -\tfrac{1}{6}n^3 \ast +\tfrac{1}{42}n,$$

$$\int n^7 = \tfrac{1}{8}n^8 + \tfrac{1}{2}n^7 + \tfrac{7}{12}n^6 \ast -\tfrac{7}{24}n^4 \ast +\tfrac{1}{12}nn,$$

$$\int n^8 = \tfrac{1}{9}n^9 + \tfrac{1}{2}n^8 + \tfrac{2}{3}n^7 \ast -\tfrac{7}{15}n^5 \ast +\tfrac{2}{9}n^3 \ast -\tfrac{1}{30}n,$$

$$\int n^9 = \tfrac{1}{10}n^{10} + \tfrac{1}{2}n^9 + \tfrac{3}{4}n^8 \ast -\tfrac{7}{10}n^6 \ast +\tfrac{1}{2}n^4 \ast -\tfrac{1}{12}nn,$$

$$\int n^{10} = \tfrac{1}{11}n^{11} + \tfrac{1}{2}n^{10} + \tfrac{5}{6}n^9 \ast -1n^7 \ast 1n^5 \ast -\tfrac{1}{2}n^3 \ast \tfrac{5}{66}n.$$

Whoever will examine the series as to their regularity may be able to continue the table. Taking c to be the power of any exponent, the sum of all n^c or

$$\int n^c = \frac{1}{c+1}n^{c+1} + \frac{1}{2}n^c + \frac{c}{2}An^{c-1} + \frac{c.c-1.c-2}{2.3.4}Bn^{c-3}$$

$$+ \frac{c.c-1.c-2.e-3.c-4}{2.3.4.5.6}Cn^{c-5}$$

$$+ \frac{c.c-1.c-2.c-3.c-4.c-5.c-6}{2.3.4.5.6.7.8}Dn^{c-7},$$

and so on, the exponents of n continually decreasing by 2 until n or nn is reached. The capital letters A, B, C, D denote in order the coefficients of the last terms in the expressions for $\int nn$, $\int n^4$, $\int n^8$ namely A, is equal to $\tfrac{1}{6}$, B is equal to $-\tfrac{1}{30}$, C is equal to $\tfrac{1}{42}$, D is equal to $-\tfrac{1}{30}$.

These coefficients are such that each one completes the others in the same expression to unity. Thus D must have the value $-\tfrac{1}{30}$ because $\tfrac{1}{9} + \tfrac{1}{2} + \tfrac{2}{3} - \tfrac{7}{15} + \tfrac{2}{9} + (+D) - \tfrac{1}{30} = 1$.

With the help of this table it took me less than half of a quarter of an hour to find that the tenth powers of the first 1000 numbers being added together will yield the sum

$$91{,}409{,}924{,}241{,}424{,}243{,}424{,}241{,}924{,}242{,}500$$

From this it will become clear how useless was the work of Ismael Bullialdus[1] spent on the compilation of his voluminous *Arithmetica Infinitorum* in which he did nothing more than compute with immense labor the sums of the first six powers, which is only a part of what we have accomplished in the space of a single page.

---

[1] [The title of Bullialdus's (1605–1694) work is *Opus novum ad arithmeticum infinitorum*. It was published in Paris 1682 and consists of six parts.]

EULER

Proof that Every Integer is a Sum of Four Squares

(Translated from the Latin by Professor E. T. Bell, California Institute of Technology, Pasadena, California.)

Léonard (Leonhard) Euler (1707–1783), a pupil of Jean (I) Bernoulli, was not only one of the greatest mathematicians and astronomers of his century, but he was also versed in theology, medicine, botany, physics, mechanics, chemistry, and the Oriental as well as the modern languages. He was a voluminous writer, and there was hardly a branch of mathematics to which he did not contribute. The selection here translated serves to illustrate his method of attacking a problem in the theory of numbers. It is taken from his *Commentationes Arithmeticae Collectae*, Petropoli, 1849, edited by P. H. Fuss and N. Fuss (Vol. I, pp. 543–546) but appeared earlier in the *Acta Eruditorum* (p. 193, Leipzig, 1773) and the *Acta Petrop.*, (p. 48, I. II., 1775. Exhib. Sept. 21, 1772). In preparing the article, the effort has been made to give a free translation that shall clearly convey Euler's meaning, in preference to following too closely the rather poor Latin of the day. Of his two proofs for the exceptional case of $n = 2$, only the simpler one has been given. From the modern point of view, the proof of the theorem is not very satisfactory, but it serves to illustrate the theory of numbers of the eighteenth century.

Lemma.—*The product of two numbers, each of which is a sum of four squares, may always be expressed as a sum of four squares.*

Let such a product be

$$(a^2 + b^2 + c^2 + d^2)(\alpha^2 + \beta^2 + \gamma^2 + \delta^2).$$

Write

$$A = a\alpha + b\beta + c\gamma + d\delta,$$
$$B = a\beta - b\alpha - c\delta + d\gamma,$$
$$C = a\gamma + b\delta - c\alpha - d\beta,$$
$$D = a\delta - b\gamma + c\beta - d\alpha.$$

Then

$$A^2 + B^2 + C^2 + D^2 = (a^2 + b^2 + c^2 + d^2)(\alpha^2 + \beta^2 + \gamma^2 + \delta^2),$$

since obviously the cross products in A^2, B^2, C^2, D^2 cancel.

THEOREM 1.—*If N is a divisor of a sum of four squares, say of $p^2 + q^2 + r^2 + s^2$, no one of which is divisible by N, then N is the sum of four squares.*

91

It will first be shown that each of the four roots p, q, r, s may be chosen less than $\frac{1}{2}N$.[1]

I. Let n be the quotient on dividing the sum of four squares by N, so that $Nn = p^2 + q^2 + r^2 + s^2$. Then we may write

$$p = a + n\alpha, \qquad q = b + n\beta, \qquad r = c + n\gamma, \qquad s = d + n\delta,$$

where each remainder a, b, c, d does not exceed $\frac{1}{2}n$ in absolute value.[2]

Hence

$$a^2 + b^2 + c^2 + d^2 < n^2.$$

II. By substituting the above values of p, q, r, s in

$$Nn = p^2 + q^2 + r^2 + s^2,$$

we get

$$Nn = a^2 + b^2 + c^2 + d^2 + 2n(a\alpha + b\beta + c\gamma + d\delta) \\ + n^2 (\alpha^2 + \beta^2 + \gamma^2 + \delta^2);$$

whence it follows that n must be a divisor of $a^2 + b^2 + c^2 + d^2$.

Put

$$a^2 + b^2 + c^2 + d^2 = nn'.$$

Then $n > n'$, or $n' < n$. By division we get

$$N = n' + 2A + n(\alpha^2 + \beta^2 + \gamma^2 + \delta^2).$$

III. Multiply now by n'. Then, since

$$nn' = a^2 + b^2 + c^2 + d^2,$$

we have, by the Lemma,

$$nn'(\alpha^2 + \beta^2 + \gamma^2 + \delta^2) = A^2 + B^2 + C^2 + D^2,$$

Combining this with the preceding equation we find

$$Nn' = n'^2 + 2n'A + A^2 + B^2 + C^2 + D^2,$$

and therefore

$$(n' + A)^2 + B^2 + C^2 + D^2 = Nn'.$$

IV. By repeating the foregoing argument we obtain a decreasing sequence of integers Nn', Nn'', etc., and hence finally we reach $N.1$ and its expression as a sum of four squares.

---

[1] [It is to be observed in the following proof that n is different from 2; this case is tacitly ignored until the so-called corollary, following the proof, which disposes of the exceptional case implicit in the argument as presented.]

[2] [But see the preceding footnote. The condition as to absolute values safeguards the assertion above, but it does not take care of all possibilities in the proof which immediately follows, unless, as with Euler, and as indicated in the preceding footnote, we attend to the corollary.]

LEONHARD EULER

Corollary.—To dispose of the apparent exception, let p, q, r, s be odd numbers and n an even number. Then, since

$$Nn = p^2 + q^2 + r^2 + s^2,$$

we have

$$\tfrac{1}{2}Nn = \left(\frac{p+q}{2}\right)^2 + \left(\frac{p-q}{2}\right)^2 + \left(\frac{r+s}{2}\right)^2 + \left(\frac{r-s}{2}\right)^2,$$

and the four squares on the right are integers. A like reduction may be performed so long as the roots of all the squares are odd. Thus the exception when $n = 2$ disappears.

THEOREM 2.—*If N is prime, not only 4 squares not divisible by N, can be found in an infinity of ways, whose sum is divisible by N, but also 3 squares.*

For, with respect to N, all numbers are of one or other of the N forms

$$\lambda N, \ \lambda N + 1, \ \lambda N + 2, \ \lambda N + 3, \ldots, \ \lambda N + N - 1.$$

Disregard the first form, λN, which contains all the multiples of N. There remain $N - 1$ forms, and we observe that the square of a number of the form $\lambda N + 1$, likewise the square of a number of the form $\lambda N + N - 1$, belongs to the same form $\lambda N + 1$. Similarly the square of a number of either form $\lambda N + 2$, $\lambda N + N - 2$ is of the form $\lambda N + 4$; and so on. Thus the squares of all numbers not of the form λN are comprised in the $\frac{1}{2}(N - 1)$ forms

$$\lambda N + 1, \quad \lambda N + 4, \quad \lambda N + 9, \quad \text{etc.,}$$

which will be called forms of the first class, and will be denoted by

$$\lambda N + a, \quad \lambda N + b, \quad \lambda N + c, \quad \lambda N + d, \text{ etc.,}$$

so that a, b, c, d,...denote the squares 1, 4, 9, 16,...or, if these exceed N, their residues on division by N. The remaining $\frac{1}{2}(N - 1)$ forms will be denoted by

$$\lambda N + \alpha, \ \lambda N + \beta, \ \lambda N + \gamma, \text{ etc.,}$$

which will be called forms of the second class. It is easy to prove the following three properties concerning these classes.[1]

I. The product of two numbers of the first class is again contained in the first class, since evidently $\lambda N + ab$ is in the first class. If $ab > N$, the residue of ab on division by N is to be understood.

---

[1] [These merely are the well known elementary properties of quadratic residues, which, since the time of Gauss, are phrased more briefly in modern terminology. The like applies to the proof given presently.]

II. Numbers of the first class a, b, c, d, etc., multiplied into any numbers of the second class α, β, γ, δ, etc., give products in the second class.

III. A product of two numbers in the second class, say $\alpha\beta$, falls into the first class.

We shall now proceed to the proof of Theorem 2, by means of a contradiction.

Suppose then that there are no three squares, not all divisible by N, whose sum is divisible by N. Then, so much the more, there are no two such squares. Hence it follows at once that the form $\lambda N - a$, or what amounts to the same, $\lambda N + (N - a)$, cannot occur in the first class. For, if there were a square of the form $\lambda N - a$, the sum of this and $\lambda N + a$ would be divisible by N, contrary to hypothesis. Hence the form $\lambda N - a$ is necessarily in the second class; the numbers -1, -4, -9, etc., are among those of the set α, β, γ, δ, etc. Let f by any number of the first class, so that there exist squares of the form $\lambda N + f$. If to one of these be added a square of the form $\lambda N + 1$, the sum of the two will have the form $\lambda N + f + 1$. Now if there were squares of the form $\lambda N - f - 1$, there would exist a sum of three squares divisible by N. Since this is denied, the form $\lambda N - f - 1$ is not contained in the first class, and hence it is in the second. But in the second class there appear the numbers -1 and $-f - 1$, and hence, by III above, their product $f + 1$ is in the first class. In the same way it may be shown that the numbers

$$f + 2, \quad f + 3, \quad f + 4, \text{ etc.,}$$

must occur in the first class. Hence, taking $f = 1$, we see that all the numbers

$$\lambda N + 1, \quad \lambda N + 2, \quad \lambda N + 3, \text{ etc.,}$$

occur in the first class, and therefore that there are none left for the second class. But, by the same reasoning, we see that the numbers -1, $-f - 1$, $-f - 2$, etc., occur in the second class, and hence all forms are in the second class. This obviously is a contradiction. It follows therefore that it is false that there are not three squares whose sum is divisible by N. Hence there are indeed three squares, and much more therefore four squares, of the prescribed kind whose sum is divisible by N.

Corollary.—From this theorem, combined with the preceding, it follows obviously that every number is a sum of four or fewer squares.

EULER

Use of the Letter e to Represent 2.718...

(Selections Translated by Professor Florian Cajori, University of California, Berkeley, California.)

Prominent among the mathematicians who have contributed notations which have met with general adoption is the Swiss Leonhard Euler (1707–1783). One of his suggestions, made when he was a young man of twenty or twenty-one, at the court in St. Petersburg, was the use of the letter e to stand for 2.718..., the base of the natural system of logarithms. It occurs in a manuscript of Euler entitled "Meditation upon Experiments made recently on the firing of Canon" (Meditatio in Experimenta explosione tormentorum nuper instituta). The manuscript was first printed in 1862 in Euler's *Opera postuma mathematica et physica*, Petropoli, 1862, edited by P. H. Fuss and N. Fuss (Vol. II, p. 800–804). In this article, seven experiments are cited, which were performed between Aug. 21 and Sept. 2, 1727. These dates, and the word "recently" (nuper) in the title, would indicate that the article was written in 1727 or 1728. In it the letter e occurs sixteen times to represent 2.718... From page 800, we translate the following:

Let c designate the diameter of a globe [spherical projectile], in scruples of Rhenish feet,[1] $m:n$ the ratio of the specific gravity of the globe to the specific gravity of the air or the medium in which the globe moves, let t seconds be the length of time of the globe in air, let also the required height to which the body rises be x. For the number whose logarithm is unity, let e be written, which is 2,7182817...whose logarithm[2] according to Vlacq is 0, 4342944. Also let N indicate the number of degrees of an arc, whose tangent is:

$$\sqrt{e^{\frac{3nx}{4mc}} - 1},$$

the sinus totus [or radius] = 1. The required altitude x may be obtained from the following equation:

$$t = \frac{m\sqrt{c}}{447650\sqrt{3n(m-n)}} \left(125N - 7162 \log.\left(\sqrt{e^{\frac{3nx}{4mc}}} - \sqrt{e^{\frac{nx}{4mc}} - 1}\right)\right).$$

That the analysis may proceed more easily, let us call $\sqrt{e^{\frac{3nx}{4mc}} - 1}$

[1] [Rhenish foot = 1000 scruples.]
[2] [That is, logarithm to the base 10.]

$= y$, then N will be the number of degrees of the arc whose tangent is $y, \ldots$

In a letter of Nov. 25, 1731, addressed to Goldbach[1] (first published in 1843), Euler solves the differential equation

$$dz - 2zdv + \frac{zdv}{v} = \frac{dv}{v}, \text{ thus:}$$

This multiplied by e^{lv-2v}, or what is the same, by $e^{-2v}v$ (e denotes that number, whose hyperbolic logarithm is $= 1$), becomes

$$e^{-2v}vdz - 2e^{-2v}zvdv + e^{-2v}zdv = e^{-2v}dv,$$

which, integrated, gives

$$e^{-2v}vz = \text{Const.} - \frac{1}{2}e^{-2v}$$

or

$$2vz + 1 = ae^{2v} \ldots$$

The earliest occurrence *in print* of the letter e for 2.718... is in Euler's *Mechanica*, 1736. It is found in Vol. I, page 68, and in other places, as well as in Vol. II, page 251, and on many of the 200 pages following. We quote, in translation, from Vol. I, page 68, where c means the velocity of the point under consideration:

Corollary II

171. Although in the foregoing equation the force p does not occur, its direction still remains, which depends upon the ratio of the elements dx and dy. Given therefore the direction of the force which moves the point and the curve along which the point moves, one can, from these data alone, derive the velocity of the point at any place. For there will be $\frac{dc}{c} = \frac{dyds}{zdx}$ or $c = e^{\int \frac{dyds}{zdx}}$, where e denotes the number whose hyperbolic logarithm is 1.

The use of the letter e, affected by imaginary exponents, in analytica expressions that were new to mathematics, occurs in a dissertation of Euler's entitled "On the sums of reciprocal series arising from the Powers of the natural Numbers" (De summis serierum reciprocarum ex potestatibus numerorum naturalium ortarum).[2] He lets s denote a circular arc and develops $\sin s$ into the now familiar infinite series. On page 177 he gives without explanation the exponential expression for $\sin s$, and the fundamental limit for e^x in the following passage:

---

[1] *Correspondance mathématique et physique de quelques célèbres géomètres du XVIII^{ime} siècle.* Par P. H. Fuss, St. Pétersbourg, 1843, Tome I, p. 58.

[2] *Miscellanea Berolinensia*, p. 172, Vol. VII, Berlin, 1743.

Hence I am now able to write down all the roots or factors of the following infinite expression

$$S - \frac{S^3}{1.2.3} + \frac{S^5}{1.2.3.4.5} - \frac{S^7}{1.2.3...7} + \frac{S^9}{1.2.3...9} - \&c.$$

Indeed that expression is equivalent to this $\frac{e^{s\sqrt{-1}} - e^{-s\sqrt{-1}}}{2\sqrt{-1}}$, e denoting the number whose logarithm is $= 1$, and, since $e^z = \left(1 + \frac{z}{n}\right)^n$, when n emerges an infinite number, the given infinite expression is reduced to this:

$$\frac{\left(1 + \frac{s\sqrt{-1}}{n}\right)^n - \left(1 - \frac{s\sqrt{-1}}{n}\right)^n}{2\sqrt{-1}} \dots$$

More systematic development is found in Euler's *Introductio in analysin infinitorum*, Vol. I, Lausannæ, 1748. We quote from § 138, in which the letter i is an infinitely great number:

... Substituting gives

$$\text{cos. } v = \frac{\left(1 + \frac{v\sqrt{-1}}{i}\right)^i + \left(1 - \frac{v\sqrt{-1}}{i}\right)^i}{2}$$

and

$$\text{sin. } v = \frac{\left(1 + \frac{v\sqrt{-1}}{i}\right)^i - \left(1 - \frac{v\sqrt{-1}}{i}\right)^i}{2\sqrt{-1}}$$

In the preceding chapter we saw that

$$\left(1 + \frac{z}{i}\right)^i = e^z$$

e denoting the base of hyperbolic logarithms; writing for z, first $+v\sqrt{-1}$, then $-v\sqrt{-1}$, there will be

$$\text{cos. } v = \frac{e^{+v\sqrt{-1}} + e^{-v\sqrt{-1}}}{2}$$

and

$$\text{sin. } v = \frac{e^{+v\sqrt{-1}} - e^{-v\sqrt{-1}}}{2\sqrt{-1}}$$

From these it is perceived how imaginary exponential quantities are reduced to the sine and cosine of real arcs. For, there is

$$e^{+v\sqrt{-1}} = \text{cos. } v + \sqrt{-1}. \text{ sin. } v$$
$$e^{-v\sqrt{-1}} = \text{cos. } v - \sqrt{-1}. \text{ sin. } v.$$

If in the formula for $e^{+v\sqrt{-1}}$ one substitutes π and v, there results the famous formula $e^{\pi\sqrt{-1}} = -1$, indicating the strange interrelation of π and e. Euler states this relation in the logarithmic form and generalized, in his paper, "De la Controverse entre Mrs. Leibnitz & Bernoulli sur les logarithmes des nombres negatifs et imaginaires," *Histoire de l'academie royale des sciences et belles lettres,* année 1749, Berlin, 1751, where on page 168 he refers to:

...this formula $\cos \varphi + \sqrt{-1}.\sin \varphi$, all logarithms of which are included in this general formula

$$l(\cos \varphi + \sqrt{-1}.\sin \varphi) = (\varphi + p\pi)\sqrt{-1},$$

p indicating any even integer, either affirmative, or negative, or even zero.   From this we derive...

$$l - 1 = (1 + p)\pi\sqrt{-1} = q\pi\sqrt{-1},$$

taking q to mark any odd integer.   One has therefore:

$$l - 1 = \pm\pi\sqrt{-1}; \pm 3\pi\sqrt{-1}; \pm 5\pi\sqrt{-1}; \pm 7\pi\sqrt{-1}; \&c.$$

HERMITE

On the Transcendence of e

(Translated from the French by Dr. Laura Guggenbühl, Hunter College, New York City.)

Charles Hermite (1822–1901) was one of the best-known writers upon the function theory in the second half of the nineteenth century. He was a professor in the Ecole Polytechnique, an honorary professor in the University of Paris, and a member of the Académie des Sciences. His memoir on the transcendence of e was published in 1873. As is well known,[1] the character of the number π was a source of disturbance in ancient times because of its connection with the classic problem of the quadrature of the circle. From the Greek period, names of famous mathematicians have been connected with transcendental numbers, but it was not until 1844 that a definite step forward was made in the general investigation of the subject. At this time, Liouville proved the existence of these numbers, thus justifying the classification of algebraic and transcendental. Liouville had already proved that e could not be a root of quadratic equation with rational coefficients. Finally, in 1873, Hermite's proof of the transcendence of e appeared. A few years later (1882), Lindemann, modeling his proof upon that of Hermite, proved the transcendence of π.

The memoir is somewhat over thirty pages long and can be divided roughly into three parts. In the first two parts, two distinct proofs of the transcendence of e are given—but as Hermite says, the second is the more rigorous of the two. In the third part, Hermite obtains, applying the method suggested in the second proof, the following approximations:[2]

$$e = \frac{58291}{21444}, \qquad e^2 = \frac{158452}{21444}$$

The translation here given includes, with indicated omissions, the portion referred to above as the second part of the memoir. Since the time when this paper first appeared, many simplifications have been made, so that now one rarely, if ever, sees more than an acknowledgement of the existence and importance of this proof. The name "Hermite's Theorem" is still, however, given to the statement that e is a transcendental number.

---

[1] *Monographs on Topics of Modern Mathematics*, edited by J. W. A. Young, Monograph IX, "The History and Transcendence of π," by D. E. Smith. Additional references are there given.

[2] Correct to six decimal places, $e = 2.718282$. This fraction gives $e = 2.718289$.

The correction of a numerical mistake pointed out by Picard, in his edition of Hermite's work, increases the accuracy of this approximation.

...But, as a more general case, take

$$F(z) = (z - z_0)^{\mu_0}(z - z_1)^{\mu_1}\ldots(z - z_n)^{\mu_n}$$

for any integral values whatever of the exponents, upon integrating both members of the identity

$$\frac{d[e^{-z}F(z)]}{dz} = e^{-z}[F'(z) - F(z)],$$

one obtains

$$e^{-z}F(z) = \int e^{-z}F'(z)dz - \int e^{-z}F(z)dz,$$

from which it follows that

$$\int_{z_0}^{Z} e^{-z}F(z)dz = \int_{z_0}^{Z} e^{-z}F'(z)dz.[1]$$

Now the formula

$$\frac{F'(z)}{F(z)} = \frac{\mu_0}{z - z_0} + \frac{\mu_1}{z - z_1} + \ldots + \frac{\mu_n}{z - z_n}$$

yields the following decomposition,

$$\int_{z_0}^{Z} e^{-z}F(z)dz = \mu_0 \int_{z_0}^{Z} \frac{e^{-z}F(z)dz}{z - z_0} + \mu_1 \int_{z_0}^{Z} \frac{e^{-z}F(z)dz}{z - z_1}$$
$$+ \ldots + \mu_n \int_{z_0}^{Z} \frac{e^{-z}F(z)dz}{z - z_n}, \ldots$$

...We shall prove that it is always possible to determine two integral polynomials of degree n, $\Theta(z)$ and $\Theta_1(z)$, such that, upon representing one of the roots $z_0, z_1, \ldots z_n$, by ζ, one has the following relation:

$$\int \frac{e^{-z}F(z)f(z)}{z - \zeta}\,dz = \int \frac{e^{-z}F(z)\Theta_1(z)}{f(z)}dz - e^{-z}F(z)\Theta(z).[2]$$

...And further, upon writing $\Theta(z, \zeta)$ in place of $\Theta(z)$, to emphasize the presence of ζ, we have

$$\Theta(z, \zeta) = z^n + \Theta_1(\zeta)z^{n-2} + \Theta_2(\zeta)z^{n-3} + \ldots + \Theta_n(\zeta).[3]$$

---

[1] [Where Z represents any one of the roots $z_0, z_1, \ldots z_n$.]

[2] $f(z) = (Z - z_0)(z - z_1)\ldots(z - z_n)$. The proof of this statement, which is given in detail in the text, is here omitted.

[3] [It is shown in the text that $\Theta_i(\zeta)$ is a polynomial of degree i in ζ, having for coefficients integral functions, with integral coefficients, of the roots z_0, $z_1, \ldots, z_n$.

$\Theta_i(\zeta)$ for $i = 1$, is not to be confused with $\Theta_1(z)$, mentioned above in connection with $\Theta(z)$.]

From this there follows, for the polynomial $\Theta_1(z)$, the formula

$$\frac{\Theta_1(z)}{f(z)} = \frac{\mu_0\Theta(z_0, \zeta)}{z - z_0} + \frac{\mu_1\Theta(z_1, \zeta)}{z - z_1} + \ldots + \frac{\mu_n\Theta(z_n, \zeta)}{z - z_n}.$$

...It is sufficient to take the integrals between the limits z_0 and Z in the relation

$$\int \frac{e^{-z}F(z)f(z)}{z - \zeta}dz = \int \frac{e^{-z}F(z)\Theta_1(z)dz}{f(z)} - e^{-z}F(z)\Theta(z),$$

and thus we obtain the equation

$$\int_{z_0}^{Z}\frac{e^{-z}F(z)f(z)}{z - \zeta}dz = \int_{z_0}^{Z}\frac{e^{-z}F(z)\Theta_1(z)}{f(z)} \, dz$$

$$= \mu_0\Theta(z_0, \zeta)\int_{z_0}^{Z}\frac{e^{-z}F(z)}{z - z_0} \, dz$$

$$+ \mu_1\Theta(z_1, \zeta)\int_{z_0}^{Z}\frac{e^{-z}F(z)}{z - z_1} \, dz$$

$$+ \ldots$$

$$+ \mu_n\Theta(z_n, \zeta)\int_{z_0}^{Z}\frac{e^{-z}F(z)}{z - z_n} \, dz.$$

We use this equation, in particular, in the case

$$\mu_0 = \mu_1 = \ldots = \mu_n = m;$$

in this case, if one writes

$$m\Theta(z_i, z_k) = (ik)$$

and if one takes ζ successively equal to $z_0, z_1, \ldots, z_n$, the above relations evidently become

$$\int_{z_0}^{Z}\frac{e^{-z}f^{m+1}(z)}{z - z_i} \, dz = (i0)\int_{z_0}^{Z}\frac{e^{-z}f^m(z)}{z - z_0} \, dz$$

$$+ (i1)\int_{z_0}^{Z}\frac{e^{-z}f^m(z)}{z - z_1} \, dz$$

$$+ \ldots$$

$$+ (in)\int_{z_0}^{Z}\frac{e^{-z}f^m(z)}{z - z_n} \, dz,$$

for $i = 0, 1, 2, \ldots, n$. But for the general case, we must still prove the following theorem.

Let Δ and δ be the determinants

$$\begin{vmatrix} \Theta(z_0, z_0) & \Theta(z_1, z_0) \ldots \Theta(z_n, z_0) \\ \Theta(z_0, z_1) & \Theta(z_1, z_1) \ldots \Theta(z_n, z_1) \\ \ldots & \ldots \quad \ldots \quad \ldots \\ \Theta(z_0, z_n) & \Theta(z_1, z_n) \ldots \Theta(z_n, z_n) \end{vmatrix}$$

and

$$\begin{vmatrix} 1 & 1 & \dots & 1 \\ z_0 & z_1 & \dots & z_n \\ z_0{}^2 & z_1{}^2 & \dots z_n{}^2 \\ \hdotsfor{4} \\ z_0{}^n & z_1{}^n & & z_n{}^n \end{vmatrix};$$

then $\Delta = \delta^2$.[1] . . . . . .

Now, let

$$\epsilon_m = \frac{1}{1.2 \dots m} \int_{z_0}^{Z} e^{-z} f^m(z)\, dz,$$

$$\epsilon_m{}^i = \frac{1}{1.2 \ \dots \ m-1} \int_{z_0}^{Z} \frac{e^{-z} f^m(z)}{z - z_i}\, dz,$$

the relation proved above

$$\int_{z_0}^{Z} e^{-z} f^m(z)\, dz = m \int_{z_0}^{Z} \frac{e^{-z} f^m(z)}{z - z_0}\, dz + m \int_{z_0}^{Z} \frac{e^{-z} f^m(z)}{z - z_1}\, dz$$
$$+ \dots + m \int_{z_0}^{Z} \frac{e^{-z} f^m(z)}{z - z_n}\, dz$$

becomes simply

$$\epsilon_m = \epsilon_m{}^0 + \epsilon_m{}^1 + \dots + \epsilon_m{}^n,$$

and the relation

$$\int_{z_0}^{Z} \frac{e^{-z} f^{m+1}(z)}{z - \zeta}\, dz = m\Theta(z_0, \zeta) \int_{z_0}^{Z} \frac{e^{-z} f^m(z)}{z - z_0}\, dz$$
$$+ m\Theta(z_1, \zeta) \int_{z_0}^{Z} \frac{e^{-z} f^m(z)}{z - z_1}\, dz$$
$$+ \dots$$
$$+ m\Theta(z_n, \zeta) \int_{z_0}^{Z} \frac{e^{-z} f^m(z)}{z - z_n}\, dz,$$

upon taking ζ successively equal to $z_0, z_1, \dots, z_n$, gives us the following substitution, which we shall represent by S_m, namely

$$\epsilon^0{}_{m+1} = \Theta(z_0, z_0)\epsilon_m{}^0 + \Theta(z_1, z_0)\epsilon_m{}^1 + \dots + \Theta(z_n, z_0)\epsilon_m{}^n,$$
$$\epsilon^1{}_{m+1} = \Theta(z_0, z_1)\epsilon_m{}^0 + \Theta(z_1, z_1)\epsilon_m{}^1 + \dots + \Theta(z_n, z_1)\epsilon_m{}^n,$$
$$\dots \dots \dots \dots$$
$$\epsilon^n{}_{m+1} = \Theta(z_0, z_n)\epsilon_m{}^0 + \Theta(z_1, z_n)\epsilon_m{}^1 + \dots + \Theta(z_n, z_n)\epsilon_m{}^n.$$

If now, one builds up in turn $S_1, S_2, \dots, S_{m-1}$, one concludes from these, expressions for $\epsilon_m{}^0, \epsilon_m{}^1 \dots, \epsilon_m{}^n$ in terms of $\epsilon_1{}^0, \epsilon_1{}^1,$ $\dots, E_1{}^n$, which we shall write as follows.

---

[1] [A short and simple proof for this statement is given in the text.]

$$\epsilon_m{}^o = A_o\epsilon_1{}^o + A_1\epsilon_1{}^1 + \ldots + A_n\epsilon_1{}^n,$$
$$\epsilon_m{}^1 = B_o\epsilon_1{}^o + B_1\epsilon_1{}^1 + \ldots + B_n\epsilon_1{}^n,$$
$$\ldots\ldots\ldots$$
$$\epsilon_m{}^n = L_o\epsilon_1{}^o + L_1\epsilon_1{}^1 + \ldots + L_n\epsilon_1{}^n,$$

and the determinant of this new substitution, being equal to the product of the determinants of the partial substitutions, will be $\delta^{2(m-1)}$. It remains for us to replace $\epsilon_1{}^o$, $\epsilon_1{}^1$, ..., $\epsilon_1{}^n$, by their values so that we shall have expressions for the quantities $\epsilon_m{}^i$ in form suitable for our purpose. These values are easily obtained, as will be seen.

For this purpose, we apply the general formula

$$\int e^{-z}F(z)dz = -e^{-z}\gamma(z),$$

taking

$$F(z) = \frac{f(z)}{z - \zeta}$$

that is

$$F(z) = z^n + \zeta \left| z^{n-1} + \zeta^2 \right| z^{n-2} + \ldots$$
$$+p_1 \qquad +p_1\zeta$$
$$+p_2$$

It is easily seen that $\gamma(z)$ will be an expression integral in z and ζ, entirely similar to $\Theta(z, \zeta)$, such that if one represents it by $\Phi(z, \zeta)$, one has

$$\Phi(z, \zeta) = z^n + \varphi_1(\zeta)z^{n-1} + \varphi_2(\zeta)z^{n-2} + \ldots + \varphi_n(\zeta),$$

where $\varphi_i(\zeta)$ is a polynomial in ζ of degree i, in which the coefficient of ζ^i is unity... and the analogy of the form with $\Theta(z, \zeta)$ shows that the determinant

$$\begin{vmatrix} \Phi(z_0, z_0) & \Phi(z_1, z_0) \ldots \Phi(z_n, z_0) \\ \Phi(z_0, z_1) & \Phi(z_1, z_1) \ldots \Phi(z_n, z_1) \\ \cdots & \cdots \cdots \cdots \\ \Phi(z_0, z_n) & \Phi(z_1, z_n) \ldots \Phi(z_n, z_n) \end{vmatrix}$$

is also equal to δ^2. Next, we conclude from the relation

$$\int_{z_0}^{Z} \frac{e^{-z}f(z)}{z - \zeta} dz = e^{-z_0}\Phi(z_o, \zeta) - e^{-Z}\Phi(Z, \zeta),$$

taking $\zeta = z_i$, the desired value

$$\epsilon_1{}^i = e^{-z_o}\Phi(z_0, z_i) - e^{-Z}\Phi(Z, z_i).$$

Consequently we have the expressions given below for $\epsilon_m{}^i$.

Let

$$\mathfrak{A} = A_o\Phi(Z, z_o) + A_1\Phi(Z, z_1) + \ldots + A_n\Phi(Z, z_n),$$
$$\mathfrak{B} = B_o\Phi(Z, z_o) + B_1\Phi(Z, z_1) + \ldots + B_n\Phi(Z, z_n),$$
$$\ldots\ldots\ldots\ldots$$
$$\mathfrak{L} = L_o\Phi(Z, z_o) + L_1\Phi(Z, z_1) + \ldots + L_n\Phi(Z, z_n),$$

and let $\mathfrak{A}_o, \mathfrak{B}_o, \ldots, \mathfrak{L}_o$ be the values obtained for $Z = z_o$; one has

$$\epsilon_m{}^0 = e^{-z_o}\mathfrak{A}_o - e^{-Z_o}\mathfrak{A}$$
$$\epsilon_m{}' = e^{-z_o}\mathfrak{B}_o - e^{-Z}\mathfrak{B}$$
$$\ldots\ldots\ldots\ldots$$
$$\epsilon_m{}^n = e^{-z_o}\mathfrak{L}_o - e^{-Z}\mathfrak{L}.$$

In these formulas, Z represents any one whatever of the quantities $z_o, z_1, \ldots, z_n$, now if we wish to state the result for $Z = z_k$, we shall agree at the outset, to represent on the one hand, by $\mathfrak{A}_k, \mathfrak{B}_k, \ldots \mathfrak{L}_k$, and on the other, by $\eta_k{}^o, \eta_k{}', \ldots, \eta_k{}^n$, the values which the coefficients $\mathfrak{A}, \mathfrak{B}, \ldots, \mathfrak{L}$, and the quantities $\epsilon_m{}^o, \epsilon_m{}', \ldots, \epsilon_m{}^n$, take on in this case. Thus one obtains the equations

$$\eta_k{}^o = e^{-z_o}\mathfrak{A}_o - e^{-z_k}\mathfrak{A}_k$$
$$\eta_k{}' = e^{-z_o}\mathfrak{B}_o - e^{-z_k}\mathfrak{B}$$
$$\ldots\ldots\ldots\ldots$$
$$\eta_k{}^n = e^{-z_o}\mathfrak{L}_o - e^{-z_k}\mathfrak{L}_k,$$

which will lead us to the second proof, we have mentioned, of the impossibility of a relation of the form

$$e^{z_o}N_o + e^{z_1}N_1 + \ldots + e^{z_n}N_n = 0,$$

where the exponents $z_o, z_1, \ldots, z_n$, as also the coefficients $N_o, N_1, \ldots, N_n$, are assumed to be integers.

Note in the first place, that $\epsilon_m{}^i$ can become smaller than any given quantity for a sufficiently large value of m. For, the exponential e^{-z} being always positive, one has, as is known,

$$\int_{z_o}^{Z} e^{-z}F(z)dz = F(\xi)\int_{z_o}^{Z} e^{-z}dz = F(\xi)(e^{-z_o} - e^{-Z}),$$

$F(z)$ being any function whatever, and ξ a quantity taken between z_o and Z, the limits of the integral. Now, upon taking

$$F(z) = \frac{f^m(z)}{z - Z_i},$$

one obtains the expression

$$\epsilon_m{}^i = \frac{f^{m-1}(\xi)}{1.2\ldots m - 1}\frac{f(\xi)}{\xi - z_i}(e^{-z_o} - e^{-Z}),$$

which demonstrates the property quoted above. Now, we obtain from the equations

$$\eta_1{}^o = e^{-z_o}\mathfrak{A}_o - e^{-z_1}\mathfrak{A}_1,$$
$$\eta_2{}^o = e^{-z_o}\mathfrak{A}_o - e^{-z_2}\mathfrak{A}_2,$$
$$\cdots\cdots\cdots$$
$$\eta_n{}^o = e^{-z_o}\mathfrak{A}_o - e^{-z_n}\mathfrak{A}_n,$$

the following relation,

$$e^{z_1}\eta_1{}^o N_1 + e^{z_2}\eta_2{}^o N_2 + \ldots + e^{z_n}\eta_n{}^o N_n$$
$$= e^{-z_o}(e^{z_1}N_1 + e^{z_2}N_2 + \ldots + e^{z_n}N_n)$$
$$- (\mathfrak{A}_1 N_1 + \mathfrak{A}_2 N_2 + \ldots + \mathfrak{A}_n N_n).$$

If the condition

$$e^{z_o}N_o + e^{z_1}N_1 + \ldots + e^{z_n}N_n = 0$$

is introduced, this relation becomes

$$e^{z_1}\eta_1{}^o N_1 + e^{z_2}\eta_2{}^o N_2 + \ldots + e^{z_n}\eta_n{}^o N_n$$
$$= -(\mathfrak{A}_o N_o + \mathfrak{A}_1 N_1 + \ldots + \mathfrak{A}_n N_n).$$

However, under the assumption that $z_o, z_1, \ldots, z_n$ are integers, the quantities $\Theta(z_i, z_k)$, $\Phi(z_i, z_k)$ and consequently $\mathfrak{A}_o, \mathfrak{A}_1, \ldots, \mathfrak{A}_n$ are also integers. Then we have a whole number

$$\mathfrak{A}_o N_o + \mathfrak{A}_1 N_1 + \ldots + \mathfrak{A}_n N_n,$$

which decreases indefinitely with $\eta_1{}^o, \eta_1{}^1, \ldots, \eta_1{}^n$, as m increases; it follows that for a certain value of m and for all larger values,

$$\mathfrak{A}_o N_o + \mathfrak{A}_1 N_1 + \ldots + \mathfrak{A}_n N_n = 0,$$

and, since one obtains similarly the relations

$$\mathfrak{B}_o N_o + \mathfrak{B}_1 N_1 + \ldots + \mathfrak{B}_n N_n = 0,$$
$$\cdots\cdots\cdots\cdots$$
$$\mathfrak{L}_o N_o + \mathfrak{L}_1 N_1 + \ldots + \mathfrak{L}_n N_n = 0.$$

the relation

$$e^{z_o}N_o + e^{z_1}N_1 + \ldots + e^{z_n}N_n = 0$$

demands that the determinant

$$\Delta = \begin{vmatrix} \mathfrak{A}_o & \mathfrak{A}_1 & \ldots & \mathfrak{A}_n \\ \mathfrak{B}_o & \mathfrak{B}_1 & \ldots & \mathfrak{B}_n \\ \ldots & \ldots & \ldots & \ldots \\ \mathfrak{L}_o & \mathfrak{L}_1 & \ldots & \mathfrak{L}_n \end{vmatrix}$$

be equal to zero. But, because of the expressions for $\mathfrak{A}_o, \mathfrak{B}_o, \ldots, \mathfrak{L}_o$, it follows that Δ is the product of these two other determinants

$$\begin{vmatrix} A_o & A_1 & \ldots & A_n \\ B_o & B_1 & \ldots & B_n \\ \ldots & \ldots & \ldots & \ldots \\ L_o & L_1 & \ldots & L_n \end{vmatrix}$$

and

$$\begin{vmatrix} \Phi(z_0, z_0) & \Phi(z_1, z_0) \ldots \Phi(z_n, z_0) \\ \Phi(z_0, z_1) & \Phi(z_1, z_1) \ldots \Phi(z_n, z_1) \\ \ldots & \ldots \quad \ldots \quad \ldots \\ \Phi(z_0, z_n) & \Phi(z, z_n) \ldots \Phi(z_n, z_n) \end{vmatrix}$$

of which the first has for its value $\delta^2(^{m-1})$, and the second δ^2. One has then $\Delta = \delta^{2m}$, and it is easily shown in an entirely rigorous manner, that the assumed relation is impossible,[1] and that therefore, the number e is not among the irrational algebraic numbers.

---

[1] [It can be shown that

$$\delta = \begin{vmatrix} 1 & 1 & \ldots & 1 \\ z_0 & z_1 & \ldots & z_n \\ z_0^2 & z_1^2 & \ldots & z_n^2 \\ \ldots & \ldots & \ldots & \ldots \\ z_0^n & z_1^n & \ldots & z_n^n \end{vmatrix} = \pm (z_n - z_{n-1})(z_n - z_{n-2}) \ldots (z_n - z_0) \\ (z_{n-1} - z_{n-2}) \ldots (z_1 - z_0)$$

and therefore that δ is not zero, assuming, as is of course assumed throughout, that the exponents, $z_0, z_1, \ldots, z_n$, are distinct.]

GAUSS

On the Congruence of Numbers

(Translated from the Latin by Professor Ralph G. Archibald, Columbia University, New York City.)

Carl Friedrich Gauss (1777–1855), the son of a day laborer, was the founder of the modern school of mathematics in Germany and was, perhaps, equally well known in the fields of physics and astronomy. Kronecker (1823–1891) said of him that "almost everything which the mathematics of our century has brought forth in the way of original scientific ideas is connected with the name of Gauss." His work in the theory of numbers began when he was a student at Göttingen, and much of it appeared in his *Disquisitiones Arithmeticae*, published in 1801, when he was only twenty-four years old. In this is found his treatment of the congruence of numbers, a translation of portions of which is here given. It also appears in the first volume of his *Werke* (Göttingen, 1870).

First Section

Concerning Congruence of Numbers in General
Congruent Numbers, Moduli, Residues, and Non-residues

1

If a number a divides the difference of the numbers b and c, b and c are said to be *congruent with respect to a;* but if not, *incongruent.* We call a the *modulus.* In the former case, each of the numbers b and c is called a *residue* of the other, but in the latter case, a *non-residue.*

These notions apply to all integral numbers both positive and negative,[1] but not to fractions. For example, -9 and $+16$ are congruent with respect to the modulus 5; -7 is a residue of $+15$ with respect to the modulus 11, but a non-residue with respect to the modulus 3. Now, since every number divides zero, every number must be regarded as congruent to itself with respect to all moduli.

2

If k denotes an indeterminate integral number, all residues of a given number a with respect to the modulus m are contained in

---

[1] Obviously, the modulus is always to be taken *absolutely,*—that is, without any sign.

107

the formula $a + km$. The easier of the propositions which we shall give can be readily demonstrated from this standpoint; but anyone will just as easily perceive their truth at sight.

We shall denote in future the congruence of two numbers by this sign, $\equiv$, and adjoin the modulus in parentheses when necessary. For example, $-16 \equiv 9 \pmod{5}$, $-7 \equiv 15 \pmod{11}$.[1]

3

THEOREM.—*If there be given the m consecutive integral numbers*
$$a, a + 1, a + 2, \ldots, a + m - 1,$$
and another integral number A, then some one of the former will be congruent to this number A with respect to the modulus m; and, in fact, there will be only one such number.

If, for instance, $\dfrac{a - A}{m}$ is an integer, we shall have $a \equiv A$; but if it is fractional, let k be the integer immediately greater (or, when it is negative, immediately *smaller* if no regard is paid to sign). Then $A + km$ will fall between a and $a + m$, and will therefore be the number desired. Now, it is evident that all the quotients $\dfrac{a - A}{m}, \dfrac{a + 1 - A}{m}, \dfrac{a + 2 - A}{m}$, etc., are situated between $k - 1$ and $k + 1$. Therefore not more than one can be integral.

Least Residues

4

Every number, then, will have a residue not only in the sequence $0, 1, 2, \ldots, m - 1$, but also in the sequence $0, -1, -2, \ldots, -(m - 1)$. We shall call these *least residues*. Now, it is evident that, unless 0 is a residue, there will always be two: one *positive*, the other *negative*. If they are of different magnitudes, one of them will be less than $\dfrac{m}{2}$; but if they are of the same magnitude, each will equal $\dfrac{m}{2}$ when no regard is paid to sign. From this it is evident that any number has a residue not exceeding half the modulus. This residue is called the *absolute minimum*.

---

[1] We have adopted this sign on account of the great analogy which exists between an equality and a congruence. For the same reason Legendre, in memoirs which will later be frequently quoted, retained the sign of equality itself for a congruence. We hesitated to follow this notation lest it introduce an ambiguity.

For example, with respect to the modulus 5, -13 has the positive least residue 2, which at the same time is the absolute minimum, and has -3 as the negative least residue. With respect to the modulus 7, $+5$ is its own positive least residue, -2 is the negative least residue and at the same time the absolute minimum.

Elementary Propositions Concerning Congruences

5

From the notions just established we may derive the following obvious properties of congruent numbers.

The numbers which are congruent with respect to a composite modulus, will certainly be congruent with respect to any one of its divisors.

If several numbers are congruent to the same number with respect to the same modulus, they will be congruent among themselves (with respect to the same modulus).

The same identity of moduli is to be understood in what follows.

Congruent numbers have the same least residues, incongruent numbers different least residues.

6

If the numbers A, B, C, etc. and the numbers a, b, c, etc. are congruent each to each with respect to any modulus, that is, if

$$A \equiv a, B \equiv b, \text{ etc.},$$

then we shall have

$$A + B + C + \text{etc.} \equiv a + b + c + \text{etc.}$$

If $A \equiv a$ and $B \equiv b$, we shall have $A - B \equiv a - b$.

7

If $A \equiv a$, we shall also have $kA \equiv ka$.

If k is a positive number, this is merely a particular case of the proposition of the preceding article when we place $A = B = C$ etc. and $a = b = c$ etc. If k is negative, $-k$ will be positive. Then $-kA \equiv -ka$, and consequently $kA \equiv ka$.

If $A \equiv a$ and $B \equiv b$, we shall have $AB \equiv ab$. For, $AB \equiv Ab \equiv ba$.

8

If the numbers A, B, C, etc. and the numbers a, b, c, etc. are congruent each to each, that is, if $A \equiv a$, $B \equiv b$, etc., the products of the numbers of each set will be congruent; that is, ABC etc. $\equiv abc$ etc.

From the preceding article, $AB \equiv ab$, and for the same reason $ABC \equiv abc$; in a like manner we can consider as many factors as desired.

If we take all the numbers A, B, C, etc. equal, and also the corresponding numbers a, b, c, etc., we obtain this theorem:

If $A \equiv a$ and if k is a positive integer, we shall have $A^k \equiv a^k$.

9

Let X be a function of the indeterminate x, of the form
$$Ax^a + Bx^b + Cx^c + \text{etc.},$$
where A, B, C, etc., denote any integral numbers, and a, b, c, etc., non-negative integral numbers. If, now, to the indeterminate x there be assigned values which are congruent with respect to any stated modulus, the resulting values of the function X will then be congruent.

Let f and g be two congruent values of x. Then by the preceding articles $f^a \equiv g^a$ and $Af^a \equiv Ag^a$; in the same way $Bf^b \equiv Bg^b$, etc. Hence
$$Af^a + Bf^b + Cf^c + \text{etc.} \equiv Ag^a + Bg^b + Cg^c + \text{etc.} \quad \text{Q. E. D.}$$

It is easily seen, too, how this theorem can be extended to functions of several indeterminates.

10

If, therefore, all consecutive integral numbers are substituted for x, and if the values of the function X are reduced to least residues, these residues will constitute a sequence in which the same terms repeat after an interval of m terms (m denoting the modulus); or, in other words, this sequence will be formed by a *period of m* terms repeated indefinitely. Let, for example, $X = x^3 - 8x + 6$ and $m = 5$. Then for $x = 0$, 1, 2, 3, etc., the values of X give the positive least residues, 1, 4, 3, 4, 3, 1, 4, etc., where the first five, namely, 1, 4, 3, 4, 3, are repeated without end. And furthermore, if the sequence is continued backwards, that is, if negative values are assigned to x, the same period occurs in the inverse order. It is therefore evident that terms different from those constituting the period cannot occur in the sequence.

11

In this example, then, X can be neither $\equiv 0$ nor $\equiv 2$ (mod 5), and can still less be $= 0$ or $= 2$. Whence it follows that the equations $x^3 - 8x + 6 = 0$ and $x^3 - 8x + 4 = 0$ cannot be solved in integral numbers, and therefore, as we know, cannot be solved in rational numbers. It is obviously true in general that, if it is impossible to satisfy the congruence $X \equiv 0$ with respect to some particular modulus, then the equation $X = 0$ has no rational root when X is a function of the unknown x, of the form
$$x^n + Ax^{n-1} + Bx^{n-2} + \text{etc.} + N,$$

where A, B, C, etc. are integers and n is a positive integer. (It is well known that all algebraic equations can be brought to this form.) This criterion, though presented here in a natural manner, will be treated at greater length in Section VIII. From this brief indication, some idea, no doubt, can be formed regarding the utility of these researches.

Some Applications

12

Many of the theorems commonly taught in arithmetic depend upon theorems given in this section; for example, the rules for testing the divisibility of a given number by 9, 11, or other numbers. *With respect to the modulus* 9, all powers of 10 are congruent to unity. Hence, if the given number is of the form $a + 10b + 100c + $ etc., it will have, with respect to the modulus 9, the same least residue as $a + b + c + $ etc. From this it is evident that, if the individual figures of the number, expressed in the denary scale, are added without regard to their position, this sum and the given number will exhibit the same least residues; and furthermore, the latter can be divided by 9 if the former be divisible by 9, and conversely. The same thing also holds true for the divisor 3. Since *with respect to the modulus* 11, $100 \equiv 1$, we shall have generally $10^{2k} \equiv 1$ and $10^{2k+1} \equiv 10 \equiv -1$. Then a number of the form $a + 10b + 100c + $ etc. will have, with respect to the modulus 11, the same least residue as $a - b + c$ etc.; whence the known rule is immediately derived. On the same principle all similar rules are easily deduced.

The preceding observations also bring out the principle underlying the rules commonly relied upon for the verification of arithmetical operations. These remarks, of course, are applicable when from given numbers we have to deduce others by addition, subtraction, multiplication, or raising to powers: in place of the given numbers, we merely substitute their least residues with respect to an arbitrary modulus (generally 9 or 11; since, as we have just now observed, in our decimal system residues with respect to these moduli can be so very easily found). The numbers thus obtained should be congruent to those which have been deduced from the given numbers. If, on the other hand, this is not the case, we infer that an error has crept into the calculation.

Now as these results and others of a similar nature are so very well known, it would serve no purpose to dwell on them further.

GAUSS

Third Proof of the Law of Quadratic Reciprocity

(Translated from the Latin by D. H. Lehmer, M.Sc., Brown University, Providence, Rhode Island.)

The theorem with which the following pages are concerned and to which Gauss gave the name of Fundamental Theorem is better known today as Legendre's Law of Quadratic Reciprocity. Although a statement of a theorem equivalent to this law is found in the works of Euler[1] without proof, the first enunciation of the law itself is attributed to Legendre,[2] whose proof, however, is invalid. It tacitly assumes that there exist infinitely many primes in certain arithmetical progressions, a fact which was first established by Dirichlet half a century later. The first proof of this theorem was given by Gauss[3] in 1801 and was followed by seven others in an interval of 17 years. The proof given below is the third one published,[4] although it is really his fifth proof. It is considered by Gauss and many others to be the most direct and elegant of his eight demonstrations.

In fact, in the first two paragraphs of the present proof Gauss expresses himself as follows:

§1. The questions of higher arithmetic often present a remarkable characteristic which seldom appears in more general analysis, and increases the beauty of the former subject. While analytic investigations lead to the discovery of new truths only after the fundamental principles of the subject (which to a certain degree open the way to these truths) have been completely mastered; on the contrary in arithmetic the most elegant theorems frequently arise experimentally as the result of a more or less unexpected stroke of good fortune, while their proofs lie so deeply embedded in the darkness that they elude all attempts and defeat the sharpest inquiries. Further, the connection between arithmetical truths which at first glance seem of widely different nature, is so close that one not infrequently has the good fortune to find a proof (in an entirely unexpected way and by means of quite another

---

[1] Euler, *Opuscula*, Vol. 1, p. 64, 1783.

[2] Legendre, *Histoire de l'Académie des Sciences*, pp. 516–517, 1785; *Théorie des Nombres*, Ed. 1, pp. 214–226, 1798; Ed. 2, pp. 198–207, 1808.

[3] Gauss, *Disquisitiones Arithmeticae*, Sect. 4, Leipzig, 1801; *Werke*, Göttingen, 1870, Bd. 1, pp. 73–111.

[4] Gauss, *Commentationes Societatis Regiæ Scientiarum Gottingensis*, Vol. 16, Göttingen, 1808; *Werke*, Göttingen, 1876. Bd. 2, pp. 1–8.

inquiry) of a truth which one greatly desired and sought in vain in spite of much effort. These truths are frequently of such a nature that they may be arrived at by many distinct paths and that the first paths to be discovered are not always the shortest. It is therefore a great pleasure after one has fruitlessly pondered over a truth and has later been able to prove it in a round-about way to find at last the simplest and most natural way to its proof.

§2. The theorem which we have called in sec. 4 of the *Disquisitiones Arithmeticae*, the *Fundamental Theorem* because it contains in itself all the theory of quadratic residues, holds a prominent position among the questions of which we have spoken in the preceding paragraph. We must consider Legendre as the discoverer of this very elegant theorem, although special cases of it had previously been discovered by the celebrated geometers Euler and Lagrange. I will not pause here to enumerate the attempts of these men to furnish a proof; those who are interested may read the above mentioned work. An account of my own trials will suffice to confirm the assertions of the preceeding paragraph. I discovered this theorem independently in 1795 at a time when I was totally ignorant of what had been achieved in higher arithmetic, and consequently had not the slightest aid from the literature on the subject. For a whole year this theorem tormented me and absorbed my greatest efforts until at last I obtained a proof given in the fourth section of the above-mentioned work. Later I ran across three other proofs which were built on entirely different principles. One of these I have already given in the fifth section, the others, which do not compare with it in elegance, I have reserved for future publication. Although these proofs leave nothing to be desired as regards rigor, they are derived from sources much too remote, except perhaps the first, which however proceeds with laborious arguments and is overloaded with extended operations. I do not hesitate to say that till now a *natural* proof has not been produced. I leave it to the authorities to judge whether the following proof which I have recently been fortunate enough to discover deserves this discription.

Inasmuch as Gauss does not give any mathematical background in the introduction to his third proof or even a formal statement of the theorem itself (these having been given in his first proof), we shall attempt to supply in a few sentences the information necessary for the proper understanding of the theorem.

The integer p is said to be a quadratic residue or non-residue of an integer q relatively prime to p according as there exist or not solutions x of the congruence $x^2 \equiv p \pmod{q}$. These two cases may be written symbolically as pRq and pNq, respectively. If p and r are both residues or both non-residues of q, then they are said to have the same *quadratic character* with respect to q. With this understanding, the fundamental theorem may be stated in words as follows: *If p and q are any distinct odd primes, then the quadratic character of p with respect to q is the same as that of q with respect to p except when both p and q are of the form $4n - 1$, in which case the characters are opposite.*

The quadratic character of p with respect to q may be expressed by the symbol of Legendre

$$\left(\frac{p}{q}\right),$$

which has the value $+1$ or -1 according as pRq or pNq. The use of this symbol enables us to state the theorem analytically as follows

$$\left(\frac{p}{q}\right)\left(\frac{q}{p}\right) = (-1)^{\frac{(p-1)(q-1)}{4}}$$

We proceed with the translation of Gauss's proof in full:

§3. THEOREM.[1]—*Let p be a positive prime number and k be any number not divisible by p. Further let A be the set of numbers*

$$1, 2, 3, \ldots, \frac{(p-1)}{2}$$

and B the set

$$\frac{(p+1)}{2}, \frac{(p+3)}{2}, \ldots, p - 1.$$

We determine the smallest positive residue modulo p of the product of k by each of the numbers in the set A. These will be distinct and will belong partly to A and partly to B. If we let μ be the number of these residues belonging to B, then k is a quadratic residue of p or a non-residue of p according as μ is odd or even.

Proof.—Let a, a', a'', ... be the residues belonging to the class A and b, b', b'', ... be those belonging to B. Then it is clear that the complements of these latter: $p - b$, $p - b'$, $p - b''$, ... are not equal to any of the numbers a, a', a'', ..., and together with them make up the class A. Consequently we have

$$1.2.3\ldots\frac{p-1}{2} = a.a'.a''\ldots(p-b)(p-b')(p-b'')\ldots$$

The right-hand product evidently becomes, modulo p:

$$\equiv (-1)^{\mu}aa'a''\ldots bb'b''\ldots \equiv (-1)^{\mu}k.2k.3k\ldots k\frac{p-1}{2}$$

$$\equiv (-1)^{\mu}k^{\left(\frac{p-1}{2}\right)}1.2.3\ldots\frac{p-1}{2}$$

---

[1] [This theorem is known to-day as Gauss's Lemma and the number μ is called the characteristic number.]

Hence

$$1 \equiv (-1)^{\mu} k^{\left(\frac{p-1}{2}\right)}$$

that is $k^{\frac{p-1}{2}} \equiv \pm 1$ according as μ is even or odd. Hence our theorem follows at once.[1]

§4. We can shorten the following discussion considerably by introducing certain convenient notations. Let the symbol (k, p)[2] represent the number of products among

$$k, 2k, 3k, \ldots k\frac{p-1}{2}$$

whose smallest positive residues modulo p exceed $p/2$. Further if x is a non-integral quantity we will express by the symbol $[x]$ the greatest integer less than x so that $x - [x]$ is always a positive quantity between 0 and 1. We can readily establish the following relations:

I. $[x] + [-x] = -1$.
II. $[x] + b = [x + b]$, whenever b is an integer.
III. $[x] + [b - x] = b - 1$.
IV. If $x - [x]$ is a fraction less than $\frac{1}{2}$, then $[2x] - 2[x] = 0$. If on the other hand $x - [x]$ is greater than $\frac{1}{2}$, then $[2x] - 2[x] = 1$.
V. If the smallest positive residue of $b(mod\ p)$ is less than $p/2$, then $[2b/p] - 2[b/p] = 0$. If however it is larger than $p/2$, then $[2b/p] - 2[b/p] = 1$.
VI. From this it follows that:

$$(k, p) = \left[\frac{2k}{p}\right] + \left[\frac{4k}{p}\right] + \left[\frac{6k}{p}\right] + \ldots + \left[\frac{(p-1)k}{p}\right]$$
$$- 2\left[\frac{k}{p}\right] - 2\left[\frac{2k}{p}\right] - 2\left[\frac{3k}{p}\right] \ldots - 2\left[\frac{k(p-1)/2}{p}\right]$$

VII. From VI and I we obtain without difficulty:

$$(k, p) + (-k, p) = \frac{p-1}{2}$$

From this it follows that the quadratic character of $-k$ with respect to p is the same as or opposite to the quadratic character

---

[1] [This follows from the famous Euler's criterion: $k^{\frac{p-1}{2}} \equiv \pm 1$ according as k is or is not a quadratic residue of p.]

[2] [The symbol (k, p) replaces the characteristic number μ of the preceding theorem.]

of k with respect to p, according as p is of the form $4n + 1$ or $4n + 3$. It is evident that in the first case -1 is a residue and in the second a non-residue of p.

VIII. We transform the formula given in VI as follows: From III we have

$$\left[\frac{(p-1)k}{p}\right] = k - 1 - \left[\frac{k}{p}\right], \quad \left[\frac{(p-3)k}{p}\right] = k - 1 - \left[\frac{3k}{p}\right],$$

$$\left[\frac{(p-5)k}{p}\right] = k - 1 - \left[\frac{5k}{p}\right]\ldots$$

When we apply these substitutions to the last $\dfrac{p \mp 1}{4}$ terms of the above series we have

first, when p is of the form $4n + 1$,

$$(k, p) = \frac{(k-1)(p-1)}{4}$$

$$- 2\left\{\left[\frac{k}{p}\right] + \left[\frac{3k}{p}\right] + \left[\frac{5k}{p}\right] + \ldots + \left[\frac{k(p-3)/2}{p}\right]\right\}$$

$$- \left[\frac{k}{p}\right] + \left[\frac{2k}{p}\right] + \left[\frac{3k}{p}\right] + \ldots + \left]\frac{k(p-1)/2}{p}\right\}$$

second, when p is of the form $4n + 3$

$$(k, p) = \frac{(k-1)(p+1)}{4}$$

$$- 2\left\{\left[\frac{k}{p}\right] + \left[\frac{3k}{p}\right] + \left[\frac{5k}{p}\right] + \ldots + \left[\frac{k(p-1)/2}{p}\right]\right\}$$

$$- \left\{\left[\frac{k}{p}\right] + \left[\frac{2k}{p}\right] + \left[\frac{3k}{p}\right] + \ldots + \left[\frac{k(p-1)/2}{p}\right]\right\}.$$

IX. In the special case $k = +2$ it follows from the above formulas[1] that $(2, p) = (p \mp 1)/4$, where we take the upper or lower sign according as p is of the form $4n + 1$ or $4n + 3$. Therefore $(2, p)$ is even and hence $2Rp$ in case p is of the form $8n + 1$ or $8n + 7$; on the other hand $(2, p)$ is odd and hence $2Np$ when p is of the form $8n + 3$ or $8n + 5$.

§5. THEOREM.—*If x is a positive non-integral quantity among whose multiples x, $2x$, $3x$,..., nx there exist no integers; putting*

---

[1] [Each term in the braces is zero in this case, since the quantities in the square brackets are less than unity.]

$[nx] = b$ we easily conclude that among the multiples of the reciprocal $\frac{1}{x}, \frac{2}{x}, \frac{3}{x} \cdots \frac{b}{x}$ there appear no integers. Then I say that:

$$\left. \begin{array}{l} [x] + [2x] + [3x] + \ldots + [nx] \\ + \left[\frac{1}{x}\right] + \left[\frac{2}{x}\right] + \left[\frac{3}{x}\right] + \ldots + \left[\frac{b}{x}\right] \end{array} \right\} = nb.$$

Proof.—In the series $[x] + [2x] + [3x] + \ldots [nx]$, which we set equal to Ω, all the terms from the first up to and including the $\left[\frac{1}{x}\right]^{th}$ are manifestly zero, the following terms up to and including the $\left[\frac{2}{x}\right]^{th}$ are equal to 1, and the following up to $\left[\frac{3}{x}\right]^{th}$ term are equal to 2 and so on. Hence we have·

$$\left. \begin{array}{l} \Omega = \quad 0 \times \left[\frac{1}{x}\right] \\ +1 \times \left\{ \left[\frac{2}{x}\right] - \left[\frac{1}{x}\right] \right\} \\ +2 \times \left\{ \left[\frac{3}{x}\right] - \left[\frac{2}{x}\right] \right\} \\ +3 \times \left\{ \left[\frac{4}{x}\right] - \left[\frac{3}{x}\right] \right\} \\ \vdots \\ +(b-1)\left\{ \left[\frac{b}{x}\right] - \left[\frac{b-1}{x}\right] \right\} \\ +b \left\{ n - \left[\frac{b}{x}\right] \right\} \end{array} \right\} = bn - \left[\frac{1}{x}\right] - \left[\frac{2}{x}\right] - \left[\frac{3}{x}\right] - \ldots - \left[\frac{b}{x}\right].$$

Q. E. D.

§6. THEOREM.—*If k and p are positive odd numbers prime to each other, we have*

$$\left. \begin{array}{l} \left[\frac{k}{p}\right] + \left[\frac{2k}{p}\right] + \left[\frac{3k}{p}\right] + \ldots + \left[\frac{k(p-1)/2}{p}\right] \\ + \left[\frac{p}{k}\right] + \left[\frac{2p}{k}\right] + \left[\frac{3p}{k}\right] + \ldots + \left[\frac{p(k-1)/2}{k}\right] \end{array} \right\} = \frac{(k-1)(p-1)}{4}.$$

Proof.—Supposing that $k < p$ we have $\dfrac{k(p-1)/2}{p} < \dfrac{k}{2}$ but $> \dfrac{k-1}{2}$, and hence

$$\left[\frac{k(p-1)/2}{p}\right] = \frac{k-1}{2}.$$

From this it is clear that the theorem follows at once from the preceding one if we set

$$\frac{k}{p} = x, \quad \frac{p-1}{2} = n, \quad \frac{k-1}{2} = b.$$

It is possible to prove in a similar way that if k is *even* and prime to p, then

$$\left.\begin{array}{l} \left[\dfrac{k}{p}\right] + \left[\dfrac{2k}{p}\right] + \left[\dfrac{3k}{p}\right] + \ldots + \left[\dfrac{k(p-1)/2}{p}\right] \\[2mm] + \left[\dfrac{p}{k}\right] + \left[\dfrac{2p}{k}\right] + \left[\dfrac{3p}{k}\right] + \ldots + \left[\dfrac{kp/2}{k}\right] \end{array}\right\} = k\frac{p-1}{4}.$$

However we will not prove this proposition as it is not necessary for our purpose.

§7. Now the main theorem follows from the combination of the last theorem with proposition VIII of paragraph 4. For if we designate by k and p any distinct, positive prime numbers[1] and put

$$(k, p) + \left[\frac{k}{p}\right] + \left[\frac{2k}{p}\right] + \left[\frac{3k}{p}\right] + \ldots + \left[\frac{k(p-1)/2}{p}\right] = L,$$

$$(p, k) + \left[\frac{p}{k}\right] + \left[\frac{2p}{k}\right] + \left[\frac{3p}{k}\right] + \ldots + \left[\frac{p(k-1)/2}{p}\right] = M,$$

then it follows from §4, VIII, that L and M will always be even numbers. It follows from the theorem of §6 that

$$L + M = (k, p) + (p, k) + \frac{(k-1)(p-1)}{4}$$

Therefore, when $(k-1)(p-1)/4$ is even, that is when one or both of the primes k or p is of the form $4n + 1$, then (p, k) and (k, p) are either both even or both odd. On the contrary when $(k-1)(p-1)/4$ is odd, that is when k and p are both of the form $4n + 3$, then necessarily one of the numbers (k, p), (p, k) is even and the other odd. In the first case the relations of k to p, and of p to k (as regards the quadratic character of one with respect to the other) are the same; in the second case they are opposite.

Q. E. D.

---

[1] [In which] k and p should also be different from 2.

KUMMER

On Ideal Numbers

(Translated from the German by Dr. Thomas Freeman Cope, National Research Fellow in Mathematics, Harvard University, Cambridge, Mass.)

Ernst Edward Kummer[1] (1810–1893), who was professor of mathematics in the University of Breslau from 1842 till 1855 and then in the University of Berlin until 1884, made valuable contributions in several branches of mathematics. Among the topics he studied may be mentioned the theory of the hypergeometric (Gaussian) series, the Riccati equation, the question of the convergency of series, the theory of complex numbers, and cubic and biquadratic residues. He was the creator of ideal prime factors of complex numbers and studied intensively surfaces of the fourth order and, in particular, the surfaces which bear his name.

In the following paper which appears in the original in Crelle's *Journal für die reine und angewandte Mathematik* (Vol. 35, pp. 319–326, 1847), Kummer introduces the notion of ideal prime factors of complex numbers, by means of which he was able to restore unique factorization in a field where the fundamental theorem of arithmetic does not hold. Although Kummer's theory has been largely supplanted by the simpler and more general theory of Dedekind, yet the ideas he introduced were of such importance that no less an authority than Professor E. T. Bell is responsible for the statement that[2] "Kummer's introduction of ideals into arithmetic was beyond all dispute one of the greatest mathematical advances of the nineteenth century." For the position of Kummer's theory in the theory of numbers, the reader is referred to the article by Professor Bell from which the above quotation is taken.

On the Theory Of Complex Numbers

(By Professor Kummer of Breslau.)

(Abstract of the *Berichten der Königl. Akad. der Wiss. zu Berlin*, March 1845.)

I have succeeded in completing and in simplifying the theory of those complex numbers which are formed from the higher roots of unity and which, as is well known, play an important rôle in cyclotomy and in the study of power residues and of forms of higher degree; this I have done through the introduction of a peculiar kind of imaginary divisors which I call *ideal complex*

---

[1] For a short biographical sketch, see D. E. Smith, *History of Mathematics*, Vol. I, pp. 507–508, Boston, 1923.

[2] *American Mathematical Monthly*, Vol. 34, pp. 66.

numbers and concerning which I take the liberty of making a few remarks.

If α is an imaginary root of the equation $\alpha^\lambda = 1$, λ a prime number, and a, a_1, a_2, etc. whole numbers, then $f(\alpha) = a + a_1\alpha + a_2\alpha^2 + \ldots + a_{\lambda-1}\alpha^{\lambda-1}$ is a complex whole number. Such a complex number can either be broken up into factors of the same kind or such a decomposition is not possible. In the first case, the number is a composite number; in the second case, it has hitherto been called a complex prime number. I have observed, however, that, even though $f(\alpha)$ cannot in any way be broken up into complex factors, it still does not possess the true nature of a complex prime number, for, quite commonly, it lacks the first and most important property of prime numbers; namely, that the product of two prime numbers is divisible by no other prime numbers. Rather, such numbers $f(\alpha)$, even if they are not capable of decomposition into complex factors, have nevertheless the nature of composite numbers; the factors in this case are, however, not actual but ideal complex numbers. For the introduction of such ideal complex numbers, there is the same, simple, basal motive as for the introduction of imaginary formulas into algebra and analysis; namely, the decomposition of integral rational functions into their simplest factors, the linear. It was, moreover, such a desideratum which prompted Gauss, in his researches on biquadratic residues (for all such prime factors of the form $4m + 1$ exhibit the nature of composite numbers), to introduce for the first time complex numbers of the form $a + b\sqrt{-1}$.

In order to secure a sound definition of the true (usually ideal) prime factors of complex numbers, it was necessary to use the properties of prime factors of complex numbers which hold in every case and which are entirely independent of the contingency of whether or not actual decomposition takes place: just as in geometry, if it is a question of the common chords of two circles even though the circles do not intersect, one seeks an actual definition of these ideal common chords which shall hold for all positions of the circles. There are several such permanent properties of complex numbers which could be used as definitions of ideal prime factors and which would always lead to essentially the same result; of these, I have chosen *one* as the simplest and the most general.

If p is a prime number of the form $m\lambda + 1$, then it can be represented, in many cases, as the product of the following $\lambda - 1$ complex factors: $p = f(\alpha) \cdot f(\alpha^2) \cdot f(\alpha^3) \ldots f(\alpha^{\lambda-1})$; when, however, a decomposition into actual complex prime factors is not possible, let ideals make their appearance in order to bring this about. If $f(\alpha)$ is an actual complex number and a prime factor of p, it has the property that, if instead of the root of the equation $\alpha^\lambda = 1$ a definite root of the congruence $\xi^\lambda \equiv 1$, mod. p, is substituted, then $f(\xi) \equiv 0$, mod. p. Hence too if the prime factor $f(\alpha)$ is contained in a complex number $\Phi(\alpha)$, it is true that $\Phi(\xi) \equiv 0$, mod. p; and conversely, if $\Phi(\xi) \equiv 0$, mod. p, and p is factorable into $\lambda - 1$ complex prime factors, then $\Phi(\alpha)$ contains the prime factor $f(\alpha)$. Now the property $\Phi(\xi) \equiv 0$, mod. p, is such that it does not depend in any way on the factorability of the number p into prime factors; it can accordingly be used as a definition, since it is agreed that the complex number $\Phi(\alpha)$ shall contain the ideal prime factor of p which belongs to $\alpha = \xi$, if $\Phi(\xi) \equiv 0$, mod. p. Each of the $\lambda - 1$ complex prime factors of p is thus replaced by a congruence relation. This suffices to show that complex prime factors, whether they be actual or merely ideal, give to complex numbers the same definite character. In the process given here, however, we do not use the congruence relations as the definitions of ideal prime factors because they would not be sufficient to represent several equal ideal prime factors of a complex number, and because, being too restrictive, they would yield only ideal prime factors of the real prime numbers of the form $m\lambda - 1$.

Every prime factor of a complex number is also a prime factor of every real prime number q, and the nature of the ideal prime factors is, in particular, dependent on the exponent to which q belongs for the modulus λ. Let this exponent be f, so that $q^f \equiv 1$, mod. λ, and $\lambda - 1 = e \cdot f$. Such a prime number q can never be broken up into more than e complex prime factors which, if this decomposition can actually be carried out, are represented as linear functions of the e periods of each set of f terms. These periods of the roots of the equation $\alpha^\lambda = 1$, I denote by $\eta, \eta_1, \eta_2, \ldots \eta_{e-1}$; and indeed in such an order that each goes over into the following one whenever α is transformed into α^γ, where γ is a primitive root of λ. As is well known, the periods are the e roots of an equation of the eth degree; and this equation, considered as a congruence for the modulus q, has always e real congruential roots which I denote by $u, u_1, u_2, \ldots u_{e-1}$ and take in an order corresponding to that of the periods, for which, besides the congruence of the eth degree, still other easily found congruences may be used. If now the complex number $c'\eta + c_1'\eta_1 + c_2'\eta_2 +$

$\ldots + c'_{e-1}\eta_{e-1}$, constructed out of periods, is denoted shortly by $\Phi(\eta)$, then among the prime numbers q which belong to the exponent f, there are always such that can be brought into the form

$$q = \Phi(\eta)\Phi(\eta_1)\Phi(\eta_2)\ldots\Phi(\eta_{e-1}),$$

in which, moreover, the e factors never admit a further decomposition. If one replaces the periods by the congruential roots corresponding to them, where a period can arbitrarily be designated to correspond to a definite congruential root, then one of the e prime factors always becomes congruent to zero for the modulus q. Now if any complex number $f(\alpha)$ contains the prime factor $\Phi(\eta)$, it will always have the property, for $\eta = u_k$, $\eta_1 = u_{k+1}$, $\eta_2 = u_{k+2}$, etc., of becoming congruent to zero for the modulus $q\cdot$ This property (which implies precisely f distinct congruence relations, the development of which would lead too far) is a permanent one even for those prime numbers q which do not admit an actual decomposition into e complex prime factors. It could therefore be used as a definition of complex prime factors; it would, however, have the defect of not being able to express the equal ideal prime factors of a complex number.

The definition of ideal complex prime factors which I have chosen and which is essentially the same as the one described but is simpler and more general, rests on the fact that, as I prove separately, one can always find a complex number $\psi(\eta)$, constructed out of periods, which is of such a nature that $\psi(\eta)\psi(\eta_1)\psi(\eta_2)\ldots$ $\psi(\eta_{e-1})$ (this product being a whole number) is divisible by q but not by q^2. This complex number $\psi(\eta)$ has always the above-mentioned property, namely, that it is congruent to zero, modulo q, if for the periods are substituted the corresponding congruential roots, and therefore $\psi(\eta) \equiv 0$, mod. q, for $\eta = u$, $\eta_1 = u_1$, $\eta_2 = u_2$, etc. I now set $\psi(\eta_1)\psi(\eta_2)\ldots\psi(\eta_{e-1}) = \Psi(\eta)$ and define ideal prime numbers in the following manner:—

If $f(\alpha)$ has the property that the product $f(\alpha)\cdot\Psi(\eta_r)$ is divisible by q, this shall be expressed as follows: $f(\alpha)$ contains the ideal prime factor of q which belongs to $u = \eta_r$. Furthermore, if $f(\alpha)$ has the property that $f(\alpha)\cdot(\Psi(\eta_r))^\mu$ is divisible by q^μ but $f(\alpha)(\Psi(\eta_r))^{\mu+1}$ is not divisible by $q^{\mu+1}$, this shall be described thus: $f(\alpha)$ contains the ideal prime factor of q which belongs to $u = \eta_r$, exactly μ times.

It would lead too far if I should develop here the connection and the agreement of this definition with those given by congruence relations as described above; I simply remark that the relation: $f(\alpha)\Psi(\eta_r)$ divisible by q, is completely equivalent to f distinct congruence relations, and that the relation: $f(\alpha)(\Psi(\eta_r))^\mu$ divisible by q^μ, can always be entirely replaced by $u \cdot f$ congruence relations. The whole theory of ideal complex numbers which I have already perfected and of which I here announce the principal theorems, is a justification of the definition given as well as of the nomenclature adopted. The principal theorems are the following:

The product of two or more complex numbers has exactly the same ideal prime factors as the factors taken together.

If a complex number (which is a product of factors) contains all the e prime factors of q, it is also divisible by q itself; if, however, it does not contain some one of these e ideal prime factors, it is not divisible by q.

If a complex number (in the form of a product) contains all the e ideal prime factors of q and, indeed, each at least μ times, it is divisible by q^μ.

If $f(\alpha)$ contains exactly m ideal prime factors of q, which may all be different, or partly or wholly alike, then the norm $Nf(\alpha) = f(\alpha)f(\alpha^2)\ldots f(\alpha^{\lambda-1})$ contains exactly the factor q^{mf}.

Every complex number contains only a finite, determinate number of ideal prime factors.

Two complex numbers which have exactly the same ideal prime factors differ only by a complex unit which may enter as a factor.

A complex number is divisible by another if all the ideal prime factors of the divisor are contained in the dividend; and the quotient contains precisely the excess of the ideal prime factors of the dividend over those of the divisor.

From these theorems it follows that computation with complex numbers becomes, by the introduction of ideal prime factors, entirely the same as computation with integers and their real integral prime factors. Consequently, the grounds for the complaint which I voiced in the *Breslauer Programm zur Jubelfeier der Universität Königsberg S.* 18, are removed:—

It seems a great pity that this quality of real numbers, namely, that they can be resolved into prime factors which for the same number are always the same, is not shared by complex numbers; if now this desirable property were part of a complete doctrine, the effecting of which is as yet beset with great difficulties, the matter could easily be resolved and brought to a successful conclusion. Etc. One sees therefore that ideal prime factors disclose the inner nature of complex numbers, make them transparent, as it were, and show their inner crystalline structure. If, in particular, a complex number is given merely in the form $a + a_1\alpha + a_2\alpha^2 + \ldots + a_{\lambda-1}\alpha^{\lambda-1}$, little can be asserted about it until one has determined, by means of its ideal prime factors (which in such a case can always be found by direct methods), its simplest qualitative properties to serve as the basis of all further arithmetical investigations.

Ideal factors of complex numbers arise, as has been shown, as factors of actual complex numbers: hence ideal prime factors multiplied with others suitably chosen must always give actual complex numbers for products. This question of the combination of ideal factors to obtain actual complex numbers is, as I shall show as a consequence of the results which I have already found, of the greatest interest, because it stands in an intimate relationship to the most important sections of number theory. The two most important results relative to this question are the following:

There always exists a finite, determinate number of ideal complex multipliers which are necessary and sufficient to reduce all possible ideal complex numbers to actual complex numbers.[1]

Every ideal complex number has the property that a definite integral power of it will give an actual complex number.

I consider now some more detailed developments from these two theorems. Two ideal complex numbers which, when multiplied by one and the same ideal number, form actual complex numbers, I shall call *equivalent* or of the same class, because this investigation of actual and ideal complex numbers is identical with the classification of a certain set of forms of the $\lambda - 1$st degree and in $\lambda - 1$ variables; the principal results relative to this classification have been found by Dirichlet but not yet published so that I do not know precisely whether or not his principle of classification coincides with that resulting from the theory of complex numbers. For example, the theory of a form of the second degree in two variables with determinant, however, a prime number λ, is closely interwoven with these investigations, and our classification in this case coincides with that of Gauss but not with that of Legendre. The same considerations also throw great light upon Gauss's classification of forms of the second degree and upon the true basis for the differentiation between *Aequivalentia propria et impropria*,[2]

---

[1] A proof of this important theorem, although in far less generality and in an entirely different form, is found in the dissertation: L. Kronecker, *De unitatibus complexis*, Berlin, 1845.

[2] [*i. e.*, proper and improper equivalence.]

which, undeniably, has always an appearance of impropriety when it presents itself in the *Disquisitiones arithmeticae*. If, for example, two forms such as $ax^2 + 2bxy + cy^2$ and $ax^2 - 2bxy + cy^2$, or $ax^2 + 2bxy + cy^2$ and $cx^2 + 2bxy + ay^2$, are considered as belonging to different classes, as is done in the above-mentioned work, while in fact no essential difference between them is to be found; and if on the other hand Gauss's classification must notwithstanding be admitted to be one arising for the most part out of the very nature of the question: then one is forced to consider forms such as $ax^2 + 2bxy + cy^2$ and $ax^2 - 2bxy + cy^2$ which differ from each other in outward appearance only, as merely representative of two new but essentially different concepts of number theory. These however, are in reality nothing more than two different ideal prime factors which belong to one and the same number. The entire theory of forms of the second degree in two variables can be thought of as the theory of complex numbers of the form $x + y\sqrt{D}$ and then leads necessarily to ideal complex numbers of the same sort. The latter, however, classify themselves according to the ideal multipliers which are necessary and sufficient to reduce them to actual complex numbers of the form $x + y\sqrt{D}$. Because of this agreement with the classification of Gauss, ideal complex numbers thus constitute the true basis for it.

The general investigation of ideal complex numbers presents the greatest analogy with the very difficult section by Gauss: *De compositione formarum*, and the principal results which Gauss proved for quadratic forms, pp. 337 and following, hold true also for the combination of general ideal complex numbers. Thus there belongs to every class of ideal numbers another class which, when multiplied by the first class, gives rise to actual complex numbers (here the actual complex numbers are the analogue of the *Classis principalis*).[1] Likewise, there are classes which, when multiplied by themselves, give for the result actual complex numbers (the *Classis principalis*), and these classes are therefore *ancipites;*[2] in particular, the *Classis principalis* itself is always a *Classis anceps*. If one takes an ideal complex number and raises it to powers, then in accordance with the second of the foregoing theorems, one will arrive at a power which is an actual complex number; if h is the smallest number for which $(f(\alpha))^h$ is an actual

---

[1] [Principal class.]

[2] [Dual, or of a double nature.]

complex number, then $f(\alpha)$, $(f(\alpha))^2$, $(f(\alpha))^3$, ... $(f(\alpha))^h$ all belong to different classes. It now may happen that, by a suitable choice of $f(\alpha)$, these exhaust all existing classes: if such is not the case, it is easy to prove that the number of classes is at least always a multiple of h. I have not gone deeper yet into this domain of complex numbers; in particular, I have not undertaken an investigation of the exact number of classes because I have heard that Dirichlet, using principles similar to those employed in his famous treatise on quadratic forms, has already found this number. I shall make only one additional remark about the character of ideal complex numbers, namely, that by the second of the foregoing theorems they can always be considered and represented as definite roots of actual complex numbers, that is, they always take the form $\sqrt[h]{\Phi(\alpha)}$ where $\Phi(\alpha)$ is an actual complex number and h an integer.

Of the different applications which I have already made of this theory of complex number, I shall refer only to the application to cyclotomy to complete the results which I have already announced in the above-mentioned *Programm*. If one sets

$$(\alpha, x) = x + \alpha x^g + \alpha^2 x^{g^2} + \ldots + \alpha^{p-2} x^{g^{p-2}},$$

where $\alpha^\lambda = 1$, $x^p = 1$, $p = m\lambda + 1$, and g is a primitive root of the prime number p, then it is well known that $(\alpha, x)^\lambda$ is a complex number independent of x and formed from the roots of the equation $\alpha^\lambda = 1$. In the *Programm* cited, I have found the following expression for this number, under the assumption that p can be resolved into $\lambda - 1$ actual complex prime factors, one of which is $f(\alpha)$:

$$(\alpha, x)^\lambda = \pm \alpha^h f^{m_1}(\alpha) \cdot f^{m_2}(\alpha^2) \cdot f^{m_3}(\alpha^3) \ldots f^{m_{\lambda-1}}(\alpha^{\lambda-1}),$$

where the power-exponents m_1, m_2, m_3, etc. are so determined that the general m_K, positive, is less than λ and $k \cdot m_k \equiv 1$, mod. λ. Exactly the same simple expression holds in complete generality, as can easily be proved, even when $f(\alpha)$ is not the actual but only the ideal prime factor of p. In order, however, in the latter case, to maintain the expression for $(\alpha, x)^\lambda$ in the form for an actual complex number, one need only represent the ideal $f(\alpha)$ as a root of an actual complex number, or apply one of the methods (although indirect) which serve to represent an actual complex number whose ideal prime factors are given.

CHEBYSHEV (TCHEBYCHEFF)

ON THE TOTALITY OF PRIMES

(Translated from the French by Professor J. D. Tamarkin, Brown University, Providence, Rhode Island.)

Pafnuty Lvovich Chebyshev (Tchebycheff, Tchebytcheff) was born on May 14, 1821, and died on Nov. 26, 1894. He is one of the most prominent representatives of the Russian mathematical school. He made numerous important contributions to the theory of numbers, algebra, the theory of probabilities, analysis, and applied mathematics. Among the most important of his papers are the two memoirs of which portions are here translated:

1. "Sur la totalité des nombres premiers inférieurs à une limite donnée," *Mémoires presentés à l'Académie Impériale des Sciences de St.-Pétersbourg par divers savants et lus dans ses assemblées*, Vol. 6, pp. 141–157, 1851 (Lu le 24 Mai, 1848); *Journal de Mathématiques pures et appliquées*, (1) Vol. 17, pp. 341–365, 1852; *Oeuvres*, Vol. 1, pp. 29–48, 1899.

2. "Mémoire sur les nombres premiers," *ibid.*, Vol. 7, pp. 15–33, 1854 (lu le 9 Septembre, 1850), *ibid.*, pp. 366–390, *ibid.*, pp. 51–70.

These memoirs represent the first definite progress after Euclid in the investigation of the function $\phi(x)$ which determines the totality of prime numbers less than the given limit x. The problem of finding an asymptotic expression for $\phi(x)$ for large values of x attracted the attention and efforts of some of the most brilliant mathematicians such as Legendre, Gauss, Lejeune-Dirichlet, and Riemann.

Gauss (1791, at the age of fourteen) was the first to suggest, in a purely empirical way, the asymptotic formula $\frac{x}{\log x}$ for $\phi(x)$. (*Werke*, Vol. X_1, p. 11, 1917.) Later on (1792–1793, 1849), he suggested another formula $\int_2^x \frac{dx}{\log x}$, of which $\frac{x}{\log x}$ is the leading term (Gauss's letter to Encke, 1849, *Werke*, Vol. II, pp. 444–447, 1876). Legendre, being, of course, unaware of Gauss's results, suggested another empirical formula $\frac{x}{A \log x + B}$ (*Essai sur la théorie des nombres*, 1st ed., pp. 18–19, 1798) and specified the constants A and B as $A = 1$, $B = -1.08366$ in the second edition of the *Essai* (pp. 394–395, 1808). Legendre's formula, which Abel quoted as "the most marvelous in mathematics" (letter to Holmboe, *Abel Memorial*, 1902, Correspondence, p. 5), is correct up to the leading term only. This fact was recognized by Dirichlet ("Sur l'usage des séries infinies dans la théorie des nombres," *Crelle's Journal*, Vol. 18, p. 272, 1838, in his remark written on the copy presented to Gauss. *Cf.* Dirichlet, *Werke*, Vol. 1, p. 372, 1889). In this note to Gauss, Dirichlet suggested another formula $\sum^{x} \dfrac{1}{\log n}$. The proof of these

results, although announced by Dirichlet, has never been published, so that Chebyshev's (Tchebycheff's) memoirs should be considered as the first attempt at a rigorous investigation of the problem by analytical methods.

Chebyshev did not reach the final goal—to prove that the ratio $\phi(x): \dfrac{x}{\log x}$

tends to 1 as $x \to \infty$. This important theorem was proved some 40 years later by Hadamard ("Sur la distribution des zéros de la fonction $\zeta(s)$ et ses conséquences arithmétiques," *Bulletin de la Societé Mathématique de France,* Vol. 24, pp. 199–220, 1896) and by de la Vallée Poussin ("Recherches analytiques sur la théorie des nombres premiers," *Annales de la Société Scientifique de Bruxelles,* Vol. 20, pp. 183–256, 1896), their work being based upon new ideas and suggestions introduced by Riemann ("Über die Anzahl der Primzahlen unter einer gegebenen Grenze," *Monatsberichte der Berliner Akademie,* pp. 671–680, 1859; *Werke,* 2nd ed., pp. 145–153, 1892).

Although Chebyshev did not prove this final theorem, still he succeeded in obtaining important inequalities for the function $\phi(x)$, which enabled him to investigate the possible forms of approximation of $\phi(x)$ by means of expressions containing algebraically x, e^x, $\log x$ (*Memoir* 1, above) with a conclusion concerning the rather limited range of applicability of Legendre's formula. In the *Memoir* 2, Chebyshev obtains rather narrow limits for the ratio $\phi(x):$

$\dfrac{x}{\log x}$, which provide a proof for the famous Bertrand postulate: "If $x \geqq 2$,

there is at least one prime number between x and $2x - 2$."

Memoir 1: On the Function which Determines the Totality of Primes Less than a Given Limit

§1. Legendre in his *Théorie des nombres*[1] proposes a formula for the number of primes between 1 and any given limit. He begins by comparing his formula with the result of counting the primes in the most extended tables, namely those from 10,000 up to 1,000,000, after which he applies his formula to the solution of many problems. Later the same formula has been the object of investigations of Mr. Lejeune-Dirichlet who announced in one of his memoirs in *Crelle's Journal,* Vol. 18, that he had found a rigorous analytical proof of the formula in question.[2] Despite the authority of the name of Mr. Lejeune-Dirichlet and the pronounced agreement of the formula of Legendre with the tables of primes we permit ourselves to raise certain doubts as to its

---

[1] Volume 2, p. 65 (3rd edition).

[2] [Naturally Chebyshev was unaware of the marginal notation made by Dirichlet in the copy of his paper presented to Gauss, to which we referred above.]

correctness and, consequently, as to the results which have been derived from this formula. We shall base our assertion on a theorem concerning a property of the function which determines the totality of primes less than a given limit,—a theorem from which one might derive numerous curious consequences. We shall first give a proof of the theorem in question; after that we shall indicate some of its applications.

§2. THEOREM 1.—*If $\phi(x)$ designates the totality of primes less than x, n is any integer, and ρ is a quantity > 0, the sum*

$$\sum_{x=2}^{x=\infty} \left[\phi(x+1) - \phi(x) - \frac{1}{\log x} \right] \frac{\log^n x}{x^{1+\rho}}$$

will have the property of approaching a finite limit as ρ converges to zero.

Proof.—We begin by establishing the property in question for the functions which are obtained by successive differentiations, with respect to ρ, of the three expressions

$$\sum \frac{1}{m^{1+\rho}} - \frac{1}{\rho}, \quad \log \rho - \sum \log \left(1 - \frac{1}{\mu^{1+\rho}} \right),$$

$$\sum \log \left(1 - \frac{1}{\mu^{1+\rho}} \right) + \sum \frac{1}{\mu^{1+\rho}}.$$

The summation over m is extended, here as well as later, over all integral values from $m = 2$ up to $m = \infty$, while that over μ is taken over primes only, likewise from $\mu = 2$ up to $\mu = \infty$.

Consider the first expression. It is readily seen that[1]

$$\int_0^\infty \frac{e^{-x}}{e^x - 1} x^\rho dx = \sum \frac{1}{m^{1+\rho}} \int_0^\infty e^{-x} x^\rho dx,$$

$$\int_0^\infty e^{-x} x^{-1+\rho} dx = \frac{1}{\rho} \int_0^\infty e^{-x} x^\rho dx,$$

consequently

$$\sum \frac{1}{m^{1+\rho}} - \frac{1}{\rho} = \frac{\int_0^\infty \left(\frac{1}{e^x - 1} - \frac{1}{x} \right) e^{-x} x^\rho dx}{\int_0^\infty e^{-x} x^\rho dx}.$$

---

[1] [The first of these formulas is obtained by expanding $\frac{e^{-x}}{(e^x - 1)}$ in the geometric series Σe^{-mx}, which, being multiplied by x^ρ and integrated termwise, yields the expression

$$\sum \int_0^\infty e^{-mx} x^\rho dx = \sum m^{-1-\rho} \int_0^\infty e^{-x} x^\rho dx.$$

The termwise integration can be readily justified.]

By virtue of this equation the derivative of any order n with respect to ρ of $\sum \frac{1}{m^{1+\rho}} - \frac{1}{\rho}$ will be equal to a fraction whose denominator is $\left[\int_0^\infty e^{-x} x^\rho dx \right]^{n+1}$ and whose numerator is a polynomial in

$$\int_0^\infty \left(\frac{1}{e^x - 1} - \frac{1}{x} \right) e^{-x} x^\rho dx, \quad \int_0^\infty \left(\frac{1}{e^x - 1} - \frac{1}{x} \right) e^{-x} x^\rho \log x \, dx,$$

$$\int_0^\infty \left(\frac{1}{e^x - 1} - \frac{1}{x} \right) e^{-x} x^\rho \log^2 x \, dx, \ldots \int_0^\infty \left(\frac{1}{e^x - 1} - \frac{1}{x} \right) e^{-x} x^\rho \log^n x \, dx,$$

$$\int_0^\infty e^{-x} x^\rho dx, \int_0^\infty e^{-x} x^\rho \log x \, dx, \int_0^\infty e^{-x} x^\rho \log^2 x \, dx, \ldots \int_0^\infty e^{-x} x^\rho \log^n x \, dx.$$

But a fraction of this type, no matter whether $n = 0$ or $n > 0$, approaches a finite limit at $\rho \to 0$; for, then the limit of the integral $\int_0^\infty e^{-x} x^\rho \, dx$ is 1, and the remaining integrals have finite limiting values.[1]

This proves that the function $\sum \frac{1}{m^{1+\rho}} - \frac{1}{\rho}$ and its successive derivatives remain finite when $\rho \to 0$.

Consider now the function

$$\log \rho - \sum \log \left(1 - \frac{1}{\mu^{1+\rho}} \right).$$

It is known that

$$\left[\left(1 - \frac{1}{2^{1+\rho}} \right)\left(1 - \frac{1}{3^{1+\rho}} \right)\left(1 - \frac{1}{5^{1+\rho}} \right) \cdots \right]^{-1}$$

$$= 1 + \frac{1}{2^{1+\rho}} + \frac{1}{3^{1+\rho}} + \frac{1}{4^{1+\rho}} + \ldots [2]$$

---

[1] [The reasoning here is justified, since all the integrals in question are uniformly convergent in ρ for $0 \leqq \rho \leqq A$, A being any fixed positive constant.]

[2] [This identity was established by Euler ("Variæ observationes circa series infinitæ," *Commentarii Academiae Scientiarum Petropolitanæ,* 9, pp. 160–188, 1737 (Theorem 8, p. 174); *Leonardi Euleri Opera Omnia,* (1) 14, pp. 216–244 (230). Euler introduces here what is now called Riemann's ζ-function as defined by the series

$$\zeta(\rho) = \sum_{\nu=1}^\infty \nu^{-\rho}, \ \rho > 1.$$

The use of this function made by Riemann (*loc. cit.*) gave a most powerful impetus to the modern theory of functions of a complex variable.

The infinite product here is absolutely convergent since $(1 - \mu^{-1-\rho})^{-1} = 1 + \left(\frac{1}{\mu^{1+\rho} - 1} \right)$ and the series $\sum \left(\frac{1}{\mu^{1+\rho} - 1} \right)$ is absolutely convergent, as well

whence, with the notation adopted above,

$$-\sum \log\left(1 - \frac{1}{\mu^{1+\rho}}\right) = \log\left(1 + \sum\frac{1}{m^{1+\rho}}\right).$$

Hence

$$\log \rho - \sum \log\left(1 - \frac{1}{\mu^{1+\rho}}\right) = \log\left(1 + \sum\frac{1}{m^{1+\rho}}\right)\rho,$$

or else

$$\log \rho - \sum \log\left(1 - \frac{1}{\mu^{1+\rho}}\right) = \log\left[1 + \rho + \left(\sum\frac{1}{m^{1+\rho}} - \frac{1}{\rho}\right)\rho\right].$$

This equation shows that all the derivatives with respect to ρ of

$$\log \rho - \sum \log\left(1 - \frac{1}{\mu^{1+\rho}}\right)$$

can be expressed in terms of a finite number of fractions whose denominators are positive integral powers of

$$1 + \rho + \left(\sum\frac{1}{m^{1+\rho}} - \frac{1}{\rho}\right)\rho,$$

and whose numerators are polynomials in ρ and the expression $\sum\frac{1}{m^{1+\rho}} - \frac{1}{\rho}$ and its derivatives with respect to ρ. The fractions of this type tend to finite limits as $\rho \to 0$: the expression $1 + \rho + \left(\sum\frac{1}{m^{1+\rho}} - \frac{1}{\rho}\right)\rho$, which figures in the denominators of these fractions, tends to 1 as $\rho \to 0$, since, as we have proved, the difference $\sum\frac{1}{m^{1+\rho}} - \frac{1}{\rho}$ remains finite; as to the numerators, they are polynomials in $\sum\frac{1}{m^{1+\rho}} - \frac{1}{\rho}$ and its derivatives, and, since all these functions tend to finite limits as $\rho \to 0$, the same will hold true for the numerators in question.

It remains to prove the same property for the derivatives of the function

$$\sum \log\left(1 - \frac{1}{\mu^{1+\rho}}\right) + \sum\frac{1}{\mu^{1+\rho}}.$$

We observe first that its first derivative is

$$\Sigma\mu^{-2-2\rho}\log \mu.(1 - \mu^{-1-\rho})^{-1}.$$

as the series $\Sigma\mu^{-1-\rho}$, which is only a part of the absolutely convergent series $\Sigma m^{-1-\rho}$. All these series and their derived series are also uniformly convergent for $\rho > 0$, which justifies the termwise differentiations in the following work.]

From this it is readily seen that the derivatives of higher order also can be expressed in terms of a finite number of expressions of the form

$$\Sigma \mu^{-2-2\rho-q} \log^p \mu \, (1 - \mu^{-1-\rho})^{-1-r},$$

with $p, q, r \geqq 0$. But, each expression of this type has a finite value for $\rho \geqq 0$, since the function under the sign Σ is of order higher than 1 in $1/\mu$.

After it has been proved that the derivatives of the three expressions above tend to finite limits as $\rho \to 0$, the same property can be established for the expression

$$\frac{d^n}{d\rho^n}\left[\sum \log\left(1 - \mu^{-1-\rho}\right) + \sum \mu^{-1-\rho} \right] +$$

$$\frac{d^n}{d\rho^n}\left[\log \rho - \sum \log\left(1 - \mu^{-1-\rho}\right) \right] + \frac{d^{n-1}}{d\rho^{n-1}}\left(\sum m^{-1-\rho} - \frac{1}{\rho}\right)$$

which, after the differentiations are performed, reduces to

$$\pm\left(\sum \frac{\log^n \mu}{\mu^{1+\rho}} - \sum \frac{\log^{n-1} m}{m^{1+\rho}} \right).$$

This result implies our theorem above, since it is readily seen that the difference

$$\sum \frac{\log^n \mu}{\mu^{1+\rho}} - \sum \frac{\log^{n-1} m}{m^{1+\rho}}$$

is identical with

$$\sum_{x=2}^{x=\infty}\left[\phi(x + 1) - \phi(x) - \frac{1}{\log x} \right]\frac{\log^n x}{x^{1+\rho}}$$

or, what is the same thing, with

$$\sum_{x=2}^{x=\infty} [\phi(x + 1) - \phi(x)]\frac{\log^n x}{x^{1+\rho}} - \sum_{x=2}^{x=\infty} \frac{\log^{n-1}}{x^{1+\rho}}.$$

To prove this we have only to observe that the first term of the difference above equals $\sum \dfrac{\log^n \mu}{\mu^{1+\rho}}$ since the coefficient $\phi(x + 1) - \phi(x)$ of $\dfrac{\log^n x}{x^{1+\rho}}$, by definition of the function $\phi(x)$ reduces to 1 or to 0 according as x is a prime or a composite number. The second term is transformed into $\sum\dfrac{\log^{n-1} m}{m^{1+\rho}}$ by replacing x by m.[1]

---

[1] [From the modern point of view the essence of Chebyshev's proof above lies in the fact that $\zeta(\rho)$ is analytic for all values of $\rho \neq 1$ while it has a simple pole at $\rho = 1$ with the residue 1, whence $\zeta(\rho) - \dfrac{1}{(\rho - 1)}$ is an entire transcendental function. (Whittaker-Watson, *Modern Analysis*, 3rd edition, 1920, p. 26.)]

This completes the proof of the theorem in question.

§3. The theorem which has been proved above leads to many curious properties of the function which determines the totality of primes less than a given limit. We first observe that the difference

$$\frac{1}{\log x} - \int^{x+} \frac{dx}{\log x}$$

for x very large is an infinitesimal of the first order in $1/x$; consequently the expression

$$\left(\frac{1}{\log x} - \int_x^{x+1} \frac{dx}{\log x}\right) \frac{\log^n x}{x^{1+\rho}}$$

will be of order $2 + \rho$ with respect to $1/x$.[1] Hence the sum

$$\sum_{x=2}^{x=\infty} \left(\frac{1}{\log x} - \int_x^{x+1} \frac{dx}{\log x}\right) \frac{\log^n x}{x^{1+\rho}}$$

remains finite for $\rho \geqq 0$. On adding this sum to the expression

$$\sum_{x=2}^{x=\infty} \left[\phi(x+1) - \phi(x) - \frac{1}{\log x}\right] \frac{\log^n x}{x^{1+\rho}}$$

for which Theorem 1 holds true, we conclude that the expression

$$\sum_{x=2}^{\infty} \left[\phi(x+1) - \phi(x) - \int_x^{x+1} \frac{dx}{\log x}\right] \frac{\log^n x}{x^{1+\rho}}$$

also remains finite as $\rho \to 0$. From this we can derive the following theorem.

THEOREM 2.—*The function $\phi(x)$ which designates the totality of primes less than x, satisfies infinitely many times, between the limits $x = 2$ and $x = \infty$, each of the inequalities*

$$\phi(x) > \int_2^x \frac{dx}{\log x} - \frac{\alpha x}{\log^n x} \quad \text{and} \quad \phi(x) < \int^x \frac{dx}{\log x} + \frac{\alpha x}{\log^n x},$$

no matter how small is the positive number α and, at the same time, how large is n.

Proof.—We shall restrict ourselves to the proof of one of these two inequalities; the second can be proved exactly in the same fashion. Take for instance the inequality

$$(1) \qquad \phi(x) < \int_2^x \frac{dx}{\log x} + \frac{\alpha x}{\log^n x}.$$

To prove that this inequality is satisfied infinitely many times let us assume the contrary and examine the consequences of

---

[1] [By this it is meant that the quotient of the difference in question by any power of $1/x$ less than $(2 + \rho)$ tends to zero as $x \to \infty$.]

this hypothesis. Let a be an integer greater than e^n and, at the same time, greater than the greatest number which satisfies (1). With this assumption we shall have, for $x > a$, the inequality

$$\phi(x) \geqq \int_2^x \frac{dx}{\log x} + \frac{\alpha x}{\log^n x}, \quad \log x > n,$$

whence

(2) $$\phi(x) - \int_2^x \frac{dx}{\log x} \geqq \frac{dx}{\log^n x}, \quad \frac{n}{\log x} < 1.$$

But, if we admit inequalities (2), it will follow, in contradiction with the facts established above, that the expression

$$\sum_{x=2}^{x=\infty} \left[\phi(x + 1) - \phi(x) - \int_x^{x+1} \frac{dx}{\log x} \right] \frac{\log^n x}{x^{1+\rho}}$$

will tend to $+\infty$ instead of converging to a finite limit as $\rho \to 0$. Indeed we can consider this expression as the limit of

$$\sum_{x=2}^{x=s} \left[\phi(x + 1) - \phi(x) - \int_x^{x+1} \frac{dx}{\log x} \right] \frac{\log^n x}{x^{1+\rho}} \text{ as } s \to \infty.$$

On assuming $s > a$, this can be presented under the form

(3) $$C + \sum_{x=a+1}^{x=s} \left[\phi(x + 1) - \phi(x) - \int_x^{x+1} \frac{dx}{\log x} \right] \frac{\log^n x}{x^{1+\rho}},$$

where

$$C = \sum_{x=2}^{x=a} \left[\phi(x + 1) - \phi(x) - \int_x^{x+1} \frac{dx}{\log x} \right] \frac{\log^n x}{x^{1+\rho}}$$

remains finite for $\rho \geqq 0$.

On setting

$$u_x = \phi(x) - \int_2^x \frac{dx}{\log x}, \qquad u_x = \frac{\log^n x}{x^{1+\rho}}$$

in the known formula

$$\sum_{a+1}^s u_x(v_{x+1} - v_x) = u_s v_{s+1} - u_a v_{a+1} - \sum_{a+1}^s v_x(u_x - u_{x-1}),$$

we transform expression (3) into

$$C - \left[\phi(a + 1) - \int_2^{a+1} \frac{dx}{\log x} \right] \frac{\log^n a}{a^{1+\rho}} + \left[\phi(s + 1) \right.$$

$$\left. - \int_2^{s+1} \frac{dx}{\log x} \right] \frac{\log^n s}{s^{1+\rho}} - \sum_{x=a+1}^{x=S} \left[\phi(x) - \int_2^x \frac{dx}{\log x} \right]$$

$$\left[\frac{\log^n x}{x^{1+\rho}} - \frac{\log^n (x - 1)}{(x - 1)^{1+\rho}} \right]$$

which, in its turn, can be written as

$$C - \left[\phi(a+1) - \int_2^{a+1} \frac{dx}{\log x} \right] \frac{\log^n a}{a^{1+\rho}} + \left[\phi(s+1) \right.$$

$$\left. - \int_2^{s+1} \frac{dx}{\log x} \right] \frac{\log^n s}{s^{1+\rho}} + \sum_{r=a+1}^{s} \left[\phi(x) - \int_a^x \frac{dx}{\log x} \right] \left[1+\rho - \frac{n}{\log(x-\theta)} \right]$$

$$\frac{\log^n (x-\theta)}{(x-\theta)^{2+\rho}}, \text{where } 0 < \theta < 1.$$

Let F denote the sum of the two first terms of this expression. Since, by virtue of condition (2), the third term is positive, we conclude that the expression above is greater than

$$F + \sum_{x=a+1}^{x=s} \left[\phi(x) - \int_2^x \frac{dx}{\log x} \right] \left[1 + \rho - \frac{n}{\log(x-\theta)} \right] \frac{\log^n (x-\theta)}{(x-\theta)^{2+\rho}}.$$

The same conditions (2) show that the function under the sign Σ in the last expression remains positive within the limits of summation. Furthermore, we have, within the same limits,

1°. $1 + \rho - \dfrac{n}{\log(x-\theta)} > 1 - \dfrac{n}{\log a}$ since $\rho > 0, x > a + 1, \theta < 1;$

2°. $\phi(x) - \displaystyle\int_2^x \frac{dx}{\log x} > \frac{\alpha(x-\theta)}{\log^n (x-\theta)}$

since, by the first of inequalities (2),

$$\phi(x) - \int_2^x \frac{dx}{\log x} \geqq \frac{\alpha x}{\log^n x},$$

while, by the second one, the derivative of $\dfrac{\alpha x}{\log^n x}$, which equals

$\dfrac{\alpha}{\log^n x}\left(1 - \dfrac{n}{\log x} \right)$, is positive, whence,

$$\frac{\alpha x}{\log^n x} > \frac{\alpha (x-\theta)}{\log^n (x-\theta)}.$$

Hence our expression is greater than the sum

$$F + \sum_{x=a+1}^{x=s} \frac{\alpha (x-\theta)}{\log^n (x-\theta)} \left(1 - \frac{n}{\log a} \right) \frac{\log^n (x-\theta)}{(x-\theta)^{2+\rho}} =$$

$$F + \alpha\left(1 - \frac{n}{\log a} \right) \sum_{x=a+1}^{s} \frac{1}{(x-\theta)^{1+\rho}}.$$

But this is obviously greater than

$$F + \alpha\left(1 - \frac{n}{\log a} \right) \sum_{x=a+1}^{s} \frac{1}{x^{1+\rho}}$$

which, for $s \to \infty$, reduces to

$$F + \alpha\left(1 - \frac{n}{\log a}\right) \sum_{x=a+1}^{x=\infty} \frac{1}{x^{1+\rho}} = F + \alpha\left(1 - \frac{n}{\log a}\right) \frac{\displaystyle\int_0^\infty \frac{e^{-ax}}{e^x - 1} x^\rho dx}{\displaystyle\int_0^\infty e^{-x} x^\rho dx} \cdot$$

It is readily seen that the expression at which we have arrived tends to $+\infty$ as $\rho \to 0$. For, we have

$$\int_0^\infty \frac{e^{-ax}}{e^x - 1} dx + \infty, \qquad \int_0^\infty e^{-x} dx = 1.$$

while both α and $1 - \dfrac{n}{\log a}$ are positive, the former by hypothesis and the latter by the second of inequalities (2).

Thus, with the assumption made, it is assured that not only the sum

$$\sum_{x=a}^{x=\infty} \left[\phi(x + 1) - \phi(x) - \int_x^{x+1} \frac{dx}{\log x} \right] \frac{\log^n x}{x^{1+\rho}},$$

but even a quantity which is less than this sum, tends to $+\infty$, whence we conclude that the assumption in question is not admissible; this immediately proves Theorem 2.

§4. On the basis of the preceding proposition it will be easy now to prove the following theorem.

THEOREM 3.—*The expression* $\dfrac{x}{\phi(x)} - \log x$ *can not have a limit distinct from* -1 *as* $x \to \infty$.

Proof.—Let L be the limit as $x \to \infty$ of the difference $\dfrac{x}{\phi(x)} - \log x$. Under this assumption we always can find a number N so large that for $x > N$ the value of $\dfrac{x}{\phi(x)} - \log x$ will be within the limits $L - \epsilon$ and $L + \epsilon$, $\epsilon > 0$ being as small as we please. For such values of x and ϵ

(4) $\qquad \dfrac{x}{\phi(x)} - \log x > L - \epsilon, \qquad \dfrac{x}{\phi(x)} - \log x < L + \epsilon.$

But, by the preceding theorem, the inequalities

$$\phi(x) > \int_2^x \frac{dx}{\log x} - \frac{\alpha x}{\log^n x}, \qquad \phi(x) < \int_2^x \frac{dx}{\log x} + \frac{\alpha x}{\log^n x}$$

are satisfied for infinitely many values of x, consequently also for values of x greater than N, for which inequalities (4) hold true. The inequalities (4), combined with those written above, imply

$$\frac{x}{\displaystyle\int_2^x \frac{dx}{\log x} - \frac{\alpha x}{\log^n x}} - \log x > L - \epsilon,$$

$$\frac{x}{\displaystyle\int_2^x \frac{dx}{\log x} + \frac{\alpha x}{\log^n x}} - \log x < L + \epsilon,$$

whence

$$L + 1 < \frac{x - (\log x - 1)\left(\displaystyle\int_2^x \frac{dx}{\log x} - \frac{\alpha x}{\log^n x}\right)}{\displaystyle\int^x \frac{dx}{\log x} - \frac{\alpha x}{\log^n x}} + \epsilon.$$

$$L + 1 > \frac{x - (\log x - 1)\left(\displaystyle\int_2^x \frac{dx}{\log x} + \frac{\alpha x}{\log^n x}\right)}{\displaystyle\int^x \frac{dx}{\log x} + \frac{\alpha x}{\log^n x}} - \epsilon.$$

Thus the absolute value of $L + 1$ does not exceed that of each of the expressions which figure in the right-hand members of the preceding inequalities. Furthermore, ϵ can be made as small as we please by taking N sufficiently large, and the same will be true also of each of the quantities

$$\frac{x - (\log x - 1)\left(\displaystyle\int_2^x \frac{dx}{\log x} \mp \frac{\alpha x}{\log^n x}\right)}{\displaystyle\int_2^x \frac{dx}{\log x} \mp \frac{\alpha x}{\log^n x}},$$

for, it can be found by the principles of the differential calculus that their common limit for $x = \infty$ is zero.

Thus it is shown that the limits between which the absolute value of $L + 1$ is included can be made arbitrarily small; hence $L + 1 = 0$ or $L = -1$, which was to be proved.

The fact established above concerning the limit of $\dfrac{x}{\phi(x)} - \log x$ for $x = \infty$ does not agree with a formula given by **Legendre** for approximate computation of the totality of primes less than a given limit. According to Legendre the function $\phi(x)$ for x large is expressed with a sufficient degree of approximation by the formula

$$\phi(x) = \frac{x}{\log x - 1.08366},$$

which gives for the limit of $\frac{x}{\phi(x)} - \log x$ the number $- 1.08366$ instead of -1.

§5. Starting from Theorem 2 it is possible to estimate the degree of approximation of the function $\phi(x)$ by any other given function $f(x)$. In what follows we shall compare the difference $(x) - \phi(x)$ with the expressions

$$\frac{x}{\log x}, \ \frac{x}{\log^2 x}, \ \frac{x}{\log^3 x}, \cdots$$

To simplify the discussion we shall say that a quantity A is of order $\frac{x}{\log^m x}$ if, as $x \to \infty$, the ratio of A to $\frac{x}{\log^m x}$ is infinite for $m > n$ and zero for $m < n$. We proceed now to prove the following theorem.

THEOREM 4.—*If the expression*

$$\frac{\log^n x}{x}\left(f(x) - \int_2^x \frac{dx}{\log x} \right)$$

has a finite [$\neq 0$] or infinite limit as $x \to \infty$, the function $f(x)$ can not represent $\phi(x)$ up to terms of order $\frac{x}{\log^n x}$ inclusive.[1]

Proof.—Let L be the limit of the expression

$$\frac{\log^n x}{x}\left(f(x) - \int_2^x \frac{dx}{\log x} \right)$$

as $x \to \infty$. Since, by hypothesis, L is distinct from zero, it is either positive or negative. Assume L to be positive; our reasoning is readily applied to the case of $L < 0$.

If $L > 0$ we can find a number N so large that for $x > N$ the expression

$$\frac{\log^n x}{x}\left(f(x) - \int_2^x \frac{dx}{\log x} \right)$$

remains always greater than a positive number l.

---

[1] [This means to imply that the difference $f(x) - \phi(x)$ can not be of order $\frac{x}{\log^m x}$ with $m > n$.]

Hence, for $x > N$,

(5)
$$\frac{\log^n x}{x}\left(f(x) - \int_2^x \frac{dx}{\log x}\right) > l.$$

But, by Theorem 2, no matter how small $\alpha = l/2$ may be, the inequality

(6)
$$\phi(x) < \int_2^x \frac{dx}{\log x} + \frac{\alpha x}{\log^n x}$$

will be satisfied for infinitely many values of x, which gives

$$f(x) - \int^x \frac{dx}{\log x} < f(x) - \phi(x) + \frac{\alpha x}{\log^n x};$$

on multiplying this by $\dfrac{\log^n x}{x}$ and observing that $\alpha = l/2$ we find

$$\frac{\log^n x}{x}\left[f(x) - \int_2^x \frac{dx}{\log x}\right] < \frac{\log^n x}{x}\,[f(x) - \phi(x)] + \frac{l}{2}$$

or, in view of (5)

$$\frac{\log^n x}{x}\,[f(x) - \phi(x)] > \frac{l}{2}.$$

Since $l/2 > 0$ and the preceding inequality, as well as inequalities (5) and (6), are satisfied for infinitely many values of x, the limit of

$$\frac{\log^n x}{x}\,[f(x) - \phi(x)]$$

as $x \to \infty$ can not be equal to zero.   Then the difference $f(x) - \phi(x)$, according to the agreement above, is either of order $\dfrac{x}{\log^n x}$ or of a lower order, which was to be proved.

On the basis of this theorem we can show that the formula of Legendre, $\dfrac{x}{\log x - 1.08366}$, for which the limit as $x \to \infty$ of the expression

$$\frac{\log^2 x}{x}\left(\frac{x}{\log x - 1.08366} - \int_2^x \frac{dx}{\log x}\right)$$

equals 0.08366, can not represent $\phi(x)$ up to terms of order $\dfrac{x}{\log^2 x}$ inclusive.

It is also easy to determine the constants A and B so that the function $\dfrac{x}{A \log x + B}$ will represent $\phi(x)$ up to terms of order $\dfrac{x}{\log^2 x}$

inclusive. By the preceding theorem the constants A and B must satisfy the equation

$$\lim \left[\frac{\log^2 x}{x} \left(\frac{x}{A \log x + B} - \int_2^x \frac{dx}{\log x} \right) \right] = 0.$$

On expanding we have

$$\frac{x}{A \log x + B} = \frac{1}{A} \frac{x}{\log x} - \frac{B}{A^2} \frac{x}{\log^2 x} + \frac{B^2}{A^3} \frac{x}{\log^3 x} - \cdots,$$

while an integration by parts yields

$$\int_2^x \frac{dx}{\log x} = \frac{x}{\log x} + \frac{x}{\log^2 x} + 2 \int_2^x \frac{dx}{\log^3 x} + C.$$

The equation above then reduces to

$$\lim_{x \to \infty} \left\{ \begin{array}{c} \dfrac{\log^2 x}{x} \left(\dfrac{1}{A} \dfrac{x}{\log x} - \dfrac{B}{A^2} \dfrac{x}{\log^2 x} + \dfrac{B^2}{A^3} \dfrac{x}{\log^3 x} - \cdots \right) \\ \cdots - \dfrac{x}{\log x} - \dfrac{x}{\log^2 x} - 2 \int_2^x \dfrac{dx}{\log^3 x} + C \end{array} \right\} = 0$$

or else to

$$\lim_{x \to \infty} \left\{ \begin{array}{c} \left(\dfrac{1}{A} - 1 \right) \log x - \left(\dfrac{B}{A^2} + 1 \right) + \dfrac{B^2}{A^3} \cdot \dfrac{1}{\log x} - \cdots \\ \cdots - 2 \dfrac{\log^2 x}{x} \int_2^x \dfrac{dx}{\log^3 x} - C \dfrac{\log^2 x}{x} \end{array} \right\} = 0.$$

On observing that all the terms beginning with the third converge to zero when x increases indefinitely, it is seen at once that the preceding equation can not be satisfied unless $\frac{1}{A} - 1 = 0$, $\frac{B}{A^2} + 1 = 0$. Hence $A = 1$, $B = -1$.

Thus among all the functions of the form $\dfrac{x}{A \log x + B}$ only $\dfrac{x}{\log x - 1}$ can represent $\phi(x)$ up to terms of order $\dfrac{x}{\log^2 x}$ inclusive.[1]

---

[1] [We omit §§6 and 7 of this memoir. In §6 Chebyshev proves by a method analogous to that used above that if $\phi(x)$ can be represented up to terms of order $\dfrac{x}{\log^n x}$ inclusive by an expression algebraic in x, $\log x$, e^x, then $\phi(x)$ can be represented also with the same degree of approximation by the expression

$$\frac{x}{\log x} + \frac{1.x}{\log^2 x} + \cdots + \frac{1.2 \ldots (n-1)x}{\log^n x}$$

which is obtained from $\int \dfrac{dx}{\log x}$ by repeated integration by parts. §7 contains

MEMOIR 2: MEMOIR ON PRIME NUMBERS[1]

§2. Let us designate by $\theta(z)$ the sum of logarithms of all the primes which do not exceed z. This function equals zero when x is less than the smallest prime, viz. 2. It is not difficult to show that this function satisfies the following equation[2]

$$
\left.
\begin{aligned}
&\theta(x) + \theta(x)^{\frac{1}{2}} + \theta(x)^{\frac{1}{3}} + \ldots \\
+\ &\theta\left(\frac{x}{2}\right) + \theta\left(\frac{x}{2}\right)^{\frac{1}{2}} + \theta\left(\frac{x}{3}\right)^{\frac{1}{3}} + \ldots \\
+\ &\theta\left(\frac{x}{3}\right) + \theta\left(\frac{x}{3}\right)^{\frac{1}{2}} + \theta\left(\frac{x}{3}\right)^{\frac{1}{3}} + \ldots \\
&\cdots\cdots\cdots\cdots\cdots\cdots\cdots \\
&\cdots\cdots\cdots\cdots\cdots\cdots\cdots
\end{aligned}
\right\} = \log 1.2.3\ldots[x],
$$

where the symbol [x] is used to designate the greatest integer contained in x.

To verify this equation we note that both its members are made up of terms of the form $K \log a$, where a is a prime and K is an integer. In the left-hand member K is equal to the number of terms in the sequence

$$ x, \quad \frac{x}{2}, \quad \frac{x}{3}, \ldots $$

(1)
$$ (x)^{\frac{1}{2}}, \quad \left(\frac{x}{2}\right)^{\frac{1}{2}}, \quad \left(\frac{x}{3}\right)^{\frac{1}{2}}, \ldots $$

$$ (x)^{\frac{1}{3}}, \quad \left(\frac{x}{3}\right)^{\frac{1}{3}}, \quad \left(\frac{x}{3}\right)^{\frac{1}{3}}, \ldots $$

which are not less than a, since the expression for $\theta(z)$ will contain the term $\log a$ only in the case where $z \geqq a$. As to the coefficient of $\log a$ in the right-hand member, it is equal to the highest power of a which divides $1.2.3\ldots[x]$. It is found however, that this power is also equal to the number of terms in the sequence (1) which are not less than a; for, the number of terms of the sequence

$$ x, \quad \frac{x}{2}, \quad \frac{x}{3}, \ldots $$

---

an attempt (not rigorous) to prove the remarkable asymptotic relations

$$ \sum_{\mu \leqq P} \frac{1}{\mu} \sim \log \log P + C_1, \quad \prod_{\mu \leqq P}\left(1 - \frac{1}{\mu}\right) \sim \frac{C_2}{\log P} $$

where C_1, C_2 are fixed constants, P is any prime number, and the summation and product are extended over all primes $\mu \leqq P$.]

[1] [We omit the introductory §1 of this memoir.]

[2] To abbreviate we write $\theta(x/n)^m$ instead of $\theta\{(x/n)^m\}$.

which are not less than a, is equal to that of the terms of the sequence

$$1, 2, 3, \ldots, [x]$$

which are divisible by a.

The same relationship exists between the number of terms of this sequence, which are divisible by a^2, a^3, a^4, ... and the number of terms of the sequence

$$(x)^{\frac{1}{2}}, \quad \left(\frac{x}{2}\right)^{\frac{1}{2}}, \quad \left(\frac{x}{3}\right)^{\frac{1}{2}}, \ldots$$

$$(x)^{\frac{1}{3}}, \quad \left(\frac{x}{2}\right)^{\frac{1}{3}}, \quad \left(\frac{x}{3}\right)^{\frac{1}{3}}, \ldots$$

. . . .

which are not less than a.

Hence both members of our equation are composed of the same terms, which proves that they are identical.

The equation just established can be presented as

$$(2) \qquad \psi(x) + \psi\left(\frac{x}{2}\right) + \psi\left(\frac{x}{3}\right) + \ldots = T(x)$$

on setting for abbreviation

$$(3) \qquad \begin{cases} \theta(z) + \theta(z)^{\frac{1}{2}} + \theta(z)^{\frac{1}{3}} + \ldots = \psi(z), \\ \log 1.2.3 \ldots [x] = T(x). \end{cases}$$

In applications of these formulas we shall observe that, in view of what has been said about the value of $\theta(z)$ when $z < 2$ the function $\psi(z)$ vanishes when $z < 2$, and consequently, equation (2) will be valid in the limiting cases $x = 0$, $x = 2$ if we agree to take zero as the value of $T(x)$ when $x < 2$.

§3. By means of this equation it is not difficult to find numerous inequalities which are satisfied by the function $\psi(x)$; those we shall use in this memoir are the following:

$$\psi(x) > T(x) + T\left(\frac{x}{30}\right) - T\left(\frac{x}{2}\right) - T\left(\frac{x}{3}\right) - T\left(\frac{x}{5}\right),$$

$$\psi(x) - \psi\left(\frac{x}{6}\right) > T(x) + T\left(\frac{x}{30}\right) - T\left(\frac{x}{2}\right) - T\left(\frac{x}{3}\right) - T\left(\frac{x}{5}\right).$$

To prove these inequalities we shall compute the value of

$$T(x) + T\left(\frac{x}{30}\right) - T\left(\frac{x}{2}\right) - T\left(\frac{x}{3}\right) - T\left(\frac{x}{5}\right)$$

by means of (2), which leads to the equation

$$(4) \quad \left\{ \begin{array}{l} \psi(x) + \psi\!\left(\dfrac{x}{2}\right) + \psi\!\left(\dfrac{x}{3}\right) + \cdots \\[2mm] + \psi\!\left(\dfrac{x}{30}\right) + \psi\!\left(\dfrac{x}{2.30}\right) + \psi\!\left(\dfrac{x}{3.30}\right) + \cdots \\[2mm] - \psi\!\left(\dfrac{x}{2}\right) - \psi\!\left(\dfrac{x}{2.2}\right) - \psi\!\left(\dfrac{x}{3.2}\right) - \cdots \\[2mm] - \psi\!\left(\dfrac{x}{3}\right) - \psi\!\left(\dfrac{x}{2.3}\right) - \psi\!\left(\dfrac{x}{3.3}\right) - \cdots \\[2mm] - \psi\!\left(\dfrac{x}{5}\right) - \psi\!\left(\dfrac{x}{2.5}\right) - \psi\!\left(\dfrac{x}{3.5}\right) - \cdots \end{array} \right\} \quad \begin{array}{l} = T(x) + T\!\left(\dfrac{x}{30}\right) \\[2mm] - T\!\left(\dfrac{x}{2}\right) - T\!\left(\dfrac{x}{3}\right) \\[2mm] - T\!\left(\dfrac{x}{5}\right). \end{array}$$

whose left-hand member reduces to

$$A_1\psi(x) + A_2\psi\!\left(\frac{x}{2}\right) + \cdots + A_n\psi\!\left(\frac{x}{n}\right) + \cdots$$

$A_1, A_2, \ldots A_n \ldots$ being numerical coefficients. Upon examining their values it is not difficult to establish that

$A_n = 1$ if $n = 30m + 1, 7, 11, 13, 17, 19, 23, 29,$

$A_n = 0$ if $n = 30m + 2, 3, 4, 5, 8, 9, 14, 16, 21, 22, 25, 26, 27,$
                                                          28,

$A_n = -1$ if $n = 30m + 6, 10, 12, 15, 18, 20, 24,$

$A_n = -1$ if $n = 30m + 30.$

Indeed, in the first case n is not divisible by any of the numbers 2, 3, 5, hence the term $\psi(x/n)$ figures only in the first line in equation (4). In the second case n is divisible by one of the numbers 2, 3, 5, hence, besides the term $\psi(x/n)$ in the first line, the term $-\psi(x/n)$ will be found in one of the last three lines, and, after reduction, the coefficient of $\psi(x/n)$ will become 0. In the third case n is divisible by two of the numbers 2, 3, 5. Hence the last three lines will contain two terms equal to $-\psi(x/n)$, while the first line contains $\psi(x/n)$ with the plus sign, so that the result will be $-\psi(x/n)$. In the last case where n is divisible by 30 we arrive at the same conclusion, since the term $\pm\psi(x/n)$ will figure in all the five lines, twice with the plus and three times with the minus sign.

    Hence for

$n = 30m + 1, 2, 3, 4, 5, 6, 7, 8, 9, 10, 11, 12, 13, 14, 15$
                16, 17, 18, 19, 20, 21, 22, 23, 24, 25, 26, 27, 28, 29, 30

we find respectively

    $A_n = 1, 0, 0, 0, 0, -1, 1, 0, 0, -1, 1, -1, 1, 0, -1,$
         $0, 1, -1, 1, -1, 0, 0, 1, -1, 0, 0, 0, 0, 1, -1,$

which shows that equation (4) reduces to

$$\psi(x) - \psi\left(\frac{x}{6}\right) + \psi\left(\frac{x}{7}\right) - \psi\left(\frac{x}{10}\right) + \psi\left(\frac{x}{11}\right) - \psi\left(\frac{x}{12}\right) + \ldots$$
$$= T(x) + T\left(\frac{x}{30}\right) - T\left(\frac{x}{2}\right) - T\left(\frac{x}{3}\right) - T\left(\frac{x}{5}\right)$$

where the terms of the left-hand member have the coefficient 1 alternately with the plus and minus signs. Furthermore, since by nature of the function $\psi(x)$ the series of the left-hand member is decreasing, its value will be included within the limits $\psi(x)$ and $\psi(x) - \psi(x/6)$. Hence, by the preceding equation, we shall have necessarily

$$\psi(x) \geqq T(x) + T\left(\frac{x}{30}\right) - T\left(\frac{x}{2}\right) - T\left(\frac{x}{3}\right) - T\left(\frac{x}{5}\right),$$
$$\psi(x) - \psi\left(\frac{x}{6}\right) \leqq T(x) + T\left(\frac{x}{30}\right) - T\left(\frac{x}{2}\right) - T\left(\frac{x}{3}\right) - T\left(\frac{x}{5}\right).$$

§4. Let us examine now the function $T(x)$ which figures in these formulas. On denoting by a the greatest integer contained in x, which we shall assume to be $\geqq 1$, we have from (3)

$$T(x) = \log 1.2.3 \ldots a$$

or, what amounts to the same thing,

$$T(x) = \log 1.2.3 \ldots a(a+1) - \log (a+1).$$

But it is known that

$\log 1.2.3 \ldots a < \log \sqrt{2\pi} + a \log a - a + \frac{1}{2} \log a +$

$\log 1.2.3 \ldots a(a+1) > \log \sqrt{2\pi} + (a+1) \log (a+1) -$
$$\frac{1}{12a}(a+1) + \frac{1}{2} \log (a+1);$$

hence

$T(x) < \log \sqrt{2\pi} + a \log a - a + \frac{1}{2} \log a + \frac{1}{12a},$

$T(x) > \log \sqrt{2\pi} + (a+1) \log (a+1) - (a+1) - \frac{1}{2} \log (a+1)$

and consequently

$$T(x) < \log \sqrt{2\pi} + x \log x - x + \frac{1}{2} \log x + \frac{1}{12},$$
$$T(x) > \log \sqrt{2\pi} + x \log x - x - \frac{1}{2} \log x,$$

since the inequalities

$$a \leqq x < a+1, \quad a \geqq 1$$

obviously imply the conditions

$$x \log x - x + \frac{1}{2} \log x + \frac{1}{12} \geqq a \log a - a + \frac{1}{2} \log a + \frac{1}{12a},$$
$$x \log x - x - \frac{1}{2} \log x \leqq (a+1) \log (a+1) - (a+1)$$
$$- \frac{1}{2} \log (a+1).$$

The inequalities above concerning $T(x)$ give

$$T(x) + T\left(\frac{x}{30}\right) < 2 \log \sqrt{2\pi} + \frac{2}{12} + \frac{31}{30}x \log x - x \log 30^{\frac{1}{30}}$$

$$-\frac{31}{30}x + \log x - \frac{1}{2} \log 30,$$

$$T(x) + T\left(\frac{1}{30}\right) > 2 \log \sqrt{2\pi} + \frac{31}{30}x \log x - x \log 30^{\frac{1}{30}} - \frac{31}{30}x$$

$$- \log x + \frac{1}{2} \log 30,$$

$$T\left(\frac{x}{2}\right) + T\left(\frac{x}{3}\right) + T\left(\frac{x}{5}\right) < 3 \log \sqrt{2\pi} + \frac{3}{12} + \frac{31}{30}x \log x$$

$$- x \log 2^{\frac{1}{2}}3^{\frac{1}{3}}5^{\frac{1}{5}} - \frac{31}{30}x + \frac{3}{2} \log x - \frac{1}{2} \log 30,$$

$$T\left(\frac{x}{2}\right) + T\left(\frac{x}{3}\right) + T\left(\frac{x}{5}\right) > 3 \log \sqrt{2\pi} + \frac{31}{30}x \log x$$

$$- x \log 2^{\frac{1}{2}}3^{\frac{1}{3}}5^{\frac{1}{5}} - \frac{31}{30}x - \frac{3}{2} \log x + \frac{1}{2} \log 30.$$

On subtracting the last of these inequalities from the first and the third from the second we find

$$T(x) + T\left(\frac{x}{30}\right) - T\left(\frac{x}{2}\right) - T\left(\frac{x}{3}\right) - T\left(\frac{x}{5}\right) < Ax + \frac{5}{2} \log x$$

$$- \frac{1}{2} \log 1800\pi + \frac{2}{12}$$

$$T(x) + T\left(\frac{x}{30}\right) - T\left(\frac{x}{2}\right) - T\left(\frac{x}{3}\right) - T\left(\frac{x}{5}\right) > Ax - \frac{5}{2} \log x$$

$$+ \frac{1}{2} \log \frac{450}{\pi} - \frac{3}{12},$$

where to abbreviate we have set

(5) $\qquad A = \log 2^{\frac{1}{2}}3^{\frac{1}{3}}5^{\frac{1}{5}}30^{-\frac{1}{30}} = 0.92129202\ldots$

The analysis used in proving these inequalities assumes that $x \geqq 30$, since, in discussing $T(x)$ we have assumed $x \geqq 1$ and after that we have replaced x successively by $x/2$, $x/3$, $x/5$ and $x/30$. It is not difficult, however, to obtain formulas which can be used for all values of $x > 1$, if we replace the preceding inequalities by simpler ones

$$T(x) + T\left(\frac{x}{30}\right) - T\left(\frac{x}{2}\right) - T\left(\frac{x}{3}\right) - T\left(\frac{x}{5}\right) < Ax + \frac{5}{2} \log x,$$

$$T(x) + T\left(\frac{x}{30}\right) - T\left(\frac{x}{2}\right) - T\left(\frac{x}{3}\right) - T\left(\frac{x}{5}\right) > Ax - \frac{5}{2} \log x - 1;$$

an examination readily shows that these inequalities are valid for values of x between 1 and 30.

§5. On combining these inequalities with those derived above for the function $\psi(x)$(§3) we arrive at two formulas

$$\psi(x) > Ax - \frac{5}{2} \log x - 1, \quad \psi(x) - \psi\left(\frac{x}{6}\right) < Ax + \frac{5}{2} \log x,$$

of which the first gives a lower limit for $\psi(x)$.

As to the second formula, it will be used in assigning another limit for $\psi(x)$. For this purpose we observe that the function

$$f(x) = \frac{6}{5}Ax + \frac{5}{4 \log 6} \log^2 x + \frac{5}{4} \log x$$

satisfies the equation

$$f(x) - f\left(\frac{x}{6}\right) = Ax + \frac{5}{2} \log x,$$

which, being subtracted from the inequality

$$\psi(x) - \psi\left(\frac{x}{6}\right) < Ax + \frac{5}{2} \log x$$

gives

$$\psi(x) - \psi\left(\frac{x}{6}\right) - f(x) + f\left(\frac{x}{6}\right) < 0$$

or else

$$\psi(x) - f(x) < \psi\left(\frac{x}{6}\right) - f\left(\frac{x}{6}\right).$$

On replacing x successively by $x/6, x/6^2, \ldots x/6^m$ in this formula we find

$$\psi(x) - f(x) < \psi\left(\frac{x}{6}\right) - f\left(\frac{x}{6}\right) < \ldots < \psi\left(\frac{x}{6^{m+1}}\right) - f\left(\frac{x}{6^{m+1}}\right).$$

Assume now that m is the greatest integer which satisfies the condition $\frac{x}{6^m} \geqq 1$. Then $x/6^{m+1}$ will be between 1 and $\frac{1}{6}$, while $\psi(z) = 0$ and $-f(z)$ remains greater than 1 within the limits $z = 1$, $z = \frac{1}{6}$. Hence $\psi(x/6^{m+1}) - f(x/6^{m+1}) < 1$, and by the preceding inequalities

$$\psi(x) - f(x) < 1.$$

Finally, on substituting the value of $f(x)$ we have

$$\psi(x) < \frac{6}{5}Ax + \frac{5}{4 \log 6} \log^2 x + \frac{5}{4} \log x + 1.$$

On the basis of the formulas just found it is not difficult to assign two limits including the value of $\theta(x)$.

Indeed, we find from (3)

$$\psi(x) - \psi(x)^{\frac{1}{2}} = \theta(x) + \theta(x)^{\frac{1}{3}} + \theta(x)^{\frac{1}{6}} + \ldots,$$
$$\psi(x) - 2\psi(x)^{\frac{1}{2}} = \theta(x) - [\theta(x)^{\frac{1}{2}} - \theta(x)^{\frac{1}{3}}] - \ldots$$

which shows that

(6) $\theta(x) \leqq \psi(x) - \psi(x)^{\frac{1}{2}}, \quad \theta(x) \leqq \psi(x) - 2\psi(x)^{\frac{1}{2}},$

since the terms

$$\theta(x)^{\frac{1}{3}}, \quad \theta(x)^{\frac{1}{6}}, \ldots, \theta(x)^{\frac{1}{2}} - \theta(x)^{\frac{1}{3}}, \ldots$$

obviously are positive or zero.

But we have found

$$\psi(x) < \frac{6}{5}Ax + \frac{5}{4 \log 6} \log^2 x + \frac{5}{4} \log x + 1,$$
$$\psi(x) > Ax - \tfrac{5}{2} \log x - 1,$$

which gives

$$\psi(x)^{\frac{1}{2}} < \frac{6}{5}Ax^{\frac{1}{2}} + \frac{5}{16 \log 6} \log^2 x + \frac{5}{8} \log x + 1,$$
$$\psi(x)^{\frac{1}{2}} > Ax^{\frac{1}{2}} - \frac{5}{4} \log x - 1,$$

and consequently

$$\psi(x) - \psi(x)^{\frac{1}{2}} < \frac{6}{5}Ax - Ax^{\frac{1}{2}} + \frac{5}{4 \log 6} \log^2 x + \frac{5}{2} \log x + 2,$$

$$\psi(x) - 2\psi(x)^{\frac{1}{2}} > Ax - \frac{12}{5}Ax^{\frac{1}{2}} - \frac{5}{8 \log 6} \log^2 x - \frac{15}{4} \log x - 3$$

Hence, by (6),

(7) $\begin{cases} \theta(x) < \dfrac{6}{5}Ax - Ax^{\frac{1}{2}} + \dfrac{5}{4 \log 6} \log^2 x + \dfrac{5}{2} \log x + 2 \\[2mm] \theta(x) > Ax - \dfrac{12}{5}Ax^{\frac{1}{2}} - \dfrac{5}{8 \log 6} \log^2 x - \dfrac{15}{4} \log x - 3. \end{cases}$ [1]

---

[1] [We omit the concluding §§6–9 of the memoir. In §6 Chebyshev gives the proof of the Bertrand postulate, taking as the point of departure the obvious inequalities

$$\theta(L) - \theta(l) > m \log l, \quad \theta(L) - \theta(l) < m \log L$$

where m is the number of primes between l and L, and using the inequalities obtained above for $\theta(x)$. §7 contains a proof of the following remarkable theorem: If for x sufficiently large $F(x)$ is positive and $\dfrac{F(x)}{\log x}$ is not increasing, then the convergence of the series $\sum \dfrac{F(m)}{\log m}$ is a necessary and sufficient condition for the convergence of the series $\Sigma F(\mu)$. The proof is based upon the simple transformation formula

$$\sum_{l,L} F(\mu) = \sum_{m=l}^{L} F(m) \left\{ \frac{\theta(m) - \theta(m-1)}{\log m} \right\}$$

where the summation over μ is extended over all primes, while that over m over all integers between the two given limits l and L.   Thus the series

$$\frac{1}{2 \log 2} + \frac{1}{3 \log 3} + \frac{1}{5 \log 5} + \cdots; \frac{1}{2 \log^2 (\log 2)} + \frac{1}{3 \log^2 (\log 3)}$$
$$+ \frac{1}{5 \log^2 (\log 5)} + \cdots$$

are convergent while the series

$$\frac{1}{2} + \frac{1}{3} + \frac{1}{5} + \cdots; \quad \frac{1}{2 \log 2} + \frac{1}{3 \log 3} + \frac{1}{5 \log 5} + \cdots$$

are divergent.   §§8 and 9 contain some applications of the above results to the approximate computation of sums of the form $\Sigma F(\mu)$ and, in the special case where $F(x) = 1$, to the computation of the totality of primes.]

NAPIER

ON THE TABLE OF LOGARITHMS

(Selections Made by Professor W. D. Cairns, Oberlin College, Oberlin, Ohio.)

John Napier (1550–1617), Baron of Merchiston, Scotland, has been given undisputed priority with regard to the publication of a table of logarithms and an account of their meaning and use. His work is the more important since, through improvements by himself, Henry Briggs, and others, it quickly became a system practical for purposes of calculation and nearly in the modern form. He published his system in 1614 in *Mirifici logarithmorum canonis descriptio* and gave therein a description of the nature of logarithms and a table of his logarithms of the sines of angles for successive minutes. The present account is, however, taken from his *Mirifici logarithmorum canonis constructio*, which appeared posthumously in 1619 but which was written several years earlier than the *Descriptio*. Sufficient extracts are given, with the original numbers of the articles, to show his method of construction of the table, his definition of logarithms, and the rules for combining these.

The *Descriptio* was translated into English by Edward Wright under the title *A Description of the Admirable Table of Logarithmes* and was published posthumously at London in 1616. The *Constructio* was translated into English by W. R. Macdonald (Edinburgh, Wm. Blackwood & Sons, Ltd., 1889). The following selections are taken from the latter work with the kind permission of the publishers, the numbers of the paragraphs being as in the original. Only the more important parts of the numbered paragraphs have been selected, there being sufficient to show Napier's method of constructing a logarithmic table. Upon the question of the invention of logarithms, see the articles on prosthaphæresis (pp. 455 and 459).

1.   A logarithmic table is a small table by the use of which we can obtain a knowledge of all geometrical dimensions and motions in space, by a very easy calculation... It is picked out from numbers progressing in continuous proportion.

2.   Of continuous progressions, an arithmetical is one which proceeds by equal intervals; a geometrical, one which advances by unequal and proportionally increasing or decreasing intervals.

16.   If from the radius with seven ciphers added you subtract its 10000000th part, and from the number thence arising its 10000000th part, and so on, a hundred numbers may very easily be continued geometrically in the proportion subsisting

between the radius and the sine less than it by unity, namely between 10000000 and 9999999; and this series of proportionals we name the First table.

Thus from the radius, with seven ciphers added for greater accuracy, namely, 10000000.0000000, subtract 1.0000000, you get 9999999.0000000; from this subtract .9999999, you get 9999998.0000001; and proceed in this way until you create a hundred proportionals, the last of which, if you have computed rightly, will be 9999900.0004950.

17.   The Second table proceeds from the radius with six ciphers added, through fifty other numbers decreasing proportionally in the proportion which is easiest, and as near as possible to that subsisting between the first and last numbers of the First table

Thus the first and last numbers of the First table are 10000000.0000000 and 9999900.0004950, in which proportion it is difficult to form fifty proportional numbers. A near and at the same time an easy proportion is 100000 to 99999, which may be continued with sufficient exactness by adding six ciphers to the radius and continually subtracting from each number its own 100000th part; and this table contains, besides the radius which is the first, fifty other proportional numbers, the last of which, if you have not erred, you will find to be 9995001.222927.[1]

18.   The Third table consists of sixty-nine columns, and in each column are placed twenty-one numbers, proceeding in the proportion which is easiest, and as near as possible to that subsisting between the first and last numbers of the Second table.

Whence its first column is very easily obtained from the radius with five ciphers added, by subtracting its 2000th part, and so from the other numbers as they arise.

In forming this progression, as the proportion between 10000000.000000, the first of the Second table, and 9995001.222927, the last of the same, is troublesome; therefore compute the twenty-one numbers in the easy proportion of 10000 to 9995, which is sufficiently near to it; the last of these, if you have not erred, will be 9900473.57808.

From these numbers, when computed, the last figure of each may be rejected without sensible error, so that others may hereafter be more easily computed from them.

---

[1] [This should be 9995001.224804.]

19. The first numbers of all the columns must proceed from the radius with four ciphers added, in the proportion easiest and nearest to that subsisting between the first and the last numbers of the first column.

As the first and the last numbers of the first column are 10000000.0000 and 9900473.5780, the easiest proportion very near to this is 100 to 99. Accordingly sixty-eight numbers are to be continued from the radius in the ratio of 100 to 99 by subtracting from each one of them its hundredth part.

20. In the same proportion a progression is to be made from the second number of the first column through the second numbers in all the columns, and from the third through the third, and from the fourth through the fourth, and from the others respectively through the others.

Thus from any number in one column, by subtracting its hundredth part, the number of the same rank in the following column is made, and the numbers should be placed in order.

Remark: The last number in the Sixty-ninth column is 4998609.4034, roughly half the original number.

21. Thus, in the Third table, between the radius and half the radius, you have sixty-eight numbers interpolated, in the proportion of 100 to 99, and between each two of these you have twenty numbers interpolated in the proportion of 10000 to 9995; and again, in the Second table, between the first two of these, namely between 10000000 and 9995000, you have fifty numbers interpolated in the proportion of 100000 to 99999; and finally, in the First table, between the latter, you have a hundred numbers interpolated in the proportion of the radius or 10000000 to 9999999; and since the difference of these is never more than unity, there is no need to divide it more minutely by interpolating means, whence these three tables, after they have been completed, will suffice for computing a Logarithmic table.

Hitherto we have explained how we may most easily place in tables sines or natural numbers progressing in geometrical proportion.

22. It remains, in the Third table at least, to place beside the sines or natural numbers decreasing geometrically their logarithms or artificial numbers increasing arithmetically.

26.   The logarithm of a given sine is that number which has increased arithmetically with the same velocity throughout as that with which the radius began to decrease geometrically, and in the same time as the radius has decreased to the given sine.[1]

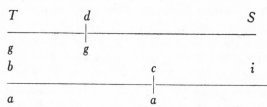

Let the line *TS* be the radius, and *dS* a given sine in the same line; let *g* move geometrically from *T* to *d* in certain determinate moments of time. Again, let *bi* be another line, infinite towards *i*, along which, from *b*, let *a* move arithmetically with the same velocity as *g* had at first when at *T*; and from the fixed point *b* in the direction of *i* let *a* advance in just the same moments of time up to the point *c*. The number measuring the line *bc* is called the logarithm of the given sine *dS*.

27.   Zero is the logarithm of the radius.

28.   Whence also it follows that the logarithm of any given sine is greater than the difference between the radius and the given sine, and less than the difference between the radius and the quantity which exceeds it in the ratio of the radius to the given sine. And these differences are therefore called the limits of the logarithm.

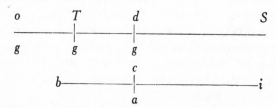

Thus, the preceding figure being repeated, and *ST* being produced beyond *T* to *o*, so that *oS* is to *TS* as *TS* to *dS*.

---

[1] [To Napier the sine was a line, or the number measuring the line, as in the present-day line representation of functions of angles.]

I say that *bc*, the logarithm of the sine *dS*, is greater than *Td* and less than *oT*. For in the same time that *g* is borne from *o* to *T*, *g* is borne from *T* to *d*, because (by 24) *oT* is such a part of *oS* as *Td* is of *TS*, and in the same time (by the definition of a logarithm) is *a* borne from *b* to *c*; so that *oT*, *Td,* and *bc* are distances traversed in equal times. But since *g* when moving between *T* and *o* is swifter than at *T*, and between *T* and *d* slower, but at *T* is equally swift with *a* (by 26); it follows that *oT* the distance traversed by *g* moving swiftly is greater, and *Td* the distance traversed by *g* moving slowly is less, than *bc* the distance traversed by the point *a* with its medium motion, in just the same moments of time; the latter is, consequently, a certain mean between the two former.

Therefore *oT* is called the greater limit, and *Td* the less limit of the logarithm which *bc* represents.

29.   To find the limits of the logarithm of a given sine.

By the preceding it is proved that the given sine being subtracted from the radius, the less limit remains, and that the radius being multiplied into the less limit and the product divided by the given sine, the greater limit is produced.

30.   Whence the first proportional of the First table, which is 9999999, has its logarithm between the limits 1.0000001 and 1.0000000.

31.   The limits themselves differing insensibly, they or anything between them may be taken as the true logarithm.

32.   There being any number of sines decreasing from the radius in geometrical proportions, of one of which the logarithm or its limits is given, to find those of the others.

This necessarily follows from the definitions of arithmetical increase, of geometrical decrease, and of a logarithm...So that, if the first logarithm corresponding to the first sine after the radius be given, the second logarithm will be double of it, the third triple, and so of the others; until the logarithms of all the sines are known.

36.   The logarithms of similarly proportioned sines differ equally.

This necessarily follows from the definitions of a logarithm and of the two motions.   Also there is the same ratio of equality between the differences of the respective limits of the logarithms, namely as the differences of the less among themselves, so also of the greater among themselves, of which logarithms the sines are similarly proportioned.

38. Of four geometrical proportionals, as the product of the means is equal to the product of the extremes; so of their logarithms, the sum of the means is equal to the sum of the extremes. Whence any three of these logarithms being given, the fourth becomes known.[1]

39. The difference of the logarithms of two sines lies between two limits; the greater limit being to the radius as the difference of the sines to the less sine, and the less limit being to the radius as the difference of the sines to the greater sine.[2]

47. In the Third table, beside the natural numbers, are to be written their logarithms; so that the Third table, which after this we shall always call the Radical table, may be made complete and perfect.

48. The Radical table being now completed, we take the numbers for the logarithmic table from it alone.

For as the first two tables were of service in the formation of the third, so this Radical table serves for the construction of the principal Logarithmic table, with great ease and no sensible error.

51. All sines in the proportion of two to one have 6931469.22 for the difference of their logarithms.[3]

52. All sines in the proportion of ten to one have 23025842.34 for the difference of their logarithms.

---

[1] [The modern theorem for the logarithm of a product does not hold here, since the logarithm of unity is not zero.]

[2] [This is proved by the principle of proportion and of Article 36. This rule is used first in Articles 40–41 as an illustration to find the logarithm of 9999975.5 from that of the nearest sine in the First table, 9999975.0000300, noting that the limits of the logarithms of the latter number are 25.0000025 and 25.0000000, that the difference of the logarithms of the two numbers by the rule just given is .4999712 and that the limits for the logarithm of 9999975.5 are therefore 24.5000313 and 24.5000288, whence he lists the logarithm as 24.5000300.

In Articles 41–45 he illustrates the fact that one may now calculate the logarithms of all the "proportionals" in the First, Second, and Third tables, as well as of the sines or natural numbers not proportionals in these tables but near or between them.]

[3] [Napier obtains this result by first calculating the logarithm of 7071068, which is to the nearest unit, the square root of 50×10^{12} and which is, to his "radius," the sine of 45°. By Article 39 its logarithm is 3465734.5, whence the result in Article 51.]

55.   As the half radius is to the sine of half a given arc, so is the
       sine of the complement of the half arc to the sine of the whole
       arc.[1]
56.   Double the logarithm of an arc of 45 degrees is the logarithm
       of half the radius.
57.   The sum of the logarithms of half the radius and any given
       arc is equal to the sum of the logarithms of half the arc and the
       complement of the half arc. Whence the logarithm of the
       half arc may be found if the logarithms of the other three are
       given.
59.   To form a logarithmic table.[2]

---

[1] [Only here does Napier begin to introduce angles into the construction of
his tables. Napier proves Articles 55–57 by geometric principles and the
preceding theorems concerning logarithms.]

[2] [Napier's table is constructed in quite the same form as used at present,
except that the second (sixth) column gives sines for the number of degrees
indicated at the top (bottom) and of minutes in the first (seventh) column,
the third (fifth) column gives the corresponding logarithm and the fourth
column gives the "differentiæ" between the logarithms in the third and fifth
columns, these being therefore essentially logarithmic tangents or cotangents.
A reproduction of one page may be seen in Macdonald's translation, page 138.

DELAMAIN

On The Slide Rule

(Edited by Professor Florian Cajori, University of California, Berkeley, California.)

The earliest publication describing a slide rule (an instrument differing from Gunter's scale, which had no sliding parts) was brought out in the year 1630 by Richard Delamain, a teacher of mathematics in London. It was a pamphlet of 30 pages, entitled *Grammelogia*[1] and describing a circular slide rule. There is a copy in the Cambridge University Library in England. This tract has no drawing of the slide rule. During the next 2 or 3 years there were issued at least four undated new editions, or impressions, of the *Grammelogia*, with new parts added. The Cambridge University Library has a copy which is the same as the 1630 publication but with an appendix[2] of 17 pages added. In the British Museum at London and in the Bodleian Library at Oxford, there are copies of another edition of 113 pages, which was published in 1632 or 1633, as is shown by its reference to Oughtred's book, the *Circles of Proportion* of 1632. It has two title pages[3] which we reproduce in facsimile.

---

[1] The full title of the *Grammelogia* of 1630 is as follows:
Gramelogia|or,|The Mathematicall Ring.|Shewing (any reasonable Capacity that hath| not Arithmeticke) bow to resolve and worke|all ordinary operations of Arithmeticke.|And those which are most difficult with greatest|facilitie: The extraction of Roots, the valuation of| Leases, &c. The measuring of Plaines|and Solids.|With the resolution of Plaine and Sphericall|Triangles.|And that onely by an Ocular Inspection,|and a Circular Motion.| Naturae secreta tempus aperit.|London printed by John Haviland, 1630.

[2] The appendix is entitled:
De Ia Mains|Appendix|Vpon his|Mathematicall|Ring. Attribuit nullo (praescripto tempore) vitae|vsuram nobis ingeniique Deus.|London,|
... The next line or two of this title page which probably contained the date of publication, were cut off by the binder in trimming the edges of this and several other pamphlets for binding into one volume.

[3] The first title page (engraved) is as follows:
Mirifica Logarithmoru' Projectio Circularis. There follows a diagram of a circular slide rule, with the inscription within the innermost ring: Nil Finis, Motvs, Circvlvs vllvs Habet.
The second title page is as follows:
Grammelogia|Or, the Mathematicall Ring.|Extracted from the Logarythmes, and projected Circular: Now published in the|inlargement thereof unto any magnitude fit for use; shewing any reason-|able capacity that hath not Arithmeticke bow to resolve and worke,|all ordinary operations of Arithmeticke:|And those that are most difficult with greatest facilitie, the extracti-|on of Rootes, the valuation of Leases, &c. the measuring of Plaines and Solids,|with the resolution of Plaine and Sphericall Triangles applied to the|Practicall parts of Geometrie, Horologographie, Geographie|Fortification, Navigation, Astronomie, &c.|And that onely by an ocular inspection, and a Circular motion, Invented and first published, by R. Delamain, Teacher, and Student of the Mathematicks.|Naturae secreta tempus aperit.|
There is no date. There follows the diagram of a second circular slide rule, with the inscription within the innermost ring: Typus proiectionis Annuli adaucti vt in Conslusione Lybri praelo commissi, Anno 1630 promisi. There are numerous drawings in the *Grammelogia*, all

156

In the *Grammelogia* of 1630, Delamain, in an address to King Charles I, emphasizes the ease of operating with his slide rule by stating that it is "fit for use...as well on Horse backe as on Foot." Speaking "To the Reader," he states that he has "for many yeares taught the Mathematicks in this Towne" and made efforts to improve Gunter's scale "by some Motion, so that the whole body of Logarithmes might move proportionally the one to the

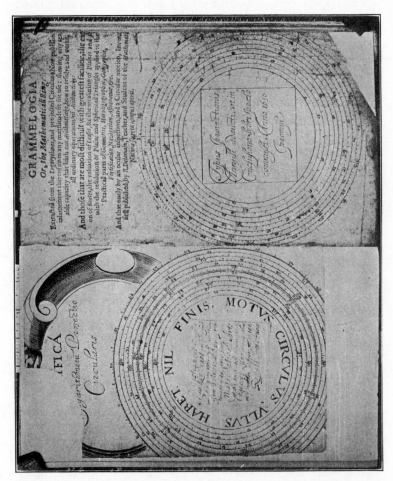

other, as occasion required. This conceit in February last [1629] I struke upon, and so composed my *Grammelogia* or *Mathematicall Ring;* by which only with an *ocular inspection*, there is had at one instant all proportionalls through

of which, excepting the drawings of slide rules on the engraved title pages were printed upon separate pieces of paper and then inserted by hand into the vacant spaces on the printed pages reserved for them. Some drawings are missing, so that the Bodleian *Grammelogia* differs in this respect slightly from the two copies in the British Museum.

the said body of Numbers." He dates his preface "first of January, 1630." The term *Grammelogia* is applied to the instrument, as well as to the book. Delamain's description of this *Grammelogia* is as follows:

The parts of the Instrument are two Circles, the one moveable, and the other fixed: The moveable is that unto which is fastened a small pin to move it by; the other Circle may be conceived to be fixed; The circumference of the moveable Circle is divided into unequall parts, charactered with figures thus, 1. 2. 3. 4. 5. 6. 7. 8. 9. these figures doe represent themselves, or such numbers unto which a Cipher or Ciphers are added, and are varied as the occasion falls out in *the speech of Numbers*, so 1. stands for 1. or 10. or 100., &c. the 2. stands for 2. or 20. or 200. or 2000., &c. the 3. stands for 30. or 300. or 3000.; &c.

"How to perform the Golden Rule" (the rule of proportion), is explained thus:

Seeke the first number in the moveable, and bring it to the second number in the fixed, so right against the third number in the moveable, is the answer in the fixed.

If the Interest of 100. li. be 8. li. in the yeare, what is the Interest of 65. li. for the same time.

Bring 100. in the movable to 8. in the fixed, so right against 65. in the movable is 5.2. in the fixed, and so much is the Interest of 65. li. for the yeare at 8. li. for 100. li. *per annum*.

The *Instrument* not removed, you may at one instant right against any summe of money in the moveable, see the Interest thereof in the fixed: the reason of this is from the *Definition of Logarithmes*.

Relating to the "resolution of Plaine and Sphericall Triangles," Delamain says:

If there be composed three Circles of equal thicknesse, A.B.C. so that the inner edge of D [should be B] and the outward edge of A bee answerably graduated with *Logarithmall signes* [sines], and the outward edge of B and the inner edge of A with *Logarithmes;* and then on the backside be graduated the *Logarithmall Tangents*, and againe the *Logarithmall signes* oppositly to the former graduations, it shall be fitted for the resolution of *Plaine* and *Sphericall Triangles*.

After twelve lines of further remarks on this point, he adds:

Hence from the forme, I have called it a *Ring*, and *Grammelogia* by annoligie of a *Lineary speech;* which *Ring*, if it were projected in the *convex* unto two yards *Diameter*, or thereabouts, and the line *Decupled*, it would worke *Trigonometrie* unto seconds, and give *proportionall numbers* unto six places only by an *ocular inspection*, which would compendiate *Astronomicall calculations*, and be sufficient for the *Prosthaphaeresis* of the Motions: But of this as God shall give life and ability to health and time.

The patent and copyright on the instrument and book are as follows:

Whereas Richard Delamain, Teacher of Mathematicks, hath presented vnto Vs an Instrument called Grammelogia, or The Mathematicall Ring, together with a Booke so instituled, expressing the use thereof, being his owne Invention; we of our Gracious and Princely favour have granted unto the said Richard Delamain and his Assignes, Privilege, Licence, and Authority, for the sole Making, Printing and Selling of the said Instrument and Booke: straightly forbidding any other to Make, Imprint, or Sell, or cause to be Made, or Imprinted, or Sold, the said Instrument or Booke within any our Dominions, during the space of ten years next ensuing the date hereof, upon paine of Our high displeasure, Given under our hand and Signet at our Palace of Westminster. the fourth day of January, in the sixth yeare of our Raigne.

OUGHTRED

On the Slide Rule

(Edited by Professor Florian Cajori, University of California, Berkeley, California.)

William Oughtred (1574–1660) was a clergyman living near London and intensely interested in mathematics. He taught mathematics at his residence, without compensation, to promising pupils. At one time, Oughtred had assisted Delamain in his mathematical studies. His *Circles of Proportion*[1] appeared in 1632, translated into English from his Latin manuscript by one of his pupils, William Forster. Forster wrote a preface in which he makes the charge (without naming Delamain) that "another...went about to preocupate" the new invention. This led to verbal disputes and to the publication by Delamain of the several new editions of the *Grammelogia*, describing further designs of circular slide rules and also stating his side of the controversy. Oughtred prepared an *Epistle*, in reply, which was published in the 1633 edition of his *Circles of Proportion*. Each combatant accuses the other of stealing the invention of the circular slide rule. After reading both sides of the controversy, we conclude that Oughtred invented the circular slide rule before the time when Delamain claimed to have made his invention, but it is not shown conclusively that the latter was dishonest; we incline to the opinion that he was an independent inventor. In 1633, Oughtred published the description of a rectilinear slide rule, in the invention of which he has no rival.

Extracts from the *Circles of Proportion*

1 There are two sides of this Instrument. On the one side, as it were in the *plaine of the Horizon*, is delineated the *proiection of the Sphere*. On the other side there are divers kindes of Circles, divided after many severall Waies; together with an *Index* to be opened after the manner of a paire of Compasses. And of this side we will speake in the first place.

---

[1] There are two title pages. The first is engraved and reads thus:

The|Circles|of|Proportion|and|The Horizontall|Instrument.|Both invented, and|the vses of both|Written in Latine by|Mr. W. O.|Translated into English: and set forth|for the publique benefit by|William Forster.|London|Printed for Elias Allen maker|of these and all other Mathe:|matical Instruments, and are to|be sold at his shop ouer against| St Clements church with out Temple-barr.|1632. T. Cecill Sculp|

The second title page is:

The|Circle|of|Proportion,|and |The Horizontall|Instrvment.|Both invented, and the vses of both|written in Latine by that learned Mathe-|matician Mr W. O.|Bvt|Translated into English: and set forth for|the publique benefit by William Forster, louer|and practizer of the Mathematicall Sciences.|London|Printed by Avg. Mathevves,|dwelling in the Parsonage Court, neere|St Brides. 1632.|

160

2 The *First,* or outermost circle is of *Sines,* from 5 degrees 45 minuts almost, vntill 90. Every degree till 30 is divided into 12 parts, each part being 5 min : from thence vntill 50 deg : into sixe parts which are 10 min : a peece : from thence vntill 75 degrees into two parts which are 30 minutes a peece. After that vnto 85 deg : they are not divided.

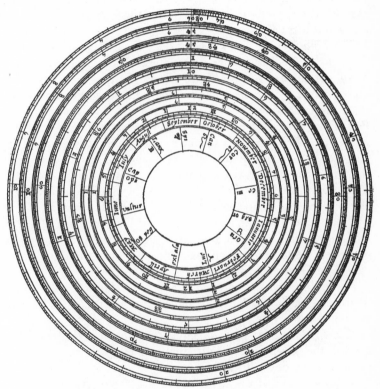

Oughtred's Circular Slide Rule, from his *Circles of Proportions,* 1632.

3 The *Second circle* is of *Tangents,* from 5 degrees 45. min : almost, untill 45 degrees. Every degree being divided into 12 parts which are 5 min : a peece.

4 The *Third circle* is of *Tangents,* from 45 degrees untill 84 degrees 15 minutes. Each degree being divided into 12 parts, which are 5 min : a peece.

5 The *Sixt circle* is of *Tangents* from 84 degrees till about 89 degrees 25 minutes.

The *Seventh circle* is of *Tangents* from about 35.Min : till 6 degrees.

The *Eight circle* is of *Sines*, from about 35 minutes til 6 degrees.

6 The *Fourth circle* is of *Vnæquall Numbers*, which are noted with the Figures 2, 3, 4, 5, 6, 7, 8, 9, 1. Whether you vnderstand them to bee single Numbers, or Tenns, or Hundreds, or Thousands, etc. And every space of the numbers till 5, is divided into 100 parts, but after 5 till 1, into 50 parts.

The *Fourth circle* also sheweth the *true* or *naturall Sines*, and *Tangents*. For if the *Index* bee applyed to any Sine or Tangent, it will cut the *true Sine* or *Tangent* in the fourth circle. And wee are to knowe that if the *Sine* or *Tangent* be in the *First*, or *Second circle*, the figures of the *Fourth circle* doe signifie so many thousands. But if the *Sine* or *Tangent* be in the *Seventh* or *Eight circle*, the figures in the *Fourth circle* signifie so many hundreds. And if the *Tangent* bee in the *Sixt circle*, the figures of the *Fourth circle*, signifie so many times tenne thousand, or whole *Radij*.

And by this meanes the Sine of 23°, 30' will bee found 3987: and the Sine of it's complement 9171. And the Tangent of 23°, 30 will be found 4348: and the Tangent of it's complement, 22998. And the Radius is 10000, that is the figure 1 with foure cyphers, or circles. And hereby you may finde out both the summe, and also the difference of Sines, and Tangents.

7 The *Fift circle* is of *Aequall numbers*, which are noted with the figures 1, 2, 3, 4, 5, 6, 7, 8, 9, 0; and every space is divided into 100 aequall parts.

This *Fift circle* is scarse of any use, but onely that by helpe thereof the given distance of numbers may be multiplied, or divided, as neede shall require.

As for example, if the space between 1|00 and 1|0833+ bee to bee septupled. Apply the Index vnto 1|0833+ in the Fourth circle, and it will cut in the Fift circle 03476+; which multiplyed by 7 makes 24333: then againe, apply the Index vnto this number 24333 in the Fift circle, and it will cut in the Fourth circle 1|7512+. And this is the space betweene 1|00 and 1|0833+ septupled, or the Ratio betweene 100 and 108⅓ seven times multiplied into it selfe.

And contrarily, if 1|7512 bee to bee divided by 7: Apply the Index vnto 1|7568 in the fourth circle, and it will cut in the fit circle 24333: which divided by 7 giveth 03476+ Then againe vnto this Number in the Fift circle apply the Index, and in the Fourth circle it wil cut vpon 1|0833+ for the Septupartion sought for.

The reason of which Operation is, because this *Fift circle* doth shew the *Logarithmes* of Numbers. *For if the Index be applyed unto any number in the Fourth circle, it will in the Fift circle cut vpon the Logarithme of the same number, so that to the Logarithme found you praefixe a Caracteristicall (as Master Brigs termes it) one lesse then in the number of the places of the integers proposed* (Which *you may rather call the* Graduall Number). So the Logarithme of the number 2 will be 0.30103. And the Logarithme of the Number 43|6 will bee found 1.63949.

Numbers are multiplied by Addition of their Logarithmes: *and they are Divided by Substraction of their* Logarithmes.

8 In the middest among the Circles, is a *double Nocturnall* instrument, to shew the hower of the night.

9 The right line passing through the Center, through 90, and 45 I call the *Line of Vnitie*, or of the *Radius*.

10 That *Arme of the Index* which in euery Operation is placed at the Antecedent, or first terme, I call the *Antecedent arme:* and that which is placed at the consequent terme, I call the *Consequent Arme.*

Oughtred's Rectilinear Slide Rule

An Addition Vnto the Vse of the Instrvment called the Circles of Proportion, For the Working of Nauticall Questions... London, 1633, contains the following description of the rectilinear slide rule, consisting of "two Rvlers:"

I call the *longer* of the two *Rulers* the *Staffe,* and the *Shorter* the *Transversarie.* And are in length one to the other almost as 3 to 2.

The *Rulers* are just four square, with right angles: and equall in bignesse: they are thus divided.

The *Transversarie* at the upper end noted with the letters S, T, N, E, on the severall sides, hath a *pinnicide* or *sight:* at the lower edge of which sight is the *line of the Radius,* or *Vnite line,* where the divisions beginne.

After explaining the different lines on the two rulers, Oughtred continues:

Thus have you on the *two Rulers* the very same lines which are in the *Circles of Proportion:* and whatsoever can be done by those Circles, may also as well be performed by the two Rulers: and the Rules which have bin here formerly set downe for that Instrument, may also be practised upon these: so that you bee carefull to observe in both the different propriety in working. It will not therfore be needfull, to make any new and long discourse, concerning these

Rulers, but onely to shew the manner, how they are to be used, for the calculation of any proportion given.

In working a Proportion by the Rulers, *hold the Transversary in your left hand, with the end at which the line of the Radius or Vnite line is, from you ward: turning that side of the Ruler upward, on which the line of the kind of the first terme is, whether it be Number, Sine, or Tangent: and therein seeke both the first terme, and the other which is homogene to it.   Then take the Staffe in your right hand with that side upward, in which the line of the kind of the fourth terme sought for is: and seeke in it the terme homogene to the fourth. Apply this to the first terme in the Transversarie: and the other homogene terme shall in the Staffe shew the fourth terme.*

As if you would multiply 355 by 48: Say

$$1 \cdot 355 :: 48 \cdot 17040.$$

For if in the line of Numbers on the Staffe you reckon 355, and apply the same to 1 in the line of Numbers on the Transversarie: then shall 48 on the Transversarie shew 17040 on the Staffe.[1]

---

[1] For additional details relating to Delamain's and Oughtred's slide rules, consult an article entitled "On the History of Gunter's Scale and the Slide Rule during the Seventeenth Century," in the *University of California Publications in Mathematics*, Vol. I, No. 9, pp. 187–209, Feb. 17, 1920.

PASCAL

On His Calculating Machine

(Translated from the French by L. Leland Locke, A. M.,
Brooklyn, New York.)

Blaise Pascal, philosopher, mathematician, physicist, inventor, was born at Clermont, June 19, 1623, and died at Paris, Aug. 19, 1662. To Pascal (see p. 67) must be given the credit of having conceived and constructed the first machine for performing the four fundamental operations of arithmetic, of which a complete description and authentic models have been preserved. His first machine was completed in 1642, and the Privilege was granted by Chancellor Seguier on May 22, 1649. Pascal's account of his invention, here reproduced, was written subsequent to the Privilege. It is found in his collected works, the most recent edition being the *Oeuvres de Blaise Pascal,*" by Brunschvieg and Boutroux, Paris, Vol. I, pp. 303–314, 1908. The perfected machine, made at the direction of and dedicated to Seguier, is one of the most interesting relics of Pascal as well as being the first significant model in the development of machine calculation.

Pascal's "Advis," the first discussion of the problem of machine calculation, may be somewhat clarified, if his accomplishment is viewed in the light of present-day design. The instrument may be classed as a machine on two grounds: First, the transfer of tens, usually designated as the "carry," is performed automatically; second, an initial installation is transmitted through the medium of intermediate parts and finally registered on the result dials. The primary conception due to Pascal is that of building a machine which would automatically produce the carry. A simple ratchet or latch is introduced between successive orders which has the property of moving the dial of higher order one unit forward as the dial of lower order passes from 9 to 0. The Pascal machine may be classed as a modern counting machine, with provision for the entry of numbers in all orders, provided such entries are made separately. The common disk and cylinder dials of today originated in this model. Pascal used crown wheels with pin teeth, a device which resulted in a minimum of friction. The chief problem in the design of a machine of this kind is so to adjust the load of the carry that a minimum of effort expended on the initial installation will produce the carry as far as desired. Such a condition arises when the dials all register 9 and when 1 is then added in the lowest order. Pascal's solution would do credit to a designer of much later date. A weighted ratchet is gradually raised as the number being installed approaches 9. As it passes from 9 to 0, the ratchet is released and in falling transfers 1 to the next higher order. If all dials stand at 9, only a slight lifting remains for each ratchet. This cumulative load would become excessive over many orders, thus definitely limiting the capacity of the machine. Pascal's statement that a thousand dials may be turned as easily as one would, of course, fail in practice.

The one feature of his design which more than any other reveals his genius is the use of the complements of numbers in subtraction, enabling him to perform all four operations with a single direction of operation, a modification of this device being still in use in many key-driven machines.

ADVERTISEMENT

Necessary to those who have curiosity to see the Arithmetic Machine, and to operate it

Dear reader, this notice will serve to inform you that I submit to the public a small machine of my invention, by means of which you alone may, without any effort, perform all the operations of arithmetic, and may be relieved of the work which has often times fatigued your spirit, when you have worked with the counters or

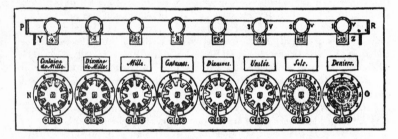

with the pen.   I can, without presumption, hope that it will not be displeasing to you, since Monseigneur le Chancelier has honored it by his favorable opinion, and since, in Paris, those who are most versed in mathematics have judged it not unworthy of their approbation.   However in order not to appear negligent in making it acquire yours also, I have felt obliged to make clear all the difficulties that I have judged capable of confronting your understanding when you take the trouble to consider it.

I have no doubt that after having seen it, there will come at once to your thought that I should have explained by writing both its construction, and its use, and that, to render the discourse intelligible, I should myself be obliged, following the method of the geometers,[1] to represent by figures the dimensions, the disposition and the relation of all of the parts and how each should be placed to compose the instrument, and to place its movement in

---

[1] [A word then used to denote mathematicians in general as well as those concerned with the study of geometric forms.]

its perfection; but do not believe that, after having spared neither time nor labor nor expense to put it in a state of being useful, I have failed to do everything necessary to satisfy you on that point, —which would indicate failure of accomplishment if I have not been prevented from doing it by a consideration so powerful that I myself hope that it will compel you to excuse me. I trust that you will approve my refraining from this phase of the work, when you reflect on the one hand on the ease with which by a brief conference the construction and the use of this machine can be explained, and on the other hand on the embarassment and the difficulty there would be in trying to express by writing the dimensions, the forms, the proportions, the position, and the rest of the properties of all the different pieces. Furthermore, you may well consider what learning means to the number of those who can be taught by word of mouth, and how an explanation in writing will be as useless as a written description of all the parts of a watch, although the verbal explanation is so easy. It is therefore apparent that such a written discourse would produce no other effect than a distaste on the part of many persons, making them conceive of a thousand difficulties at every point where there is none at all.

Now, dear reader, I deem it necessary to say that I foresee two things capable of forming some clouds in your spirit. I know that there are a number of persons who make profession of finding fault everywhere, and that among them will be found those who will say that the machine may be simplified, and this is the first mist that I feel it necessary to dispel. Such a proposition can only be made by certain persons who have indeed some knowledge of mechanics or of geometry, but who, not knowing how to join the one to the other, and both of these to physics, flatter themselves or are deceived by their imaginary conceptions, and persuade themselves that many things are possible which are not. Having only an imperfect knowledge in general, this is not sufficient to make them forsee the inconveniences arising, either from the nature of the case or as to the places which the pieces of the machine should occupy. The movements of these parts are different, and they must be so free as not to interfere with one another. When, therefore, those whose knowledge is so imperfect propose that this machine be simplified, I ask you to say to them that I will reply for myself, if they will simply ask me; and to assure them on my part, that I will let them see, whenever they wish, many other models, together with a perfect instrument which is much less complex, and which I have publicly operated for six months. It will thus appear that I am quite aware that the machine may be simplified. In particular I could, if I had wished, institute the movement of the operation on the front face,[1] but this could only be substituted with much inconvenience for that which it is now done on the top face with all the convenience that one should wish and with pleasure. You may also say to them that my design does not always have in view the reducing in controlled movement all the operations of arithmetic. [Hence] I am persuaded that it will be successful only if the movement is simple, easy, convenient and quick of execution, and if the machine is durable, solid, and capable of undergoing without alteration the strain of transportation. Finally you may say that if they had thought as much as I on this matter and had considered all the means which I have taken to reach my goal, experience would have shown them that a more simple instrument could not have all of the qualities that I have successfully given to this little machine.

As for the simplicity of movement of the operations, I have so devised it that, although the operations of arithmetic are in a way opposed the one to the other,—as addition to subtraction, and multiplication to division,—nevertheless they are all performed on this machine by a single unique movement.

The facility of this movement of operation is very evident since it is just as easy to move one thousand or ten thousand dials, all at one time, if one desires as to make a single dial move, although all accomplish the movement perfectly. (I do not know if there remains another principle in nature such as the one upon which I have based this ease of operation.) In addition to the facility of movement in the operation, if you wish to appreciate it, you may compare it with the methods of counters and with the pen. You know that, in operating with counters, the calculator (especially when he lacks practice) is often obliged, for fear of making an error, to make a long series and extension of counters, being afterward compelled to gather up and retake those which are found to be extended unnecessarily, in which you see these two useless tasks, with the double loss of time. This machine facili-

---

[1] [The ratchet design was based on a horizontal position of the intermediate shaft. The stylus-operated dial, being on the top face with a vertical shaft, required a pair of crown wheels at right angles to transmit the motion to the horizontal shaft. Pascal here proposes placing the dial on the front face.]

tates the work and eliminates all unnecessary features. The most ignorant find as many advantages as the most experienced. The instrument makes up for ignorance and for lack of practice, and even without any effort of the operator, it makes possible shortcuts by itself, whenever the numbers are set down. In the same way you know that in operating with the pen one is obliged to retain or to borrow the necessary numbers, and that errors slip in, in these retentions and borrowings, except through very long practice, and in spite of a profound attention which soon fatigues the mind. This machine frees the operator from that vexation; it suffices that he have judgment; he is relieved from the failing of memory; and without any retaining or borrowing, it does by itself what he wishes, without any thinking on his part. There are a hundred other advantages which practice will reveal, the details of which it would be wearisome to mention.

As to the amount[1] of movement, it is sufficient to say that it is imperceptible, going from left to right and following our method of common writing except that it proceeds in a circle.

And, finally, its speed is evident at once in comparing it with the other two methods of the counters and the pen. If you still wish a more particular explanation of its rapidity, I shall tell you that it is equal to the agility of the hand of the operator. This speed is based, not only on the facility of the movements which have no resistance, but also on the smallness of the dials which are moved with the hand. The result is that, the key board being very short, the movement can be performed in a short time. Thus, the machine is small and hence is easily handled and carried.

And as to the lasting and wearing qualities of the instrument, the durability of the metal of which it is made should be a sufficient warrant: I have been able to give entire assurance to others only after having had the experience of carrying the instrument over more than two hundred and fifty leagues of road, without its showing any damage.

Therefore, dear reader I ask you again not to consider it an imperfection for this machine to be composed of so many parts, because without these I could not give to it all the qualities which I have explained, and which are absolutely necessary. In this you may notice a kind of paradox, that to render the movement of operation more simple, it is necessary that the machine should be constructed of a movement more complex.

---

[1] This has reference to the movement of the stylus in setting down a number.

The second possibility for distrust, dear reader, might be the imperfect reproductions of this machine which have been produced by the presumption of certain artisans. In these cases I beg of you to carefully consider [the product], to guard yourself from surprise, to distinguish between "la lepre et la lepre,"[1] and not to judge the true original by the imperfect productions of the ignorance and the temerity of the mechanics. The more excellent they are in their art, the more we should fear that vanity forces them to consider themselves capable of undertaking and of producing new instruments, of which the principles and the rules of which they are ignorant. Intoxicated by that false persuasion, they grope aimlessly about, without precise measurements carefully determined and without propositions. The result is that after much time and labor, either they do not produce anything equal to what they have attempted, or, at most, they produce a small monstrosity of which the principal members are lacking, the others being formless and without any proportion. These imperfections, rendering it ridiculous, never fail to attract the contempt of all those who see it, and most of them blame without reason, the inventor instead of inquiring about it from him, and then censuring the presumption of these artisans, who by their unjustified daring undertake more than they are equal to, producing these useless abortions. It is important to the public to recognize their weakness and to learn from them that, for new inventions, it is necessary that art should be aided by theory until usage has made the rules of theory so common that it has finally reduced them to an art and until continued practice has given the artisans the habit of following and practicing these rules with certainty. It was not in my power, with all the theory imaginable, to execute alone my own design without the aid of a mechanic who knew perfectly the practice of the lathe, of the file, and of the hammer to reduce the parts of the machine in the measures and proportions that I prescribed to him. Likewise it is impossible for simple artisans, skillful as they may be in their art, to make perfectly a new instrument which consists, like this one, of complicated movements, without the aid of a person who, by the rules of theory, gives him the measures and proportions of all of the pieces of which it shall be composed.

Dear reader, I have good reason to give you this last advice, after having seen with my own eyes a wrong production of my idea

---

[1] [Bossut reads, "between the copy and the copy."]

by a workman of the city of Rouen, a clockmaker by profession, who, from a simple description which had been given him of my first model, which I had made some months previously, had the presumption, to undertake to make another; and what is more, by another type of movement. Since the good man has no other talent than that of handling his tools skillfully, and has no knowledge of geometry and mechanics (although he is very skillful in his art and also very industrious in many things which are not related to it), he made only a useless piece, apparently true, polished and well filed on the outside, but so wholly imperfect on the inside that it was of no use. Because of its novelty alone, it was not without value to those who did not understand about it; and, notwithstanding all these essential defects which trial shows, it found in the same city a place in a collector's cabinet which is filled with many other rare and curious pieces. The appearance of that small abortion displeased me to the last degree and so cooled the ardor with which I had worked to the accomplishment of my model, that I at once discharged all my workmen, resolved to give up entirely my enterprise because of the just apprehension that many others would feel a similar boldness and that the false copies which they would produce of this new idea would only ruin its value at its beginning and its usefulness to the public. But, some time afterward, Monseigneur le Chancelier, having deigned to examine my first model and to give testimony of the regard which he held for that invention, commanded me to perfect it. In order to eliminate the fear which held me back for some time, it pleased him to check the evil at its root, and to prevent the course it could take in prejudicing my reputation and inconveniencing the public. This was shown in the kindness that he did in granting me an unusual privilege, and which stamped out with their birth all those illegitimate abortions which might be produced by others than by the legitimate alliance of the theory with art.

For the rest, if at any time you have thought of the invention of machines, I can readily persuade you that the form of the instrument, in the state in which it is at present, is not the first attempt that I have made on that subject. I began my project by a machine very different from this both in material and in form, which (although it would have pleased many) did not give me entire satisfaction. The result was that in altering it gradually I unknowingly made a second type, in which I still found incon-

veniences to which I would not agree.   In order to find a remedy,
I have devised a third, which works by springs and which is very
simple in construction.   It is that one which, as I have just said,
I have operated many times, at the request of many persons, and
which is still in perfect condition.   Nevertheless, in constantly
perfecting it, I have found reasons to change it, and finally recognizing in all these reasons, whether of difficulty of operation, or in
the roughness of its movements, or in the disposition to get out of
order too easily by weather or by transportation, I have had the
patience to make as many as fifty models, wholly different, some
of wood, some of ivory and ebony, and others of copper, before
having arrived at the accomplishment of this machine which I
now make known.   Although it is composed of many different
small parts, as you can see, at the same time it is so solid that, after
the experience of which I have spoken before, I assure you that
all the jarring that it receives in transportation, however far, will
not disarrange it.

Finally, dear reader, now that I deem it ready to be seen, and
in order that you yourself can see and operate it, if you are interested, I pray you to grant me the liberty of hoping that this same
idea of finding a third method of performing all the operations of
arithmetic, totally new, and which has nothing in common with
the two ordinary methods of the pen and of the counters, will
receive from you some esteem.   I hope that in approving my aim
of pleasing and assisting you, you will be grateful to me for the
care that I have taken to make all of the operations, which by the
preceding methods are painful, complex, long, and uncertain,
hereafter easy, simple, prompt, and assured.

LEIBNIZ

On His Calculating Machine

(Translated from the Latin by Dr. Mark Kormes, New York City.)

Pascal's calculating machine, described in the preceding article, was intended to add numbers mechanically. The first one made for the purpose of multiplying was constructed by Gottfried Wilhelm, Freiherr von Leibniz (1646–1716) about the year 1671. One of these machines is still to be seen in the Kästner Museum in Hannover, the city in which Leibniz spent his later years. An article by Jordan, published in *Die Zeitschrift für Vermessungswesen*, in 1897, brought to light a manuscript by Leibniz describing his machine and is now in the Royal Library of the same city. This manuscript was written in 1685, some years after the machine was invented, and it bears the title: "Machina arithmetica in qua non additio tantum et subtractio sed et multiplicatio nullo, divisio vero pæne nullo animi labore peragantur."

When, several years ago, I saw for the first time an instrument which, when carried, automatically records the numbers of steps

taken by a pedestrian, it occurred to me at once that the entire arithmetic could be subjected to a similar kind of machinery so that not only counting but also addition and subtraction, multiplication and division could be accomplished by a suitably arranged machine easily, promptly, and with sure results.

The calculating box of Pascal was not known to me at that time. I believe it has not gained sufficient publicity. When I noticed, however, the mere name of a calculating machine in the preface of his "posthumous thoughts" (his arithmetical triangle I saw

173

first in Paris) I immediately inquired about it in a letter to a Parisian friend. When I learned from him that such a machine exists I requested the most distinguished Carcavius by letter to give me an explanation of the work which it is capable of performing. He replied that addition and subtraction are accomplished by it directly, the other [operations] in a round-about way by repeating additions and subtractions and performing still another calculation. I wrote back that I venture to promise something more, namely, that multiplication could be performed by the machine as well as addition, and with greatest speed and accuracy.

He replied that this would be desirable and encouraged me to present my plans before the illustrious King's Academy of that place.

In the first place it should be understood that there are two parts of the machine, one designed for addition (subtraction) the other for multiplication (division) and that they should fit together.

The adding (subtracting) machine coincides completely with the calculating box of Pascal. Something, however, must be added for the sake of multiplication so that several and even all the wheels of addition could rotate without disturbing each other, and nevertheless anyone of them should precede the other in such a manner that after a single complete turn unity would be transferred into the next following. If this is not performed by the calculating box of Pascal it may be added to it without difficulty.

The multiplying machine will consist of two rows of wheels, equal ones and unequal ones. Hence the whole machine will have three kinds of wheels: the wheels of addition, the wheels of the multiplicand and the wheels of the multiplier. The wheels of addition or the decadic wheels are now visible in Pascal's adding box and are designated in the accompanying figure by the numbers 1, 10, 100, etc. Everyone of these wheels has ten fixed teeth.

The wheels which represent the multiplicand are all of the same size, equal to that of the wheels of addition, and are also provided with ten teeth which, however, are movable so that at one time there should protrude 5, at another 6 teeth, etc., according to whether the multiplicand is to be represented five times or six times, etc. For example, the multiplicand 365 consists of three digits 3, 6 and 5. Hence the same number of wheels is to be used. On these wheels the multiplicand will be set, if from the right wheel there protrude 5 teeth, from the middle wheel 6, and from the left wheel 3 teeth.

In order that this could be performed quickly and easily a peculiar arrangement would be needed, the exposition of which would lead too far into details. The wheels of the multiplicand should now be adjoined to the wheels of addition in such a manner that the last corresponds to the last, the last but one to the last but one, and that before the last but one to that before the last but one, or 5 should correspond to 1, 6 to 10, and 3 to 100. In the addition box itself there should show through small openings the number set as 0, 0, 0, etc. or zero. If after making such an arrangement we suppose that 365 be multiplied by one, the wheels 3, 6, and 5 must make one complete turn (but while one is being rotated all are being rotated because they are equal and are connected by cords as it will be made apparent subsequently) and their teeth

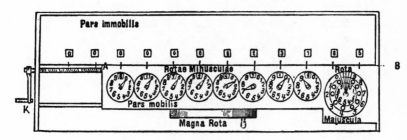

now protruding will turn the same number of fixed teeth of the wheels 100, 10, 1 and thus the number 365 will be transferred to the addition box.

Assuming, however, that the number 365 is to be multiplied by an arbitrary multiplier (124) there arises the need of a third kind of wheels, or the wheels of the multiplier. Let there be nine such wheels and while the wheels of the multiplicand are variable so that the same wheel can at one time represent 1 and at another time 9 according to whether there protrude less or more teeth, the wheels of the multiplier shall on the contrary be designated by fixed numbers, one for 9, one for 1, etc.

This is accomplished in the following manner: Everyone of the wheels of the multiplier is connected by means of a cord or a chain to a little pulley which is affixed to the corresponding wheel of the multiplicand: Thus the wheel of the multiplier will represent a number of units equal to the number of times the diameter of the multiplier-wheel contains the diameter of the corresponding pulley. The pulley will turn namely this number of times while the wheel turns but once.   Hence if the diameter of the wheel contains the diameter of the pulley four times the wheel will represent 4.

Thus at a single turn of the multiplier-wheel to which there corresponds a pulley having a quarter of its diameter the pulley will turn four times and with it also the multiplicand-wheel to which it [the pulley] is affixed.   When, however, the multiplicand-wheel is turned four times its teeth will meet the corresponding wheel of addition four times and hence the number of its units will be repeated as many times in the box of addition.

An example will clarify the matter best: Let 365 be multiplied by 124.   In the first place the entire number 365 must be multi-

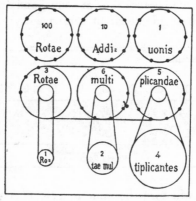

plied by four.   Turn the multiplier-wheel 4 by hand once; at the same time the corresponding pulley will turn four times (being as many times smaller) and with it the wheel of the multiplicand 5, to which it is attached, will also turn four times.   Since the wheel 5 has five teeth protruding at every turn 5 teeth of the corresponding wheel of addition will turn once and hence in the addition box there will be produced four times 5 or 20 units.

The multiplicand-wheel 6 is connected with the multiplicand-wheel 5 by another cord or chain and the multiplicand-wheel 3 is connected with wheel 6.   As they are equal, whenever wheel 5 turns four times, at the same time wheel 6 by turning four times will give 24 tens (it namely catches the decadic addition-wheel 10) and wheel 3 catching the addition-wheel 100 will give twelve hundred so that the sum of 1460 will be produced.

In this way 365 is multiplied by 4, which is the first operation. In order that we may also multiply by 2 (or rather by 20) it is necessary to move the entire adding machine by one step so to say, so that the multiplicand-wheel 5 and the multiplier-wheel 4 are under addition-wheel 10, while they were previously under 1, and in the same manner 6 and 2 under 100 and also 3 and 1 under 1000. After this is done let the multiplier-wheel 2 be turned once: at the same time 5 and 6 and 3 will turn twice and 5 catching twice [the addition-wheel] 10 will give 10 tens, 6 catching 100 will give twelve hundred and 3 catching 1000 will give six thousand, together 7300. This number is being added at the very same turn to the previous result of 1460.

In order to perform as the third operation, the multiplication by 1 (or rather by 100), let the multiplication machine be moved again (of course the multiplicand-wheels together with the multiplier-wheels while the addition-wheels remain in their position) so that the wheels 5 and 4 be placed under 100 and in the same way 6 and 2 under 1000 and 3 and 1 under 10,000. If wheel 1 be turned once at the same time the wheels 3, 6, and 5 will turn once and thus add in the addition box that many units, namely, 36,500. As a product we obtain, therefore:

$$\begin{array}{r} 1,460 \\ 7,300 \\ 36,500 \\ \hline 45,260 \end{array}$$

It should be noted here that for the sake of greater convenience the pulleys should be affixed to the multiplicand-wheels in such a manner that the wheels must move when the pulleys move but that the pulleys do not need to move while the wheels are turned. Otherwise when one multiplier-wheel (*e. g.*, 1) be turned and thus all the multiplicand-wheels moved, all the other multiplier wheels (*e. g.*, 2 and 4) would necessarily move, which would increase the difficulty and perturb the motion.

It should be also noted that it does not make any difference in what order the multiplier-wheels 1, 2, 4, etc. be arranged but they could very well be placed in numerical order 1, 2, 3, 4, 5. For even then one is at liberty to decide which one to turn first and which afterwards.

In order that the multiplier-wheel, *e. g.*, the one representing 9 or whose diameter is nine times as great as the diameter of the corresponding pulley, should not be too large we can make the pulley so much smaller preserving the same proportion between the pulley and the wheel.

In order that no irregularity should follow the tension of the cords and the motion of pulleys tiny iron chains could be used in place of the cords and on the circumference of the wheels and pulleys where the chains would rest there should be put little brass teeth corresponding always to the individual links of the chain; or in place of cords there could be teeth affixed to both the pulleys and the wheels so that the teeth of the multiplier-wheel would immediately catch the teeth of the pulley.

If we wanted to produce a more admirable machine it could be so arranged that it would not be necessary for the human hand to turn the wheels or to move the multiplication machine from operation to operation: Things could be arranged in the beginning so that everything should be done by the machine itself. This, however, would render the machine more costly and complicated and perhaps in no way better for practical use.

It remains for me to describe the method of dividing on the machine, which [task] I think no one has accomplished by a machine alone and without any mental labor whatever, especially where great numbers are concerned.

But whatever labor remains to be done in [the case of] our machine it could not be compared with that intricate labyrinth of the common division which is in the case of large numbers the most tedious [procedure] and [the one] most abundant in errors that can be conceived. Behold our method of division! Let the number 45,260 be divided by 124. Begin as usual and ask for the first simple quotient or how many times 452 contains 124.

It is but very easy for anyone with mediocre ability to estimate the correct quotient at first sight. Hence let 452 contain 124 thrice. Multiply the entire divisor by this simple quotient which can be easily accomplished by one simple turn of the wheel. The product will be 372. Subtract this from 452. Combine the remainder 80 with the rest of the dividend 60. This gives 8060. (But that will be effected by itself in the machine during the multiplication if we arrange in it the dividend in such a manner that whatever shall be produced by multiplication will be automatically deducted. The subtraction also takes place in the machine if we arrange in it the dividend in the beginning; the performed multiplications are then deducted from it and a new dividend is given by the machine itself without any mental labor whatever.)

Again divide this [8060] by 124 and ask how many times 806 contains 124. It will be clear to every beginner at first sight that it is contained six times. Multiply 124 by 6. (One turn of the multiplier wheel) gives 744. Subtract this result from 806, there remains 62. Combine this with the rest of the dividend, giving 620. Divide this third result again by 124. It is clear immediately that it is contained 5 times. Multiply 124 by 5; [this] gives 620. Deduct this from 620 and nothing remains; hence the quotient is 365.

The advantage of this division over the common division consists mostly in the fact (apart from infallibility) that in our method there are but few multiplications, namely as many as there are digits in the entire quotient or as many as there are simple quotients. In the common multiplication a far greater number is needed, namely, as many as [are given by] the product of the number of digits of the quotient by the number of the digits of the divisor. Thus in the preceding example our method required three multiplications because the entire divisor, 124, had to be multiplied by the single digits of the quotient 365,—that is, three. In the common method, however, single digits of the divisor are multiplied by single digits of the quotient and hence there are nine multiplications in the given example.

It also does not make any difference whether the few multiplications are large, but in the common method there are more and smaller ones; similarly one could say that also in the common method few multiplications but large ones could be done if the entire divisor be multiplied by an arbitrary number of the quotient. But the answer is obvious, our single large multiplication being so easy, even easier than any of the other kind no matter how small. It is effected instantly by a simple turn of a single wheel and at that without any fear of error. On the other hand in the common method the larger the multiplication the more difficult it is and the more subject to errors. For that reason it seemed to the teachers of arithmetic that in division there should be used many and small multiplications rather than one large one. It should be added that the largest part of the work already so trifling consists in the setting of the number to be multiplied, or to change according to the circumstances the number of the variable teeth on the multiplicand-wheels. In dividing, however, the multiplicand (namely the divisor) remains always the same, and only the multiplier (namely the simple quotient) changes without the necessity of moving the machine. Finally, it is to be added that our method does not require any work of subtraction; for while multiplying in the machine the subtraction is done automatically. From the above it is apparent that the advantage of the machine becomes the more conspicuous the larger the divisor.

It is sufficiently clear how many applications will be found for this machine, as the elimination of all errors and of almost all work from the calculations with numbers is of great utility to the government and science. It is well known with what enthusiasm the calculating rods [baculi] of Napier,[1] were accepted, the use of which, however, in division is neither much quicker nor surer than the common calculation. For in his [Napier's] multiplication there is need of continual additions, but division is in no way faster than by the ordinary [method]. Hence the calculating rods [baculi] soon fell into disuse. But in our [machine] there is no work when multiplying and very little when dividing.

Pascal's machine is an example of the most fortunate genius but while it facilitates only additions and subtractions, the difficulty of which is not very great in themselves, it commits the multiplication and division to a previous calculation so that it commended itself rather by refinement to the curious than as of practical use to people engaged in business affairs.

And now that we may give final praise to the machine we may say that it will be desirable to all who are engaged in computations which, it is well known, are the managers of financial affairs, the administrators of others' estates, merchants, surveyors, geographers, navigators, astronomers, and [those connected with] any of the crafts that use mathematics.

But limiting ourselves to scientific uses, the old geometric and astronomic tables could be corrected and new ones constructed by the help of which we could measure all kinds of curves and figures, whether composed or decomposed and unnamed, with no less certainty than we are now able to treat the angles according to the work of Regiomontanus and the circle according to that of Ludolphus of Cologne, in the same manner as straight lines. If this could take place at least for the curves and figures that are most important and used most often, then after the establishment of tables not only for lines and polygons but also for ellipses, parabolas, hyperbolas, and other figures of major importance, whether described by motion or by points, it could be assumed that geometry would then be perfect for practical use.

---

[1] [See p. 182.]

Furthermore, although optical demonstration or astronomical observation or the composition of motions will bring us new figures, it will be easy for anyone to construct tables for himself so that he may conduct his investigations with little toil and with great accuracy; for it is known from the failures [of those] who attempted the quadrature of the circle that arithmetic is the surest custodian of geometrical exactness. Hence it will pay to undertake the work of extending as far as possible the major Pythagorean tables; the table of squares, cubes, and other powers; and the tables of combinations, variations, and progressions of all kinds, so as to facilitate the labor.

Also the astronomers surely will not have to continue to exercise the patience which is required for computation. It is this that deters them from computing or correcting tables, from the construction of Ephemerides, from working on hypotheses, and from discussions of observations with each other. For it is unworthy of excellent men to lose hours like slaves in the labor of calculation, which could be safely relegated to anyone else if the machine were used.

What I have said about the construction and future use [of the machine], should be sufficient, and I believe will become absolutely clear to the observers [when completed].

NAPIER

The Napier Rods

(Translated from the Latin by Professor Jekuthiel Ginsburg, Yeshiva College, New York City.)

John Napier (1550–1617), Laird of Merchiston, Edinburgh (see p. 149), was known in his time quite as widely for his computing rods as for his invention of logarithms. While these rods are almost unknown at the present time, their advent was a distinct step in advance in mechanical computation. As is well known, they consist merely in putting on rods a scheme of multiplication which had long been in use among the Arabs and then using the rods for other operations as well. The following translation is from certain particularly significant parts of the *Rabdologiæ, seu nvmerationis per virgulas libri duo,* Edinburgh, 1617 (posthumously published). The word *rabdologia* is from the Greek ράβδος (*rhab'dos.* "rod") and λογία (*logi'a,* "collection"). When Leybourn published his English translation (*The Art of Numbring By Speaking-Rods: Vulgarly termed Nepeir's Bones,* London, 1667), he used a false etymology, not recognizing Napier's use of λογία.

Napier gives (p. 2) the number of the rods. Ten rods will suffice for calculations with numbers less than 11,111; twenty for numbers less than 111, 111, 111; and thirty rods for 13-place numbers less than 111, 111, 111, 111, 1.

Each rod is divided lengthwise into ten equal parts in the following way: nine parts in the middle, one half of a part above and another half below. Horizontal lines joining the points of division will divide the surface into nine squares plus two half squares. The diagonals are then drawn as here shown.

To mark the faces of the rods: the face turned toward the eye during the marking is called the "first;" the one to the right side of the observer, the "second;" the one toward the left, the "fourth."

The nine little areas on each face serve for entering the multiples of one of the nine digits by 1, 2, 3, 4, 5, 6, 7, 8, 9. If the products are expressed by one digit, the lower half of the square is used; if by two, then one of the digits namely, the digits of the tens) is put in the upper area and the other in the lower one.

The first four rods are marked as follows: In the squares of the first face of each (that is, the face turned to the eye of the observer) we put zeros. This uses up four of the sixteen available faces.

Then, turning around each rod lengthwise so that the third face will now be turned toward the eye, but upside down, we write in the nine squares the

182

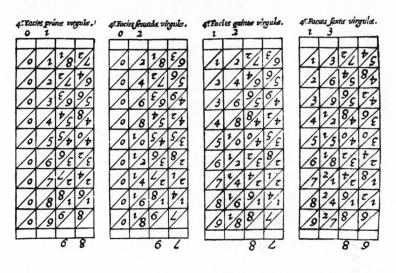

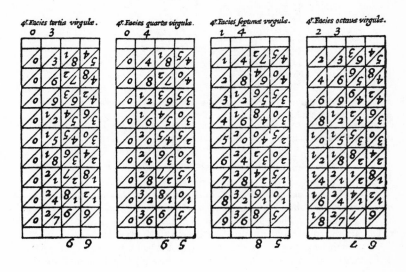

products of 9 by 1, 2, 3, 4, 5, 6, 7, 8, 9—namely, the numbers 9, 18, 27, 36, 45, 54, 63, 72, 81.

This takes care of four more of the available sixteen faces, leaving eight faces for the remaining eight digits. These will be filled in the following way: The second face of the first rod will be given to the multiples of 1 by the first nine digits (that is, the numbers 1, 2, 3, 4, 5, 6, 7, 8, 9), while the opposite face will be given to similar multiples of its complement to the number 9—namely, the multiples of 8 (8, 16, 24, 32, 40, 48, 56, 64, 72).

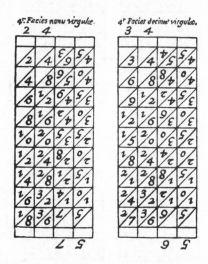

Similarly, the second and fourth faces of rod 2 will be marked, respectively, by the multiples of 2 and 7 by the first nine digits.

On the second and fourth faces of the third rod will be inscribed the products of the numbers 3 and 6, while the same faces of the rod will serve the numbers 4 and 5.

Hence, the first four rods will contain all the products of the first nine numbers by each other, besides four zero columns and three 9 columns, making in all four 9 columns. The twenty-four faces of the remaining six rods will have to contain the columns of other digits repeated three times each.

On the first face of each of the following three rods (namely, the fifth, sixth, and seventh), we enter the unit column (i. e., 1, 2, 3, 4, 5, 6, 7, 8, 9) on the opposite face (the third) of each of these columns—the corresponding product of its complement to 9, namely, 8 (the numbers 8, 16, 24, 32, 40, 48, 56, 64, 72). Hence, each of the columns 0, 1, 8, 9 has been repeated four times.

Of the remaining faces, we enter in the second place of each rod the columns headed by 2, 3, 4 and the columns headed by the complements 7, 6, 5 on the fourth place. Hence, we used up seven rods and we entered the columns 0, 1, 8, 9, . . . four times each and the columns 2, 3, 4, 5, 6 twice. We still have three rods (the eighth, ninth, and tenth). On the first face of the eighth and ninth, we enter the column headed by 2, and on the third face of each the column headed by 7, its complement. The remaining two second faces we give to 3 and 4, and the opposite faces to their complements 6 and 5.

If an inventory be taken now, we still find that each of the columns 0, 1, 2, 7, 8, 9, has occurred just four times, while each of the columns 3, 4, 5, 6, only three times, and we still have one unused rod.

Hence, we enter on this the columns 3, 4, 5, 6 in the way indicated. So that now each column is found to have occurred just four times.

The translation of Napier's rule for multiplying numbers by the use of rods (pp. 16–17) follows.

Set up one of the numbers given for multiplication (preferably the larger) by means of the rods. Write the other on paper with a line under it. Then under each written figure put that multiple found in the rods of which the figure is so to speak an index. It makes no difference whether the first figures on the right side of each multiple follow each other obliquely in the same order as the numbers signifying their indexes, or as the first figures to the left. The multiples thus arranged are to be added arithmetically and this will give the product of the multiplication.

Thus let it be required to multiply the year of the Lord 1615 by 365.

The first number is to be formed by the rods, the second written on paper as here shown. The triple, sextuple, and quintuple of the tabulated numbers are taken, corresponding to the figures in the numbers on paper (3, 6, 5) which are the indices.

365	365
4845	8075
9690	9690
8075	4845
589475	589475

Thus the triple of the number 1615 which is to be transcribed from the rods is 4845. The sextuple which is 9690 and the quintuple 8075 are written obliquely under their indices 3, 6, 5, either beginning under them as in the first scheme, or terminating under them as in the second... The multiples arranged in this way are to be added arithmetically, and the desired number 589,475 will thus be obtained, which is the product of the multiplication.

GALILEO GALILEI

On the Proportional or Sector Compasses

(Translated from the Italian by Professor David Eugene Smith, Teachers College, Columbia University, New York City.)

Galileo Galilei (1564–1642), the greatest physicist, astronomer, and mathematician of Italy in his time, and one of the greatest in the world, was interested not only in the higher branches of his chosen subjects but also in the improvement of methods of computation and of measuring. Before the slide rule was invented (see p. 156) or logarithms were known (see p. 149), he devised the simple but ingenious proportional compasses, or, as he called them, the geometric and military compasses (*compasso*). They were first described in *Le Operazioni del Compasso Geometrico et Militare* (Padua, 1606). The following extract from this work will suffice to make the general purpose of the instrument known.

The Operations of the Geometric and Military Compasses.[1]
On Arithmetic Lines. Division of the Line. First Operation

Coming to the special explanation of the methods of using the new geometric and military compasses (Fig. 1), we will first consider the side in which are shown four pairs of lines, with their divisions and numbers. Of these we shall first speak of the innermost ones. These are called the arithmetic lines because their divisions are in arithmetic proportion; that is, they proceed by equal increments up to 250. We shall find several ways of using these lines. First, we shall by their help show how to divide a proposed straight line into as many equal parts as we wish, using any one of several methods mentioned below. When the proposed line is of medium length, not exceeding the spread of the instrument, we open an ordinary pair of compasses[2] the full length of the line and transfer this length to any number on these arithmetic lines, taking care that there is a smaller number that is contained in this one as often as the part of the proposed line is contained in the whole...[For example], to divide the line into five equal parts, let us take two numbers, one being five times the

---

[1] The Italian usage is *compasso*, the singular form.

[2] He speaks of the "geometric and military compasses" as "the instrument," and of ordinary compasses used in transferring lengths as "compasses."

other,—say 100 and 20. Now open the instrument so that the given line as transferred by the compasses shall reach from 100

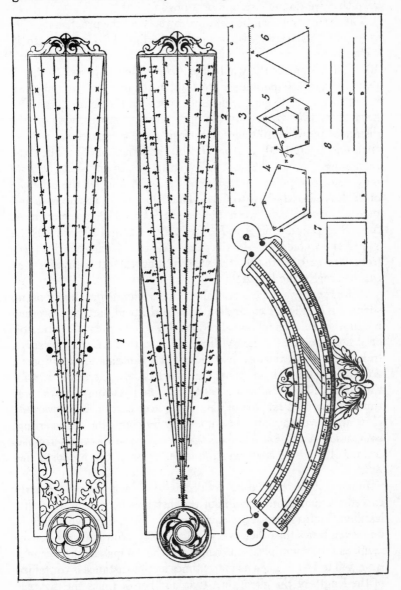

[on one leg] to 100 [on the other]. Now, without moving the instrument, let us take the distance between the points marked 20 and 20, and this will manifestly be the fifth part of the proposed line. In the same way we can find every other division, taking care that we do not use numbers beyond 250...

The same result will be obtained by solving the problem another way, like this: If we wish to divide the line *AB* (Fig. 2) into 11 parts, take a number that is eleven times another,—say 110 and 10. Then transfer the whole line *AB* by the compasses so that it reaches from 110 [on one leg] to 110 [on the other]. It is impossible in this figure to get the distances between the points 10 and 10, because each is covered by the nut. Instead of this, we take the distances between 100 and 100, closing the compasses a little so that one point [100] lies on *B* and the other on *C*. Then the remaining distance *AC* will be $\frac{1}{11}$ of *AB*. In the same way we may place one point of the compasses on *A* and let the other lie on *E*, leaving *EB* equal to *CA*. Then close up the compasses and take the distance between the points 90 and 90, transferring it from *B* to *D* and from *A* to *F*, after which *CD* and *EF* will each be $\frac{1}{11}$ of the whole line. In the same way, transferring the distances from 80 to 80, 70 to 70, etc., we shall find the other divisions, as can be seen in the line *AB*.

If, however, we have a very short line to divide into many parts, such as *AB* (Fig. 3) to be divided into thirteen parts, we proceed by another rule, as follows: Produce *AB* to any point *C*, laying off on it as many lines as you wish, say six, so that *AC* shall be seven times *AB*. It is then evident that if *AB* contains 13 equal parts, *AC* will contain 91 [of the same length]. We therefore transfer the distance between 90 and 90 to the line *CA* from *C* toward *A*, thus leaving the 91st part of *CA*, or the 13th part of *AB*, toward A. If we wish, we may now close up, point by point, the [transferring] compasses at 89, 88, 87, etc., transferring the distances from *C* toward *A*, and we shall find the other parts of the proposed line *AB*.

Finally, if the line to be divided is very long, so as to greatly exceed the maximum opening of the instrument, we can nevertheless divide it, say into seven equal parts. First, take two numbers, one seven times the other,—say 140 and 20. Now open the instrument as far as you please, taking with the compasses the distance from 140 to 140. Then as many times as this distance is contained in the length of the given line, that number of times the distance from 20 to 20 will be the seventh part of it...

Galileus Galileus   Florentinus

28

Superior.   licentia

16   24

Eques Octauius Leonis   Roman' pictor fecit

(Facing page 188.)

How from a Proposed Line we can take any stated Parts.

Second Operation

This operation is much more useful and necessary [than the first], since without our instrument it would be very difficult, while with it the solution is found at once. Suppose, for example, we are required to take from the 197 parts of a given line 113 parts. We open the instrument until the given line can be transferred by the compasses so that it reaches from 197 [on one leg] to 197 [on the other]. Without moving it, the distance from 113 to 113 will then be $113/_{197}$ of the given line...

How the Same Lines furnish two or even an infinite number of Scales for increasing or decreasing the Scale of a Drawing.

Third Operation

If we wish to reduce a drawing to another scale, it is evidently necessary to use two scales, one for the given drawing and the other for the new one. Such scales are at once given by the instrument. One will be the line as already divided into equal parts, and will be used in measuring the given figure. The other will be used for the new drawing, and this has to be adjustable; that is, it must be constructed so that we can lengthen or shorten it according as the new drawing is to be larger or smaller. Such an adjustable scale is the one that we get from the same lines by adjusting the instrument. That you may understand more clearly the process, consider this example:

Suppose that we have the figure *ABCDE* (Fig. 4) and wish to draw a similar figure with side *FG* corresponding to side *AB*. We must evidently use two scales, one to measure the lines of *ABCDE* and the other to measure those of the new drawing, these being longer or shorter than the former according to the ratio which *FG* has to *AB*. Take therefore the length of *AB* with a pair of compasses and then place one of the points at the vertex of the instrument, noting where the other falls on one of the lines,—say at 60. Then transfer *FG* with the compasses so that one point rests on this 60 and the other on the corresponding 60 [on the other arm of the instrument]. If the instrument be now allowed to remain fixed, all the lines in the given figure can be measured on the straight scale, and the corresponding lines of the new figure can be measured transversely. For example, if we wish the length of *CH* corresponding to the given *BC*, we simply lay off *BC* from the vertex,—say to 66,—and then turn the other [leg of the measuring compasses] until the point rests on the 66 [of the other arm of the instrument]. This will then have to *BC* the same ratio as *FG* to *AB*.

If you wish to greatly enlarge a figure, you will need to use two scales in the opposite way [from that shown above]; that is, you will have to use the straight scale [on the arm] for the required drawing and the transverse measurement [from one arm to the other] for the given one. For example, suppose that we have the figure *ABCDEF* (Fig. 5) which we wish to enlarge so that *GH* corresponds to *AB*. We measure *GH*, supposing it to be, say, 60 points on one of the arms. We then open the instrument so that the distance from 60 to 60 is *AB*. Leaving the instrument fixed, we then find *HI* corresponding to *BC* by seeing what two corresponding points, say 46 and 46, determine the ends of *BC*. Then the length from the vertex to 46 will be *HI*[1]. . .

The Rule of Three. Solved by Means of the Compasses and the same Arithmetic Lines. Operation IV

The lines [of the proportional compasses] serve not so much for solving geometric linear problems as for certain arithmetic rules, among which we place one corresponding to one of Euclid's problem, thus: Given three numbers, find their fourth proportional. This is merely the Golden Rule, which experts call the Rule of Three,—to find the fourth number proportional to three that are proposed. To illustrate by examples for the purpose of a clearer understanding,—if 80 gives us 120, what will 100 give? We now have three numbers in this order: 80, 120, 100, and to find the fourth number sought [we proceed as follows:] Find on one arm 120; connect this with 80 on the other arm; find 100 [on the same arm as 80] and draw a parallel to the connecting line[2] and what you find will be 150, the fourth number sought. Observe also that the same thing would result if instead of taking the second number [120] you had taken the third [100], and instead of the third you had taken the second [120][3]. . .

---

[1] [Galileo then proceeds to show how the vertices are found, but this is obvious.]

[2] [In the original:. . .prendi sopra lo strumento rettamente il secondo numero de' proposti, cioè 120, ed applicato trasversalmente al primo, cioè all' 80; dipoi prendi trasversalmente il terzo numero, cioè 100, e mesuralo rettamente sopra la scala, equello che troverai, cioè 150, sarà il quarto numero cercato.]

[3] [Galileo then proceeds to discuss the question when the numbers are such as to require other adjustments, as in the "First Operation" already explained.]

Inverse Rule of Three, solved by means of the Same Lines.
Operation V

In the same way we can solve problems involving the inverse Rule of Three, as in this example: If there is food sufficient for 100 soldiers for 60 days, how many would it feed for 75 days. The numbers may be arranged as 60, 100, 75. Find 60 on one arm of the instrument. Connect it with the third number, 75, on the other arm. Without moving it, take 100 on the same arm as 60 and draw a parallel to the connecting line and what you find will be 80, the number sought...

Rule of Exchange. Operation VI

By means of these same arithmetic lines we can change money by finding the equal values. This is done very easily and quickly as follows: Adjust the instrument by finding on one of the lines the value of the piece of money to be exchanged. Connect it with the value of the other piece which we wish to exchange; but in order that you may understand the matter more clearly, we shall illustrate it by an example. Suppose that we wish to exchange gold scudi into Venetian ducats, and that the value of the gold scudo is 8 lire and the value of the Venetian ducat is 6 lire 4 soldi. Since the ducat is not precicely measured by the lire, there being 4 soldi to be considered, it is best to reduce both to soldi, the value of the scudo being 160 soldi and that of the ducat 124 [soldi]. To adjust the instrument for translating scudi into ducats lay off the value of the scudo, or 160, and then open the instrument and connect the 160 to 124, the value of the ducat. Now leave the instrument unchanged. Then any proposed number of scudi can be changed into ducats by laying off the number of scudi on the arm [of ducats] and drawing a parallel to the line already drawn from 160 to 124. For example. 186 scudi will then be found equal to 240 ducats.[1]

---

[1] [This section closes with the *Rule of Compound Interest,...Operation VII.* The next section discusses geometric lines; the third, stereometric lines, including cube root; the fourth, "metallic lines," finding the size of bodies with respect to weight; and the rest dealing with mensuration, closing with an extended discussion of operations with the quadrant.]

D'OCAGNE

On Nomography

(Translated from the French by Nevin C. Fisk, M.S., University of Michigan,
Ann Arbor, Michigan.)

Philbert Maurice d'Ocagne was born in Paris, March 25, 1862. His education was received at the Collège Chaptal, the Lycée Fontanges, and the Ecole
Polytechnique.

For many years he has been professor of geometry at the Ecole Polytechnique and professor of topometry and applied geometry at the Ecole des Ponts
et Chaussées. He is a member of the Académie des Sciences and an officer of
the Légion d'Honneur.

D'Ocagne has published numerous books and articles on nomography,
graphical and mechanical calculus, and geometry. The selections following
are taken from his *Traité de Nomographie*, published by Gauthier-Villars,
Paris, in 1899. A second edition of this book appeared in 1921.

D'Ocagone's *Traité de Nomographie* presents a collection and correlation
of important developments in graphical proceedure during the latter part of
the nineteenth century. Outstanding among these developments is the alignment chart, the principle of which is due to d'Ocagne himself. D'Ocagne may
also be credited with the application of the alignment chart to many engineering formulas.

The subject of nomography received much of its impetus from the problems
arising in connection with the construction of railroads in France. Most of the
men contributing to its growth during the nineteenth century were engineers.
Nomography has thus been essentially a branch of applied mathematics finding
use in engineering, military science, and industry. At present it is one of the
most useful mathematical tools of the technical man.

The[1] purpose of Nomography is to reduce to simple readings on
graphical charts, constructed once for all, the computations which
necessarily intervene in the practice of various technical arts.
If one makes a system of geometric elements (points or lines)
correspond to each of the variable connected by a certain equation,
the elements of each system being numbered[2] in terms of the values
of the corresponding variable, and if the relationship between the
variables established by the equation may be translated geometri-

---

[1] [Introduction, page v. Pages given in the footnotes refer to the *Traité
de Nomographie*.]

[2] [French; *côtés*.]

192

cally into terms of a certain relation of position easy to set up between the corresponding geometric elements, then the set of elements constitutes a chart[1] of the equation considered. This is the theory of charts, that is to say the graphical representation of mathematical laws defined by equations in any number of variables, which is understood today under the name of Nomography.

1. *Normal Scale of a Function.*[2]—Let $f(\alpha)$ be a function of the variable α, taken in an interval where it is uniform, that is, where it has for each value of α only a single determinate value. Let us lay off on an axis Ox, starting from the origin O, the lengths

$$x_1 = lf(\alpha_1), \quad x_2 = lf(\alpha_2), \quad x_3 = lf(\alpha_3), \ldots$$

l being an arbitrarily chosen length, and let us inscribe beside the

points which limit these segments, points which are marked by a fine stroke perpendicular to the axis, the corresponding values of the variables α_1, α_2, α_3, ... The set of points thus obtained constitutes the scale of the function $f(\alpha)$. The length l is called the modulus of this scale.

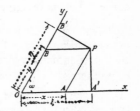

· · · · · · · · · ·

3. *Geometrical Construction of a Scale.*[3]—In order to construct the scale of the function $f(\alpha)$, we may have recourse to the curve C whose equation is

$$x = lf(y)$$

It is sufficient to take on the curve the point whose ordinate is α in order that the extremity of its abcissa may give on Ox the point numbered α for the desired scale. If the curve C may be obtained point by point by means of a simple geometric construction, all calculations can be dispensed with.

· · · · · · · · · ·

II. CHARTS OF EQUATIONS WITH TWO VARIABLES.

9. *Charts with adjacent[4] scales.*[5] Let us first take the equation to be represented under the form

$$\alpha_2 = f_1(\alpha_1),$$

---

[1] [French; *abaque.*]
[2] [Page 1 et seq.]
[3] [Page 7.]
[4] [French; *accolées.*]
[5] [Page 17.]

a form frequently occurring in practice. Let suppose the scales

$$x = l\alpha_2 \text{ and } x = lf_1(\alpha_1)$$

to be constructed on the same axis, starting from the same origin.
Then two values of α_1 and α_2, corresponding by virtue of the
preceding equation, are inscribed at the same point of the axis
bearing the two scales. If a value of one of the variables, say α_1
is given, the corresponding value of α_2 is read from the second scale
at the point graduated α_1 on the first.

. . . .

12. *Cartesian Charts for Two Variables.*[1]—We may apply a
uniform scale to each of the two variables by establishing the
linkage between corresponding points through the medium of a
curve. Let us imagine that the scales

$$x = l_1\alpha_1 \text{ and } y = l_2\alpha_2$$

are carried on two rectangular axes Ox and Oy, and let us suppose
that perpendiculars are erected at the points of division marked
on each axis. If the values α_1 and α_2 together satisfy the equation

(1) $F(\alpha_1, \alpha_2) = 0$

the perpendiculars to the axes at the points graduated α_1 and α_2
intersect at a certain point. The points corresponding to various
couples of values of α_1 and α_2 satisfying the equation (1) are
distributed along a curve C whose equation referred to the axes
Ox and Oy is

$$F\left(\frac{x}{l_1}, \frac{y}{l_2}\right) = 0$$

The various points of the curve C determined individually are
easily marked on the plane, thanks to the cross-section[2] system
defined above, and one observes that the curve C obtained by
connecting all these points constitutes a chart of the equation (1).
Such a chart derived by the use of cartesian coordinates is called
cartesian.

In order to find one of the variables, say α_2, when α_1 is given, it
is sufficient to note the point (P) where the curve C is met by the
perpendicular to Ox passing through the point on that axis
numbered α_1, and to read the graduation α_2 at the foot of the
perpendicular dropped from the point (P) upon the axis Oy.

. . . .

---

[1] [Page 24 et seq.]
[2] [French; *quadrillage*.]

16. *Cartesian Charts for Three Variables.*[1]—Suppose it be desired
to construct a chart for the equation

(1) $$F(\alpha_1, \alpha_2, \alpha_3) = 0$$

The first plan to present itself is this. Let us give a determined
value to one of the variables, preferably that one which will
usually be calculated as a function of the other two, say α_3. We
shall then have an equation in the two variables α_1 and α_2 which
we may represent as indicated in section 12 by mean of a curve
traced on the cross-section network[2] defined by the equations

(α_1) $\qquad\qquad\qquad x = l_1\alpha_1$

(α_2) $\qquad\qquad\qquad y = l_2\alpha_2$

l_1 and l_2 being moduli chosen to give the most satisfactory chart.
The equation of this curve will be

(α_3) $$F\left(\frac{x}{l_1}, \frac{y}{l_2}, \alpha_3\right) = 0$$

This curve along which the element α_3 conserves a constant value
has been called by Lalanne a curve "d'égal élément," and by the
German author Vogler an isopleth curve. The latter term has
since been adopted by Lalanne. We shall call it simply a
numbered curve.[3] In the same manner as above let us construct
curves corresponding to a series of values of α_3 increasing by regular
steps, taking care to label each curve with the corresponding value
of α_3. Let us remark further that it is necessary only to trace
the portion of each curve contained within a rectangle bounded
by the perpendiculars erected to Ox and Oy respectively at the
points corresponding to the limiting values a_1 and b_1 for α_1, and
a_2 and b_2 for α_2, values which are given in the problem since we
have assumed that α_1 and α_2 are the independent variables. We
thus obtain within a ruled[4] rectangle a system of numbered curves
which furnishes the representation desired within the limits
admitted for the independent variables. This ruled rectangle,
resembling a sort of checkerboard, has given the name "abaque"
to diagrams of this kind, and, by extension, to every sort of
numbered chart. Making the convention once for all of designating by the terms horizontal and vertical the lines parallel to Ox
and Oy respectively, we may state that the method of using such a

---

[1] [Page 32 et seq.]
[2] [French; *quadrillage.*]
[3] [French; *courbe cotée.*]
[4] [French; *quadrillé.*]

chart in order to obtain the value of α_3 when α_1 and α_2 are given is to read the graduation α_3 of the curve passing through the point of intersection of the vertical numbered α_1 with the horizontal numbered α_2.

. . . .

24. *Principle.*[1]—We have seen in section 15 that in substituting other functional scales for uniform scales which at first sight one would be inclined to use along the axes Ox and Oy, we may always transform into a straight line the curve representative of an equation linking the variables to which the two scales correspond.   In what case may such a modification applied to the scales Ox and Oy of a cartesian chart for three variables transform simultaneously all the curves of the chart into straight lines?   The answer to this question is easy to obtain.   In order that the curves (α_3) constitute a straight line diagram with graduations

(α_1) $\qquad\qquad\qquad\quad x = l_1 f_1(\alpha_1)$
(α_2) $\qquad\qquad\qquad\quad y = l_2 f_2(\alpha_2)$

it is necessary and sufficient that their equation be of the form

(α_3) $\qquad\qquad \dfrac{x}{l_1} f_3(\alpha_3) + \dfrac{y}{l_2}\varphi_3(\alpha_3) + \psi_3(\alpha_3) = 0$

This will be the case if the proposed equation is of the form

$$f_1(\alpha_1)f_3(\alpha_3) + f_2(\alpha_2)\varphi_3(\alpha_3) + \psi_3(\alpha_3) = 0$$

We thus obtain at the same time the form of the equations to which this artifice is applicable, and an indication of the way in which it may be put into play.

In the case in which a single curve constitutes the chart for an equation in two variables as in section 15, such a transformation offers no appreciable advantage, the work required for the establishment of a functional scale being practically equivalent to that required for the determination of points for the corresponding curve; the sole difference is in the tracing of the curve joining the points individually obtained.   This is not the case here and the advantage becomes appreciable.   If the labor demanded by the change in graduation is equivalent to that involved in the construction of a curve, one sees that when there are n curves to be drawn the economy achieved may be represented approximately by the work required to draw $n - 1$ curves.   In fact, once the new scale system is established, it is necessary to locate only two

---

[1] [Page 50 et seq.]

points to determine each of the straight lines intended to replace the curves which had to be constructed point by point in the primitive system, straight lines which have the further advantage of being easy to draw with accuracy.

The principle of such a transformation was indicated for the first time by Léon Lalanne who gave it the name "geometrical anamorphosis."[1] It was under the form indicated in section 28[2] that the idea first occurred to him in connection with applications treated in sections 29[3] and 108.[4]

. . . .

56. *Principle of Aligned Points.*[5]—We have already explained in section 30 the reasons for which it is desirable whenever possible to have only points appear as numbered elements in the representation of an equation. We have seen furthermore how the use of a "transparent"[6] with three indices allows the realization of this end for equations representable by three systems of parallel straight lines, (section 26) that is to say, equations of the form[7]

$$f_1 + f_2 = f_3$$

We shall now expound another method which allows the attainment of the same end for the much more general category of equations representable by three systems of any straight lines whatsoever, comprising as a consequence the foregoing as a particular case; that is to say, those equations which are of the form

$$\begin{vmatrix} f_1 & \varphi_1 & \psi_1 \\ f_2 & \varphi_2 & \psi_2 \\ f_3 & \varphi_3 & \psi_3 \end{vmatrix} = 0$$

The idea which allows us a priori to take account of the possibility of such a result is blended with that of the principle of duality

---

[1] "Mémoire sur les tables graphiques et sur la Géométrie anamorphique," *Annales des Ponts et Chausées ponts chaussées, -erer semestre,* 1846.

[2] [Section 28 of the present work treats of logarithmic anamorphosis. It appears that Lalanne is to be credited with the invention of logarithmic paper.]

[3] [Section 29 of the *Traité* presents a straight-line chart on logarithmic paper for the multiplication of two variables.]

[4] [Section 108 treats of superposed charts with logarithmic graduations.]

[5] [Page 123 *et seq.* This principle was first announced by d'Ocagne in the *Annales des Ponts et Chausées* for November, 1884, p. 531, under the title "Procédé nouveau de calcul graphique."]

[6] [A sheet of celluloid or similar transparent material on which straight lines are engraved. In the case referred to, three intersecting lines were used.]

[7] [The author has made the convention of writing f_1 for $f(\alpha_1)$, f_2 for $f(\alpha_2)$, etc.]

which is fundamental in the field of pure geometry today. We know that it is possible in an infinity of ways to construct a figure composed of points corresponding to a given figure composed of straight lines, so that to any three concurrent lines of the given figure there correspond three collinear points on the other. Every transformation possessing such a property, of which the typical case is transformation by polar reciprocals, is said to be dualistic.

Suppose then that we have applied such a transformation to a chart made up of three systems of straight lines, retaining, let it be well understood, the graduation of each element in the passage

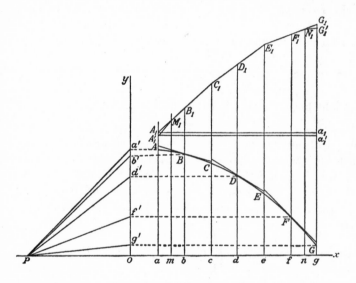

from one figure to the other. We thus obtain a new diagram on which to each of the variables α_1, α_2, and α_3 there corresponds a system of numbered points distributed along a curve called their support. In the transformation effected, this curve will be the correlative of the envelope of the corresponding system of straight lines on the first chart. These three systems of numbered points constitute curvilinear scales. Just as on the first chart the three straight lines, numbered in terms of a system of values of α_1, α_2, α_3 satisfying the equation represented, are concurrent, so here the three corresponding points are collinear. The method of using the chart follows from this fact. The straight line joining the points numbered α_1 and α_2 on the first two curvilinear scales intersects the third scale at the point graduated α_3.

To avoid drawing this line, one may make use of a transparent with one index line or a fine thread which is stretched between the points α_1 and α_2.

. . . .

88. *General Principle.*[1]—Suppose that the variables α, α_1 and α_2 on the one side and α, α_3 and α_4 on the other are linked by equations such as

$$(E) \qquad \begin{vmatrix} f(\alpha) & \varphi(\alpha) & \psi(\alpha) \\ f_1(\alpha_1) & \varphi_1(\alpha_1) & \psi_1(\alpha_1) \\ f_2(\alpha_2) & \varphi_2(\alpha_2) & \psi_2(\alpha_2) \end{vmatrix} = 0$$

$$(E') \qquad \begin{vmatrix} f(\alpha) & \varphi(\alpha) & \psi(\alpha) \\ f_3(\alpha_3) & \varphi_3(\alpha_3) & \psi_3(\alpha_3) \\ f_4(\alpha_4) & \varphi_4(\alpha_4) & \psi_4(\alpha_4) \end{vmatrix} = 0$$

Each of these will be representable by an alignment chart, and since the functions f, φ, ψ are the same in the two equations, we observe that their curvilinear scale (α) will be the same in the two

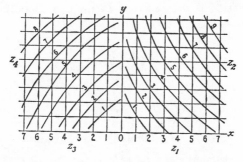

charts. Consequently the two charts can be constructed with this scale in common. If values are given for three of the four variables α_1, α_2, α_3, α_4, the equations (E) and (E') allow the calculation of the fourth as well as the value of α. On the chart the straight line passing through the points numbered α_1 and α_2 and the straight line passing through the points numbered α_3 and α_4 intersect in a point numbered α.

Now it may happen that an equation in four variables α_1, α_2, α_3, α_4 results from the elimination of an auxiliary variable α between two equations such as (E) and (E'). In this case the chart which has just been constructed furnishes a representation of the equation considered. The method of proceedure to obtain say α_4 when α_1, α_2 and α_3 are known is reduced to the following.

---

[1] [Page 213, *et seq.*]

Make the index pass through the points numbered α_1 and α_2, then pivot the index bout the point where it intersects the scale (α) until it passes through the point numbered α_3. It then cuts the last scale in the point numbered α_4. Since in general it is not necessary to know the corresponding value of the auxiliary variable α, we may dispense with graduating the scale of this variable; it is sufficient to draw its support which will be called the pivot line. If however it is desired in any case to note the position of the pivot, the line may be graduated in any manner whatsoever. The chart thus constructed by combining two alignment charts having a scale in common is called a double alignment chart in order to recall the way in which it is used.[1]

. . . .

In practice it is rarely necessary to apply this method except in the case in which the auxiliary scale is uniform, that is to say, when the function $f(\alpha)$ reduces to α, the function φ reduces to 1, and the function ψ reduces to 0 in the equations (E) and (E'). These equations may then be written

$$\begin{vmatrix} \alpha & 1 & 0 \\ f_1 & \varphi_1 & \psi_1 \\ f_2 & \varphi_2 & \psi_2 \end{vmatrix} = 0$$

$$\begin{vmatrix} \alpha & 1 & 0 \\ f_3 & \varphi_3 & \psi_3 \\ f_4 & \varphi_4 & \psi_4 \end{vmatrix} = 0$$

The elimination of α immediately carried out gives

$$(2) \qquad \begin{vmatrix} \psi_1 & f_1 \\ \psi_2 & f_2 \end{vmatrix} \cdot \begin{vmatrix} \varphi_3 & \psi_3 \\ \varphi_4 & \psi_4 \end{vmatrix} = \begin{vmatrix} \psi_3 & f_3 \\ \psi_4 & f_4 \end{vmatrix} \cdot \begin{vmatrix} \varphi_1 & \psi_1 \\ \varphi_2 & \psi_2 \end{vmatrix}.$$

---

[1] [The portion of Sec. 88 omitted at this point deals with a generalization of the principle under discussion.]

II. FIELD OF ALGEBRA

CARDAN'S TREATMENT OF IMAGINARY ROOTS

(Translated from the Latin by Professor Vera Sanford, Western Reserve University, Cleveland, Ohio.)

For a biographical note on Cardan see page 203. Although Cardan (1501–1576) spoke of the complex roots of a certain equation as "impossible," he seems to have been the first to use such numbers in computation, and he even devoted a full page of his *Ars Magna* (1545) to showing the solution of the problem in which this question occurred. The translation which follows was made from the first edition of the *Ars Magna*, ff. 65v. and 66r.

A second type of false position[1] makes use of roots of negative numbers.[2] I will give as an example: If some one says to you, divide 10 into two parts, one of which multiplied into the other shall produce 30 or 40, it is evident that this case or question is impossible. Nevertheless, we shall solve it in this fashion. Let us divide 10 into equal parts and 5 will be its half. Multiplied by itself, this yields 25. From 25 subtract the product itself, that is 40, which, as I taught you in the chapter on operations in the sixth book[3] leaves a remainder m: 15. The root[4] of this added and then subtracted from 5 gives the parts which multiplied together will produce 40. These, therefore, are 5 p: ℞ m: 15 and 5 m: ℞m: 15.[5]

Proof

That the true significance of this rule may be made clear, let the line *AB* which is called 10, be the line which is to be divided

---

[1] [The preceding section of this chapter discusses the solution of equations of the type $x^2 = 4x + 32$, which Cardan wrote in the form

$$\text{qdratū aeq̄tur 4 rebus p: 32.]}$$

[2] ["... est per radicem m."]

[3] [The *Ars Magna* begins with Book X, the preceding nine being Cardan's arithmetic, the *Practica arithmetice*, Milan, 1539.]

[4] [For "root," Cardan uses the symbol ℞.]

[5] [Although the symbols + and − appeared in print in Widman's arithmetic of 1489, the signs were not generally adopted for some time, and the use of the letters p and m continued in Italy until the beginning of the seventeenth century.

It should be noted that Cardan made use of the letter ℞ to represent both an unknown quantity (*res*) and a root (*radix*).]

into two parts whose rectangle is to be 40. Now since 40 is the quadruple of 10, we wish four times the whole of *AB*. Therefore, make *AD* the square on *AC*, the half of *AB*. From *AD* subtract four times *AB*. If there is a remainder, its root should be added to and subtracted from *AC* thus showing the parts (into which *AB* was to be divided). Even when such a residue is minus, you will nevertheless imagine ℞ m:15 to be the difference between

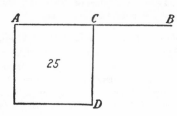

AD and the quadruple of *AB* which you should add and subtract from *AC* to find what was sought. That is 5 p: ℞v:25 m:40[1] and 5 m:℞v:25 m:40 or 5 p: ℞ − 15 and 5 m:℞ − 15. Multiplying 5 p:℞m:15 by 5 m:℞m:15, the imaginary parts being lost,[2] gives 25 m:m:15 which is p. 15. Therefore the product is 40. However, the nature of *AD* is not the same as that of 40 or *AB*

5 p:℞m:15
5 m:℞m:15
|25 m:m:15 qd. est 40

because a surface is far from a number or a line. This, however, is closest to this quantity which is truly imaginary[3] since operations may not be performed with it as with a pure negative number, nor as in other numbers. Nor can we find it by adding the square of half the number in producing the number and take away from the root of the sum and add half of the dividend. For example, in the case of dividing 10 into two parts whose product is 40, you add 25, the square of one half of 10, to 40 making 65. From the root of this subtract 5 and then add 5 and according to similar reasoning you will have ℞ 65 p:5 and ℞ 65 m:5. But these numbers differ by 10, and do not make 10 jointly. This subtility results from arithmetic of which this final point is as I have said as subtile as it is useless.

---

[1] [The v acts as a sign of aggregation and might be considered an abbreviation for the *radix universalis*, or *vniversalis*.]

[2] ["...dimissis incruciationibus."]

[3] [...uere est sophistica.]

CARDAN

Solution of the Cubic Equation

(Translated from the Latin by Professor R. B. McClenon, Grinnell College, Grinnell, Iowa.)

In his *Ars Magna* (Nürnberg, 1545) Girolamo Cardano (Hieronymus Cardanus, 1501–1576) states that Scipio del Ferro discovered the method of solving an equation of the type $x^3 + px = q$ about the year 1515. Nicolo Tartaglia (in the Latin texts, Tartalea) agrees to this but claims for himself the method of solving the type $x^3 + px^2 = q$ and also the independent discovery already made by Scipio del Ferro. Cardan secured the solution from Tartaglia and published it in his work above mentioned. The merits of the discoveries and the ethics involved in the publication may be found discussed in any of the histories of mathematics.

The selection here made is from Chapter XI of the *Ars Magna*, "De cubo & rebus æqualibus numero," the first edition, the type considered being $x^3 + px = q$, the particular equation being cub⁸ *p*; 6 reb⁸ æq̄lis 20; that is, $x^3 + 6x = 20$. The edition of 1570 differs considerably in the text. A facsimile of the two pages is given in Smith's *History of Mathematics*, vol. II, pp. 462, 463.

The translation can be more easily followed by considering the general plan as set forth in modern symbols.

Given

$$x^3 + 6x = 20.$$

Let

$$u^3 - v^3 = 20 \text{ and } u^3v^3 = (\tfrac{1}{3} \times 6)^3 = 8.$$

Then

$$(u - v)^3 + 6(u - v) = u^3 - v^3,$$

for

$$u^3 - 3u^2v + 3uv^2 - v^3 + 6u - 6v = u^3 - v^3,$$

whence

$$3uv(v - u) = 6(v - u)$$

and

$$uv = 2.$$

Hence

$$x = u - v.$$

But

$$u^3 = 20 + v^3 = 20 + \frac{8}{u^3},$$

whence

$$u^6 = 20u^3 + 8,$$

which is a quadratic in u^3. Hence u^3 can be found, and therefore v^3, and therefore $u - v$.

Concerning a Cube and "Things"[1] Equal to a Number

Chapter XI

Scipio del Ferro of Bologna about thirty years ago invented [the method set forth in] this chapter, [and] communicated it to Antonio Maria Florido of Venice, who when he once engaged in a contest with Nicolo Tartalea of Brescia announced that Nicolo also invented it; and he [Nicolo] communicated it to us when we asked for it, but suppressed the demonstration. With this aid we sought the demonstration, and found it, though with great difficulty, in the manner which we set out in the following.

Demonstration

For example, let the cube of *GH* and six times the side *GH* be equal[2] to 20. I take two cubes *AE* and *CL* whose difference shall

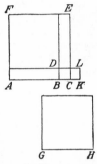

be 20, so that the product of the side *AC* by the side *CK* shall be 2,—*i.e.*, a third of the number of "things;"[3] and I lay off *CB* equal to *CK*, then I say that if it is done thus, the remaining line *AB* is equal to *GH* and therefore to the value of the "thing," for it was supposed of *GH* that it was so [*i. e.*, equal to *x*], therefore I complete, after the manner of the first theorem of the 6th chapter of this book, the solids *DA, DC, DE, DF,* so that we understand by *DC* the cube of *BC,* by *DF* the cube of *AB,* by *DA* three times *CB* times the square of *AB,* by *DE* three times *AB*[4] times the square of *BC.* Since therefore from *AC* times *CK* the result is 2, from 3 times *AC* times *CK* will result 6, the number of "things;" and

---

[1] [We shall render by "thing" Cardan's *res* or *positio,* the two words he employs to designate the unknown quantity in an equation.]

[2] [This is, $x^3 + 6x = 20$.]

[3] [Here $AC = u$, $CK = v$, $uv = 2 = \frac{1}{3}$ of the coefficient of x.]

[4] [In modern form, we have $DC = v^3$, $DF = (u - v)^3 = x^3$, $DA = 3(u - v)^2v$, and $DE = 3(u - v)v^2$.]

Cardan

(Facing page 204.)

therefore from AB times 3 AC times CK there results 6 "things" AB, or 6 times AB, so that 3 times the product of AB, BC, and AC is 6 times AB. But the difference of the cube AC from the cube CK, and likewise from the cube BC, equal to it by hypothesis, is 20;[1] and from the first theorem of the 6th chapter, this is the sum of the solids DA, DE, and DF, so that these three solids make 20.[2] But taking BC *minus*, the cube of AB is equal to the cube of AC and 3 times AC into the square of CB and minus the cube of BC and minus 3 times BC into the square of AC.[3] By the demonstration, the difference between 3 times CB times the square of AC, and 3 times AC times the square of BC, is [3 times][4] the product of AB, BC, and AC.[5] Therefore since this, as has been shown, is equal to 6 times AB, adding 6 times AB to that which results from AC into 3 times the square of BC there results 3 times BC times the square of AC, since BC is minus.[6] Now it has been shown that the product of CB into 3 times the square of AC is minus; and the remainder which is equal to that is plus, hence 3 times CB into the square of AC[7] and 3 times AC into the square of CB and 6 times AB make nothing.[8] Accordingly, by common sense, the difference between the cubes AC and BC is as much as the totality of the cube of AC, and 3 times AC into the square of CB, and 3 times CB into the square of AC (minus), and the cube of BC (minus), and 6 times AB.[9] This therefore is 20, since the difference of the cubes AC and CB was 20.[10] Moreover, by the second theorem of the 6th chapter, putting BC minus, the cube of AB will be equal to the cube of AC and 3 times AC into the square of BC minus the cube of BC and minus 3 times BC into the square of AC.[11] Therefore the cube of AB, with 6 times AB, by common sense, since it is equal to the cube of AC and 3 times AC into the square of CB, and minus 3 times CB into the square of AC,[12] and

---

[1] [That is, $u^3 - v^3 = 20$.]

[2] [That is, $(u - v)^3 + 3(u - v)^2 v + 3(u - v)v^2 = 20$.]

[3] [That is, $(u - v)^3 = u^3 + 3uv^2 - v^3 - 3vu^2$.]

[4] [The original omits "triplum" here.]

[5] [That is, $3vu^2 - 3uv^2 = 3(u - v)uv$.]

[6] [That is, $6(u - v) + 3uv^2 = 3u^2 v$.]

[7] [In the text this is AB.]

[8] [That is $-3vu^2 + 3uv^2 + 6(u - v) = 0$.]

[9] [That is, $u^3 - v^3 = u^3 + 3uv^2 - 3vu^2 - v^3 + 6(u - v) = 20$.]

[10] [That is, $u^3 - v^3 = 20$.]

[11] [That is, $(u - v)^3 = u^3 + 3uv^2 - v^3 - 3vu^2$.]

[12] [The text has AB.]

minus the cube of *CB* and 6 times *AB*, which is now equal to 20, as has been shown, will also be equal to 20.[1] Since therefore the cube of *AB* and 6 times *AB* will equal 20, and the cube of *GH*, together with 6 times *GH*, will equal 20, by common sense and from what has been said in the 35th and 31st of the 11th Book of the *Elements*,[2] *GH* will be equal to *AB*, therefore *GH* is the difference of *AC* and *CB*. But *AC* and *CB*, or *AC* and *CK*, are numbers or lines containing an area equal to a third part of the number of "things" whose cubes differ by the number in the equation, wherefore we have the

RULE

Cube the third part of the number of "things," to which you add the square of half the number of the equation,[3] and take the root of the whole, that is, the square root, which you will use, in the one case adding the half of the number which you just multiplied by itself,[4] in the other case subtracting the same half, and you will have a "binomial" and "apotome" respectively; then subtract the cube root of the apotome from the cube root of the binomial, and the remainder from this is the value of the "thing."[5] In the example, the cube and 6 "things"[6] equals 20; raise 2, the 3rd part of 6, to the cube, that makes 8; multiply 10, half the number, by itself, that makes 100; add 100 and 8, that makes 108; take the root, which is $\sqrt{108}$, and use this, in the first place adding 10, half the number, and in the second place subtracting the same amount, and you will have the binomial $\sqrt{108} + 10$, and the apotome $\sqrt{108} - 10$; take the cube root of these and subtract that of the apotome from that of the binomial, and you will have the value of the "thing," $\sqrt[3]{\sqrt{108} + 10} - \sqrt[3]{\sqrt{108} - 10}$.

---

[1] [That is, $x^3 + 6x = u^3 + 3uv^2 - 3vu^2 - v^3 + 6(u - v) = 20$.]

[2] [Evidently an incorrect reference to Euclid. It does not appear in the edition of 1570.]

[3] [That is, if the equation is $x^3 + px = q$, take $(\frac{1}{3}p)^3 + (\frac{1}{2}q)^2$.]

[4] [That is, adding $\frac{1}{2}q$.]

[5] $\left[\text{That is, } \sqrt[3]{\sqrt{(\frac{1}{3}p)^3 + (\frac{1}{2}q)^2} + \frac{1}{2}q} - \sqrt[3]{\sqrt{(\frac{1}{3}p)^3 + (\frac{1}{2}q)^2} - \frac{1}{2}q}. \right]$

[6] $[x^3 + 6x = 20.]$

FERRARI-CARDAN

Solution of the Biquadratic Equation

(Translated from the Latin by Professor R. B. McClenon, Grinnell College, Grinnell, Iowa, with notes by Professor Jekuthiel Ginsburg, Yeshiva College, New York City.)

Luigi (Ludovico) Ferrari (1522–c. 1560), a man of humble birth, was taken into Cardan's household as a servant at the age of fifteen. He showed such unusual ability that the latter made him his secretary. After three years of service Ferrari left and took up the work of teaching. Such was his success that he became professor of mathematics at Bologna but died in the first year of his service there. Zuanne de Tonini da Coi, a teacher at Brescia had proposed a problem which involved the equation

$$x^4 + 6x^2 + 36 = 60x.$$

Cardan, being unable to solve it, gave it to Ferrari. The latter succeeded in finding a solution and this was published, with due credit, by Cardan in his *Ars Magna* (Nürnberg, 1545). For an outline of the solution in modern symbolism see Smith, *History of Mathematics* (Boston, Mass., 1925), vol. II, p. 468.

Rule II

Another rule...is due to Luigi Ferrari, who invented it at my request. By it we have the solutions of absolutely all types of fourth powers, squares, and numbers; or fourth powers, cubes, squares, and numbers [1]...

Demonstration

Let the square *AF* be divided into two squares *AD* and *DF*, and two supplementary parts *DC* and *DE*; and I wish to add the gnomon *KFG* around this so that the whole *AH* may remain a square. I say that such a gnomon consists of twice the product of *GC*, the added line, by *CA*, with the square of *GC*; for *FG* is con-

---

[1] [Cardan uses "square-square" for fourth power. He now proceeds to state all types of biquadratics, beginning with the equivalents of

$$(1) \quad x^4 = ax^2 + bx + c,$$
$$(2) \quad x^4 = ax^2 + bx^3 + c,$$
$$(3) \quad x^4 = ax^3 + b.$$

His list includes twenty types.
He then considers one of these types, as shown in the translation.]

tained by the lines *GC* and *CF*, from the definition given at the beginning of the 2nd [book] of the *Elements*[1]; and *CF* is equal to *CA*, from the definition of a square; and by the 44th [proposition] of the 1st [book] of the *Elements*,[2] *KF* is equal to *FG*. Therefore the two areas *GF* and *FK* consist of *GC* into twice *CA*. Also the square of *GC* is *FH*, in consequence of the 4th [proposition] of the 2nd [book] of the *Elements*.[3] Therefore the proposition is evident.[4]

If therefore *AD* is made 1 square-square, and *CD* and *DE* [are made] 3 "squares," and *DF* [is made] 9,[5] *BA* will necessarily be a

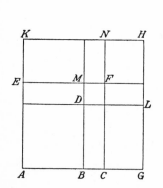 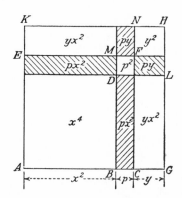

square and *BC* will necessarily be 3. Since we wish to add some "squares"[6] to *DC*[7] and *DE*, let these [additions] be [the

---

[1] [See Heath's *Euclid*, vol. I, p. 370. The general plan of attack will be better understood from the diagram here shown, which should be compared with Cardan's as given in the text. What he and Ferrari meant to do was to geometrize

$$(x^2 + p + y)^2$$

With this diagram before the reader, the proof will be more clearly understood. It shows the components of

$$(x^2 + p + y)^2 = x^4 + p^2 + y^2 + 2x^2p + 2x^2y + 2py$$

[2] [The 43*d* as usually numbered in later Editions.]

[3] [See Heath's *Euclid*, vol. I, p. 380.]

[4] [$(AC + CG)^2 = \overline{AC^2} + 2AC.CG + \overline{CG}.^2$]

[5] [He assumes the side of the square to be itself a square, say x^2. Then the increase *BC* will be 3. Then the area of the square *AD* is x^2, the area of rectangle *DE* will be $3x^2$, that of *DC* will be the same as that of *DE*, or $3x^2$, and that of *DF* will be 9.]

[6] [$AB = x^2$, $BC = 3$, $CG = y$. Each of *CL* and *KM* equals x^2y.]

[7] [Which, as stated above, is $3s^2$, as is also *DE*.]

rectangles] *CL* and *KM*.[1] Then in order to complete the square it will be necessary to add the area *LNM*. This has been shown to consist of the square on *GC*, which is half the number of [added] squares, since *CL* is the area [made] from [the product of] *GC* times *AB*, where *AB* is a square, *AD* having been assumed to be a fourth power.[2] But *FL* and *MN* are each equal to *GC* times *CB*, by Euclid, I, 42, and hence the area *LMN*, which is the number to be added, is a sum composed of the product of *GC* into twice *CB*, that is, into the number of squares which was 6, and *GC* into itself, which is the number of squares to be added. This is our proof.

This having been completed, you will always reduce the part containing the square-square to a root, *viz.*, by adding enough to each side so that the square-square with the square and number may have a root.[3] This is easy when you take half the number of the squares as the root of the number; and you will at the same time make the extreme terms on both sides plus, for otherwise the trinomial or binomial changed to a trinomial will necessarily fail to have a root. Having done this, you will add enough squares and a number to the one side, by the 3rd rule,[4] so that the same being added to the other side (in which the unknowns were) will make a trinomial having a square root by assumption; and you will have a number of squares and a number to be added to each side, after which you will extract the square root of each side, which will be, on the one side, 1 square plus a number (or minus a number)

---

[1] [Such an addition will convert the original figure, *AF* into the following.]

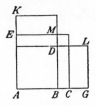

[2] [Cardan uses *quadratum* to mean both the second power of a number and a square figure.]

[3] [Let the equation $x^4 + px^2 + qx + r = 0$ be given. This may be written

$$x^4 + px^2 = -(qx + r).$$

Adding $px^2 + p^2$ to each side,

$$x^4 + 2px^2 + p^2 = p^2 + px^2 - qx - r,$$

or

$$(x^2 + p)^2 = p^2 + px^2 - qx - r.]$$

[4] [Given elsewhere in the *Ars Magna*.]

and on the other side 1 unknown or more, plus a number (or minus a number; or a number minus unknowns) wherefore by the 5th chapter of this book you will have what has been proposed.

Question V

Example.—Divide 10 into 3 parts in continued proportion such that the 1st multiplied by the 2nd gives 6 as product. This problem was proposed by Johannes Colla, who said he could not solve it. I nevertheless said I could solve it, but did not know how until Ferrari found this solution. Put then 1 unknown as the middle number, then the 1st will be $\dfrac{6}{1 \text{ unknown}}$, and the 3rd will be ⅙ of a cube. Hence these together will be equal to 10. Multiplying all by 6 unknowns we shall have 60 unknowns equal to one square-square plus 6 squares plus 36. Add, according to the 5th rule, 6 squares to each side, and you will have 1 square-square plus 12 squares plus 36, equal to 6 squares plus 60 unknowns; for if equals are added to equals, the totals are equal. But 1 square-square plus 12 squares plus 36 has a root, which is 1 square plus 6.

1q̄dq̄d. *p*: 6 q̄d. p:36	æqualia 60 pos.[1]
6 q̄d.	6 q̄d.
1q̄dq̄d. p:12 q̄d. p:36	æq̄lia 6 q̄d. p:60 pos.
2 pos.	1 q̄d. p:12 pos.

If 6 squares plus 60 unknowns also had a root, we should have the job done; but they do not have; hence we must add so many squares and a number to each side, that on the one side there may remain a trinomial having a root, while on the other side it should be made so. Let therefore a number of squares be 1 unknown[2] and since, as you see in the figure of the 3rd rule, *CL* and *MK* are formed from twice *GC* into *AB*, and *GC* is 1 unknown,[3] I

---

[1] [That is, $x^4 + 6x^2 + 36 = 60x$, hence $x^4 + 12x^2 + 36 = 6x^2 + 60x$.]

[2] [Having reduced the equation to the form

$$(x^2 + p)^2 = p^2 + px^2 - qx - r,$$

he makes use of another unknown for the purpose of converting the left side into $(x^2 + p + y)^2$. This is done by adding $2y(x^2 + p) + y^2$ to each side. The equation then becomes

$$(x^2 + p + y)^2 = p^2 + px^2 - qx - r + 2y(x^2 + p) + y^2,$$

an equation in the form

$$x^2 + a = bx + c.$$

The problem now reduces to one of finding such a value of y as shall make the right side a square.]

[3] [That is, $GC = y$, and y is half the coefficient of x^2 in the part to be added.]

will always take the number of squares to be added as 2 unknowns, that is, twice GC; and since the number to be added to 36 is LNM it therefore is the square of GC together with the product of twice GC into CB or of GC into twice CB, which is 12, the number of the squares in the original equation. I will therefore always multiply 1 unknown, half the number of squares to be added, into the number of squares in the original equation and into itself and this will make 1 square plus 12 unknowns to be added on each side, and also 2 unknowns for the number of the squares.[1] We shall therefore have again, by common sense, the quantities written below equal to each other; and each side will have a root, the first, by the 3rd rule, but the 2nd

| 1 q̄dq̄d. p:2 pos. p:12. q̄d ℞ p:1 q̄d. p:12 pos. additi numeri p:36 æqualia. |
| 2 pos. 6 q̄dratorū, p:60 pos. p:1 q̄d. p:12 pos. numeri additi.[2] |

quantity by an assumption as to y. Therefore the first part of the trinomial multiplied by the third makes the square of half the 2nd part of the trinomial. Thus from half the 2nd part multiplied by itself there results 900, a square, and from the 1st [multiplied] into the 3rd there results 2 cubes plus 30 squares plus 72 unknowns. Likewise, this may be reduced ... since equals divided by equals produce equals, as 2 cubes plus 30 squares plus 72 unknowns equals 900,[3] therefore 1 cube plus 15 squares plus 36 unknowns equals 450.[4]

---

[1] [The problem has been reduced to

$$x^4 + 12x^2 + 36 = 6x^2 + 60x,$$

or

$$(x^2 + 6)^2 = 6x^2 + 60x.$$

To convert the left-hand side into $(x^2 + 6 + y)^2$, it is necessary to add $2y(x^2 + 6) + y^2$ to both sides, which converts the equation into

$$(x^2 + 6 + y)^2 = 6x^2 + 60x + y^2 + 12y + 2yx^2.]$$

[2] [That is,

$$x^4 + (2y + 12)x^2 + y^2 + 12y + 36$$
$$= (2y + 6)x^2 + 60x + y^2 + 12y$$

in which the first member reduces to $(x^2 + 6 + y)^2$.]

[3] [To find the value of y that will make the second member a square, Cardan had to consider the trinomial $ax^2 + 2bx + c$, as we should write it. This is a square when $b^2 = ac$, for then $b^2 - ac = 0$. But here $b = 30$, and so b^2 ("the square of half the second part") is 900, and a ("the first") is $2y + 6$, and $c = y^2 + 12y$. Then "the first into the third" is ac, or

$$(2y + 6)(y^2 + 12y) = 2y^3 + 30y^2 + 72y,$$

which Cardan describes as "2 cubes plus 30 squares plus 72 unknowns."]

[4] [Since $2y^3 + 30y^2 + 72y = 900$, $y^3 + 15y^2 + 36y = 450$.]

It is therefore sufficient for reducing to the rule, to have always 1 cube plus the number of the former squares, with a 4th of it added to it plus such a multiple of the assumed quantity as the first number of the equation indicates;[1] so that if we had 1 square-square plus 12 squares plus 36 equals 6 squares plus 60 unknowns we should have 1 cube plus 15 squares plus 36 unknowns equal to 450, half the square of half the number of unknowns. And if we had 1 square-square plus 16 squares plus 64 equal to 80 unknowns we should have 1 cube plus 20 squares plus 64 unknowns equal to 800.[2] And if we had 1 square-square plus 20 squares plus 100 equal to 80 unknowns we should have 1 cube plus 25 squares plus 100 unknowns equal to 800.[3] This being understood, in the former example we had 1 cube plus 15 squares plus 36 unknowns equal to 450; therefore the value of the unknown, by the 17th chapter, is

$$\sqrt[3]{287\tfrac{1}{2} + \sqrt{+\,80449\tfrac{1}{4}}} + \sqrt[3]{287\tfrac{1}{2} - \sqrt{80449\tfrac{1}{4}}} - 5$$

This then is the number of squares which is to be doubled and added to each side (since we assumed 2 unknowns to be added) and the number to be added to each side, by the demonstration, is the square of this, with the product of this by 12, the number of squares.[4]

---

[1] $[y^3 + (12 + 1\tfrac{3}{4})y^2 + 36y = \tfrac{1}{2}(6\tfrac{6}{2})^2$. The "number of former squares" means the coefficient of x^2, 12; and the "first number of the equation" means the constant term, 36.]

[2] $[y^3 + (16 + 1\tfrac{6}{4})y^2 + 64y = \tfrac{1}{2}(8\tfrac{6}{2})^2.]$

[3] $[y^3 + (20 + 2\tfrac{4}{4})y^2 + 100y = \tfrac{1}{2}(8\tfrac{6}{2})^2.]$

[4] $[2yx^2 + 12y + y^2$, 12 being the coefficient of x^2 in the original equation, $x^4 + 12x^2 + 36 = 60x + 6x^2.]$

FERMAT

NOTE ON THE EQUATION $x^n + y^n = z^n$

(Translated from the French by Professor Vera Sanford, Western Reserve University, Cleveland Ohio.)

Pierre de Fermat (c. 1608–1665), a member of the provincial parliament of Toulouse, became interested in the theory of numbers through Bachet's translation of Diophantus. Fermat's many discoveries in this field were given in letters to other mathematicians or were noted on the pages of the books which he read. The theorem which follows appears beside the eighth proposition of the second book of Diophantus:—"To divide a square number into two other square numbers." Fermat's note[1] reads:

To divide a cube into two other cubes, a fourth power, or in general any power whatever into two powers of the same denomination above the second is impossible, and I have assuredly found an admirable proof of this, but the margin is too narrow to contain it.

---

[1] *Précis des Oeuvres Mathématiques de P. Fermat et de l'Arithmétique de Diophante*, E. Brassinne, Paris, 1853, pp. 53–54. It should be noted that no one as yet has proved this theorem except for special cases.

FERMAT

The So-called Pell Equation

(Translated from the Latin by Professor Edward E. Whitford, College of the City of New York.)

Pierre de Fermat (c. 1608–1665) was the first to assert that the equation

$$x^2 - Ay^2 = 1$$

where A is any non-square integer, always has an unlimited number of solutions in integers. This equation may have been suggested to him by the study of some of the double equations of Diophantus; for he says in a note on the works of the latter (IV, 39), "Suppose if you will, that the double equation to be solved is

$$2m + 5 = \text{square},$$
$$6m + 3 = \text{square}.$$

The first square must be made equal to 16 and the second to 36; and others will be found ad infinitum satisfying the equation. Nor is it difficult to propound a general rule for the solution of this kind of equation."

Fermat was a profound scholar in all branches of learning and a mathematician of exceptional power. He has left the impression of his genius upon all branches of mathematics known in his time.

Fermat[1] first proposed the general problem of the Pell equation as a challenge problem to the English mathematicians Lord Brouncker and John Wallis (see p. 46). This was written in Latin in the form of a letter. In these contests of wits the Englishmen did not use French and the Frenchmen did not use English and the letters passed through intermediaries. The name Pell equation originated in a mistaken notion of Léonard Euler[2] (see p. 91) that John Pell was the author of the solution which was really the work of Lord Brouncker. Euler in his cursory reading of Wallis's algebra must have confused the contributions of Pell and Brouncker.[3] Nevertheless it seems not improbable that Pell solved the equation, for we find it discussed in Rahn's algebra[4] under the form

$$x = 12yy - 33.$$

This shows that Pell had some acquaintance with the general equation, and that Euler was not so far out of the way when he attributed to him some

---

[1] *Oeuvres de Fermat*, publiées par les soins de MM. Paul Tannery et Charles Henry, Paris, 1894, vol. II, p. 333–5.

[2] P. H. Fuss, editor, *Correspondance mathématique et physique de quelques célèbres géometres du XVIII ième siècle*, letter IX of L. Euler to C. Goldbach, Aug. 10, 1732, St. Petersburg, 1843, p. 37.

[3] G. Wertheim, "Über den Ursprung des Ausdruckes 'Pellsche Gleichung,'" *Bibliotheca Mathematica*, vol. II (3), p. 360, Leipzig, 1901.

[4] J. H. Rahn, *An introduction to algebra, translated out of the High Dutch into English by Thomas Brancker, M. A. Much altered and augmented by D. P.*, London, 1668, p. 143.

work upon it. Pell was an extensive contributor to Rahn's algebra and is referred to in the title of this book by the initials D. P.

The Pell equation affords the simplest case of Dirichlet's elegant and very general theorem on the existence of units in any algebraic field or domain. It is of great importance in the theory of binary quadratic forms. The problem to find all the rational solutions of the most general equation of the second degree in two unknowns reduces readily to that for $x^2 - Ay^2 = B$, all of whose solutions follow from the solution of $x^2 - Ay^2 = 1$. The honor of having first recognized the deep importance of the Pell equation for the general solution of the indeterminate equation of the second degree belongs to Euler.[1] The first admissible proof of the solvability of the equation $x^2 - Ay^2 = 1$ was given by Lagrange.[2]

Useful tables of solutions have been given by Euler, Legendre, Degen, Tenner, Koenig, Arndt, Cayley, Stern, Seeling, Roberts, Bickmore, Cunningham, and Whitford.

The letter of Fermat, dated February, 1657, which is called the second challenge of Fermat to the mathematicians, runs as follows:

There is scarcely any one that sets forth purely arithmetical questions, and scarcely any one that understands them. Is it not because arithmetic has heretofore been treated geometrically rather than arithmetically? This is certainly intimated by many works of ancient and modern writers, including Diophantus himself. Although he got away from geometry a little more than the rest, while limiting his analysis to rational numbers only, yet the "Zetetica" of Vieta, in which the method of Diophantus is extended to continuous quantity and therefore to geometry, sufficiently proves that this branch is not wholly separated from geometry.

Therefore arithmetic claims for itself the theory of whole numbers as its own estate. Arithmeticians ("children of arithmetic") should strive either to advance or restore it, which was only imperfectly represented by Euclid in his *Elements*, and moreover not sufficiently perfected by those who followed him. Perhaps it lies concealed in those books of Diophantus which the damages done by time have destroyed.

To these, in order to show them the light which may lead the way, I propose the following theorem or problem to be either proved or solved. Moreover, if they discover this, they will admit that questions of this sort are not inferior to the more celebrated ones from geometry, either in subtlety or in difficulty or in method of proof.

---

[1] L. Euler. "De solutione problematum Diophantaeorum per numeros integros," *Commentarii Academiae scientiarum imperialis Petropolitanae*, 1732, vol. VI, p. 175, St. Petersburg, 1738.

[2] J. L. Lagrange, "Solution d'un problème d'arithmétique," *Miscellanea Taurinensis*, vol. IV, p. 41, Turin, 1766. *Oeuvres de Lagrange*, Paris, 1867, vol. I, p. 671

Given any number not a square, then there are an infinite number of squares which, when multiplied into the given number, make a square when unity is added.

Example.—Given 3, a non-square number; this number multiplied into the square number 1, and 1 being added, produces 4, which is a square.

Moreover, the same 3 multiplied into the square 16, with 1 added makes 49, which is a square.

And instead of 1 and 16, an infinite number of squares may be found showing the same property; I demand, however, a general rule, any number being given which is not a square.

It is sought, for example, to find a square which when multiplied into 149, 109, 433, etc., becomes a square when unity is added.

In the same month (February, 1657) Fermat, in a letter to Frénicle, suggests the same problem, and expressly states the important condition implied in the foregoing that the solution be in integers:

Every non-square is of such a nature that one can find an infinite number of squares by which if you multiply the number given and if you add unity to the product, it becomes a square.

Example: 3 is a non-square number, which multiplied by 1, which is a square, makes 3, and by adding unity makes 4, which is a square.

The same 3, multiplied by 16, which is a square, makes 48, and with unity added makes 49, which is a square.

There is an infinity of such squares which when multiplied by 3 with unity added likewise make a square number.

I demand a general rule,—given a non-square number, find squares which multiplied by the given number, and with unity added, make squares.

What is for example the smallest square which multiplied by 61 with unity added, makes a square?

Moreover, what is the smallest square which, when multiplied by 109 and with unity added, makes a square?

If you do not give me the general solution, then give the particular solution for these two numbers, which I have chosen small in order not to give too much difficulty.

After I have received your reply, I will propose another matter. It appears without saying that my proposition is to find integers which satisfy the question, for in the case of fractions the lowest type of arithmetician could find the solution.

WALLIS

On General Exponents

(Translated from the Latin by Professor Eva M. Sanford, College for Women, Western Reserve University, Cleveland, Ohio.)

John Wallis (1616–1703), Savilian professor of geometry at Oxford (1649–1703), contemporary of Newton, was the first writer to set forth with any completeness the meaning of negative and fractional exponents. Steps in this direction had already been taken by Nicole Oresme (c. 1360), Chuquet (1484), Stifel (1544), and Girard (1629), but it remained for Wallis (1655) and Newton (1669) to generalize the subject for rational exponents. The following extract is from Wallis's *Arithmetica Infinitorum* as published in his *Opera Mathematica*, Oxford, 1695, vol. I, pp. 410, 411. The *Arithmetica Infinitorum* first appeared in 1655, and the use of the generalized exponent occurs in connection with the study of series, Proposition CVI.

Prop. CVI

If any series of reciprocals be multiplied or divided by another series (whether reciprocal or direct) or even if the series multiplies or divides another; the same laws are to be observed as in direct series (see propositions 73 and 81).

Example.—If the series of the reciprocals of squares ($\frac{1}{1}$, $\frac{1}{4}$, $\frac{1}{9}$, &c.) whose index is -2 be multiplied term by term into the series of the reciprocals of cubes ($\frac{1}{1}$, $\frac{1}{8}$, $\frac{1}{27}$, &c.) whose index is -3, the product will be a series of the reciprocals of the fifth powers[1] ($\frac{1}{1}$, $\frac{1}{32}$, $\frac{1}{243}$, &c.) whose index $-5 = -2 - 3$ as is evident.

Furthermore, if a series of the reciprocals of cubes ($\frac{1}{1}$, $\frac{1}{8}$, $\frac{1}{27}$, &c.) whose index is -3 be multiplied term by term by a series of squares (1, 4, 9, &c.) whose index is 2, the result is the series $\frac{1}{1}$, $\frac{4}{8}$, $\frac{9}{27}$, &c. This is 1, $\frac{1}{2}$, $\frac{1}{3}$, &c., a series of the reciprocals of first powers whose index $-1 = -3 + 2$.

Likewise, if the series of the reciprocals of the square roots[2]

$$\frac{1}{\sqrt{1}}, \frac{1}{\sqrt{2}}, \frac{1}{\sqrt{3}}, \text{ &c.}$$

---

[1] [*Subquintanis.*]
[2] [*Subsecundans.*]

whose index is $-\frac{1}{2}$ be multiplied term by term by the series of squares (1, 4, 9, &c.) whose index is 2, the product will be the series

$$\frac{1}{\sqrt{1}}, \frac{4}{\sqrt{2}}, \frac{9}{\sqrt{3}}, \&\text{c.},$$

or

$$\tfrac{1}{1}\sqrt{1}, \tfrac{4}{2}\sqrt{2}, \tfrac{9}{3}\sqrt{3}, \&\text{c.},$$

or

$$\sqrt{1}, \sqrt{8}, \sqrt{27}, \&\text{c.},$$

the square roots of the cubes or third powers, whose index $\frac{3}{2} = -\frac{1}{2} + 2$.

Furthermore, if a series of the reciprocals of squares whose index is -2 divides a series of the reciprocals of integers whose index is -1, the product will be the series of first powers whose index $1 = -1 + 2$, or -1 minus -2.

Likewise if a series of the reciprocals of integers whose index is -1 divides a series of the reciprocals of squares whose index is -2, then the product will be a series of the reciprocals of first powers whose index $-1 = -2 + 1$, that is, -2 minus -1.

Likewise if a series of reciprocals of first powers whose index is -1 divides a series of squares whose index is 2, the product will be a series of third powers whose index $3 = 2 + 1$, that is 2 minus -1.

Likewise if a series of the reciprocals of first powers whose index is -1 be divided by a series of squares whose index is 2, the product will be a series of the reciprocals of third powers whose index $-3 = -1 - 2$, that is -1 minus 2.

And the same thing will happen in any other cases whatsoever of this sort, and hence the proposition is proved.[1]

---

[1] [In the wide page of the original there are arranged alongside the above paragraphs, beginning with the fourth one, the following series.

$\frac{1}{1}$)	$\frac{1}{1}$	$(\frac{1}{1} = 1$
$\frac{1}{4}$)	$\frac{1}{2}$	$(\frac{4}{2} = 2$
$\frac{1}{9}$)	$\frac{1}{3}$	$(\frac{9}{3} = 3$
	&c.	
$\frac{1}{1}$)	$\frac{1}{1}$	$(\frac{1}{1} = \frac{1}{1}$
$\frac{1}{2}$)	$\frac{1}{4}$	$(\frac{2}{4} = \frac{1}{2}$
$\frac{1}{3}$)	$\frac{1}{9}$	$(\frac{3}{9} = \frac{1}{3}$
	&c.	
1)	$\frac{1}{1}$	$(\frac{1}{1}$
4)	$\frac{1}{2}$	$(\frac{1}{8}$
9)	$\frac{1}{3}$	$(\frac{1}{27}$
	&c.]	

WALLIS AND NEWTON

On the Binomial Theorem for Fractional and Negative Exponents

(Selected from the English version by Professor David Eugene Smith, Teachers College, Columbia University, New York City.)

John Wallis (1616–1703), in his work *De Algebra Tractatus, Historicus & Practicus* was instrumental in making known several discoveries made by Newton. Among them is Newton's generalization of the Binomial Theorem to include fractional and negative exponents. This was first published in Latin, and was later translated by Wallis into English. The following extract is from this translation. In it Wallis assigns credit to Newton and sets forth his results, as yet unpublished. These results appear in the article which follows this one.

CHAP. XCI.[1]

The Doctrine of Infinite Series, *further prosecuted by* Mr. Newton.

Now (to return where we left off:) Those Approximations (in the Arithmetick of Infinites) above mentioned, (for the Circle or Ellipse, and the Hyperbola;) have given occasion to others (as is before intimated,) to make further inquiry into that subject; and seek out other the like Approximations, (or continual approaches) in other cases. Which are now wont to be called by the name of *Infinite Series*, or *Converging Series*, or other names of a like import. (Thereby intimating, the designation of some particular quantity, by a regular Progression or rank of quantities, continually approaching to it; and which, if infinitely continued, must be equal to it.) Though it be but little of this nature which hath yet been made publick in print.

Of all that I have seen in this kind; I do not find any that hath better prosecuted that notion, nor with better success, than Mr. *Isaac Newton*, the worthy Professor of Mathematicks in *Cambridge*: Who about the Year 1664, or 1665, (though he did afterwards for divers years intermit those thoughts, diverting to other Studies,) did with great sagacity apply himself to that Speculation. This I find by Two Letters of his (which I have seen,) written to Mr.

[1] Page 330.

Oldenburg, on that Subject, (dated *June* 13, and *Octob.* 24. 1676,) full of very ingenious discoveries, and well deserving to be made more publick. In the latter of which Letters, he says, that by the Plague (which happened in the Year 1665), he was driven from *Cambridge*; and gave over the prosecution of it for divers years. And when he did again resume it, about the Year 1671, with intention then to make it publick; (together with his new discoveries concerning the Refractions of Light,) he was then by other accidents diverted.

He doth therein, not only give us many such Approximations fitted to particular cases; but lays down general Rules and Methods, easily applicable to cases innumerable; from whence such Infinite Series or Progressions may be deduced at pleasure; and those in great varieties for the same particular case. And gives instances, how those Infinite or Interminate Progressions may be accommodated, to the Rectifying of Curve Lines (Geometrick or Mechanick;) Squaring of Curve-lined Figures; finding the length of Archs, by their given Chords, Sines, or Versed Sines; and of these by those; fitting Logarithms to Numbers, and Numbers to Logarithms given; with many other of the most perplexed Inquiries in Mathematicks.

In order hereunto, he applies not only Division in Species; (such as we have before described;) but Extraction of Roots in Species, (Quadratick, Cubick, and of other consequent, and intermediate Powers;) as well in Single, as in Affected Equations.

How this was by him made use of in the way of Interpolation, we have shewed before; upon a discovery that the *Vnciæ* or Numbers prefixed to the members of Powers, created from a Binomial Root, (the Exponent of which Powers respectively he calls *m*,) doth arise from such continual Multiplication as this,

$$1 \times \frac{m-0}{1} \times \frac{m-1}{2} \times \frac{m-2}{3} \times \frac{m-3}{4} \times \frac{m-4}{5}, \times \textit{&c.}[1]$$

Which Process, if *m* (the Exponent of the Power) be an Integer will (after a certain number of places, such as the nature of each Power requires) terminate again at 1, as it did begin: But if *m* be a Fraction, it will (passing it) run on to Negative numbers infinitely.

According to this notion; having found the numbers answering the Power commonly expressed by $\sqrt{q}$, (which is the intermediate

---
[1] Page 331.

between an Unite and the Lateral,) whose Exponent is $\frac{1}{2}=m$; to be these

$$1 \cdot \tfrac{1}{2} \cdot - \tfrac{1}{8} \cdot + \cdot \tfrac{1}{16} \cdot - \tfrac{5}{128} \cdot + \tfrac{7}{256} \cdot - \textit{e}^{\jmath}c.$$

He applys this (for instance) to that of mine, (accommodated as is before shewed, to the Quadrature of the Circle, or a Quadrant thereof, ($\sqrt{}:RR-cc$; or (putting $R=1$,) $\sqrt{}:1-cc$. And finds $\sqrt{}:1-cc:=1-\tfrac{1}{2}cc-\tfrac{1}{8}c^4-\tfrac{1}{16}c^6$, &c. (Which multiplied into itself, restores $1-cc$.) The Process thus.

$$1-cc(1,-\tfrac{1}{2}cc,-\tfrac{1}{8}c^4,-\tfrac{1}{16}c^6, \quad \text{&c.}$$
$$1$$
$$\overline{0-cc}$$
$$-cc+\tfrac{1}{4}c^4$$
$$\overline{\qquad -\tfrac{1}{4}c^4}$$
$$-\tfrac{1}{4}c^4+\tfrac{1}{8}c^6+\tfrac{1}{64}c^3$$
$$\overline{\qquad -\tfrac{1}{8}c^6-\tfrac{1}{64}c^3}$$
$$\text{&c.} \quad \text{&c.}$$

$$into \quad \begin{array}{l} 1-\tfrac{1}{2}cc-\tfrac{1}{8}c^4-\tfrac{1}{16}c^6 \quad \text{&c.} \\ 1-\tfrac{1}{2}cc-\tfrac{1}{8}c^4-\tfrac{1}{16}c^6 \quad \text{&c.} \\ \hline 1-cc-\tfrac{1}{4}c^4-\tfrac{1}{8}c^6 \quad \text{&c.} \\ +\tfrac{1}{4}c^4+\tfrac{1}{8}c^6 \quad \text{&c.} \\ \hline \quad\quad\quad \text{&c.} \\ \hline 1-cc. \end{array}$$

From whence (and from others of the like nature) he derives this Theorem for such Extractions,

$$\overline{P+PQ}\Big|\tfrac{m}{n}=P\tfrac{m}{n}+\tfrac{m}{n}AQ+\tfrac{m-n}{2n}BQ+\tfrac{m-2n}{3n}CQ+\tfrac{m-3n}{4n}DQ+\textit{e}^{\jmath}c.$$

Where $P+PQ$ is the Quantity, whose Root is to be extracted, or any Power formed from it, or the Root of any such Power extracted. P is the first Term of such Quantity; Q, the rest (of such proposed Quantity) divided by that first Term. And $\frac{m}{n}$ the Exponent of such Root or Dimension sought. That is, in the present case, (for a Quadratick Root,) $\frac{1}{2}$.

(Note here, for preventing mistakes, that whereas it is usual to express the Exponent of a Power, or the number of its Dimensions, by a small Figure, at the head of the letter, as a^3 for *aaa*; the same is here done by a Fraction, when such Exponent is not an Integer Number, as a $\frac{3}{2}$ for $\sqrt{aaa}$; which Fraction is so to be understood, as if the whole of it were above the letter; and signifies the Exponent of the Power; not as at other times, a Fraction adjoined, as if it were $a+\frac{3}{2}$: And the same is to be understood afterwards in many places; where the like happens, by reason that there is not room to set the whole Fraction above the Letter, but equal with it.)

And according to this Method; if of any such Quantity proposed, we seek a Square, Cube, or Higher Power, whose Exponent is an

Integer; we shall find for it, a Series terminated, consisting of so many members as the nature of each Power requires; (the Side of 2, the Square of 3; the Cube of 4; &c.) But if a Root or Intermediate Power be sought, whose Exponent is a Fraction, or an Integer[1] with a Fraction annexed, (as $\frac{1}{2}$, $1\frac{1}{2}$, $2\frac{1}{2}$, &c; that is, $\frac{1}{2}$, $\frac{3}{2}$, $\frac{5}{2}$, &c: Or $\frac{1}{3}$, $\frac{2}{3}$, $1\frac{1}{3}$, $1\frac{2}{3}$, that is, $\frac{1}{3}$, $\frac{2}{3}$, $\frac{4}{3}$, $\frac{5}{3}$, &c:) We shall have (for its value) an Interminate or Infinite Series; to be continued as far as we please. And the farther it is continued, the more exactly doth it represent the quantity sought.

Of this Process, he giveth divers Examples; which (because they are not yet Extant in Print,) I have thought fit here to transcribe.

Example I. $\sqrt{}:cc+xx$, or $\overline{cc+xx}|\frac{1}{2}$, $=c+\dfrac{xx}{2c}-\dfrac{x^4}{8c^3}+\dfrac{x^6}{16c^6}-\dfrac{5x^8}{128c^7}$

$+\dfrac{7x^{10}}{256c^9}$&c. For in this case, is $P=cc$. $Q=\dfrac{xx}{cc}$. $m=1$. $n=2$.

$A(=\overline{P}|\dfrac{m}{n}=\overline{cc}|\frac{1}{2},)=c$. $B(=\dfrac{m}{n}AQ)=\dfrac{xx}{2c}$. $C=\dfrac{m-n}{2n}BQ)=\dfrac{-x^4}{8c^3}$.&c.

Examp. II. $\sqrt{}^5:c^5+c^4x-x^5$: or $\overline{c^5+c^4x-x^5}|\frac{1}{5}$.

$=c+\dfrac{c^4x-x^5}{5c^4}, \dfrac{-2c^8xx+4c^4x^6-2x^{10}}{25c^9}+$&c. As will be evident by substituting $1=m$. $5=n$. $c^5=P$. and $c^5)c^4x-x^5(Q$.

Or we might in like manner substitute $-x^5=P$, and $-x^5)c^4x+c^5$ (Q.

And then $\sqrt{}^5:c^5+c^4x-x^5:=-x+\dfrac{c^4x+c^5}{5x^4}+\dfrac{2c^8xx+4c^9+c^{10}}{25x^9}+$&c.

The former way is most eligible, if x be very small; the latter if x be very great.

Examp. III. $\dfrac{N}{\sqrt{}^3:y^3-aay:}$ That is, $N\times\overline{y^3-aay}|^{-\frac{1}{3}}$. $=N$ into

$\dfrac{1}{y}+\dfrac{aa}{3y^3}+\dfrac{a^4}{9y^5}+\dfrac{7a^6}{81y^7}+$&c. For here, $P=y^3$. $Q=\dfrac{-aa}{yy}$. $m=-1$.

$n=3$. $A(=\overline{P}|\dfrac{m}{n}=y^3\times-\frac{1}{3})=y^{-1}$, that is, $\dfrac{1}{y}$. $B\left(=\dfrac{m}{n}AQ=-\frac{1}{3}\times\dfrac{1}{y}\times\right.$

$\left.\dfrac{-aa}{yy}\right)=\dfrac{aa}{3y^3}$. &c.

Examp. IV. The Cubick Root of the Biquadrate of $d+e$; that is, $\overline{d+e}|\frac{4}{3}$. is $d\frac{4}{3}+\dfrac{4ed\frac{1}{3}}{3}+\dfrac{2ee}{9d\frac{2}{3}}-\dfrac{e^3}{9d\frac{2}{3}}+$&c. For $P=d$. $d)e(Q$. $m=4$.

$n=3$. $A\left(=P\dfrac{m}{n}\right)=d\frac{4}{3}$. &c.

Examp. V. After the same manner may Single Powers be formed; as the Sursolid, or Fifth Power of $d+e$: That is, $\overline{d+e}|^5$, or $\overline{d+e}|^{\frac{5}{1}}$. For then $P=d$. $d)e(Q$. $m=5$. $n=1$. $A\left(=P\frac{m}{n}\right)=$ d^5. $B\left(=\frac{m}{n}AQ\right)=5d^4e$. $C=10d^3ee$. $D=10dde^3$. $E=5dc^4$. $F=e.^5$ $G\left(=\frac{m-5n}{6n}FQ\right)=0$. That is, $\overline{d+e}|^5=d^5+5d^4e+10d^3ee+10dde^3$ $+5de^4+e^5$.

Examp. VI. And even bare Divison, (whether single, or repeated,) may be performed by the same Rule. As $\frac{1}{d+e}$, that is $\overline{d+e}|^{-1}$, or $\overline{d+e}|^{-\frac{1}{1}}$. For then $P=d$. $d)e(Q$. $m=-1$. $n=1$. $A\left(=P\frac{m}{n}=d^{-1}\right)=d^{-1}$, or $\frac{1}{d}$. $B\left(=\frac{m}{n}AQ=-1\times\frac{1}{d}\times\frac{e}{d}\right)=\frac{-e}{dd}$. And in like manner, $C=\frac{ee}{d^3}$. $D=\frac{-e^3}{d^4}$. &c.

That[1] is, $\frac{1}{d+e}=\frac{1}{d}-\frac{e}{dd}+\frac{ee}{d^3}-\frac{e^3}{d^4}+$&c.

Examp. VII. In like manner $\overline{d+e}|^{-3}$: That is, an Unite **Three** times divided by $d+e$, or divided by the Cube of $d+e$: Is $\frac{1}{d^3}-\frac{3e}{d^4}$ $+\frac{6ee}{d^5}-\frac{10e^3}{d^6}+$&c.

Examp. VIII. And $N\times\overline{d+e}|^{-\frac{1}{3}}$; That is, N divided by the Cubick Root of $d+e$: is $N:\times\frac{1}{d^{\frac{1}{3}}}-\frac{e}{3d^{\frac{4}{3}}}+\frac{2ee}{9d^{\frac{7}{3}}}-\frac{14e^3}{81d^{\frac{10}{3}}}+$&c.

Examp. IX. And $N\times\overline{d+e}|^{-\frac{3}{5}}$; That is, N divided by the Sursolidal Root of the Cube of $d+e$: Or $\frac{N}{\sqrt{5}:d^3+3d^2e+3dee+e^3}$: Is N into: $\frac{1}{d^{\frac{3}{5}}}-\frac{3e}{5d^{\frac{8}{5}}}+\frac{12ee}{25d^{\frac{13}{5}}}-\frac{52e^3}{125d^{\frac{18}{5}}}+$&c.

And by the same Rule, we may in Numbers (as well as Species,) perform the Generation of Powers; Division by Powers, or by Radical Quantities; and the Extraction of Roots of higher Powers; and the like.

[1] Page 333.

NEWTON

On the Binomial Theorem for Fractional and Negative Exponents

(Translated from the Latin by Professor Eva M. Sanford, College for Women, Western Reserve University, Cleveland, Ohio.)

Isaac Newton (1642–1727) was the first to state the binomial theorem for negative and fractional exponents. The formula appears in a letter written on June 13, 1676, to Oldenburg, the Secretary of the Royal Society, for transmission to Leibniz who had asked for information regarding Newton's work with infinite series On the receipt of this communication, Leibniz requested further details and Newton replied on October 24th of the same year. Both letters were printed in the *Commercium Epistolicum* (1712) with other papers that bore upon the Newton-Leibniz controversy. For a biographical note on Newton, see page 613.

Letter of June 13,1676[1]

Although the modesty of Dr. Leibniz in the Excerpts which you recently sent me from his Letter, attributes much to my work in certain Speculations regarding *Infinite Series,*[2] rumor of which is already beginning to spread, I have no doubt that he has found not only a method of reducing any Quantities whatsoever into Series of this type, *as he himself asserts,* but also that he has found various Compendia, similar to ours if not even better.

Since, however, he may wish to know the discoveries that have been made in this direction by the English (I myself fell into this Speculation some years ago) and in order to satisfy his wishes to some degree at least, I have sent you certain of the points which have occurred to me.

Fractions may be reduced to Infinite Series by Division, and Radical Quantities may be so reduced by the Extraction of Roots. These Operations may be extended to Species[3] in the same way as

---

[1] [*Commercium Epistolicum* (1712; 1725 edition, pp. 131–132).]

[2] [Probably as early as 1666, Newton had told Barrow and others of his work in infinite series in connection with the problem of finding the area under a curve, but this work was not published until 1704 when it appeared as an appendix to Newton's *Opticks.*]

[3] [That is "to algebraic numbers." In his *Arithmetica Universalis* (1707; 1728 edition) Newton says, "Computation is either perform'd by *Numbers,* as in Vulgar Arithmetick, or by *Species,* as usual among Algebraists..."]

that in which they apply to Decimal Numbers. These are the Foundations of the Reductions.

The Extractions of Roots are much shortened by the Theorem

$$\overline{P + PQ}\left|\frac{m}{n}\right. = P\frac{m}{n} + \frac{m}{n}AQ + \frac{m-n}{2n}BQ + \frac{m-2n}{4n^1}CQ$$

$$+ \frac{m-3n}{4n}DQ + \&c.$$

where $P + PQ$ stands for a Quantity whose Root or Power or whose Root of a Power is to be found, P being the first Term of that quantity, Q being the remaining terms divided by the first term, and $\frac{m}{n}$ the numerical Index of the powers of $P + PQ$. This may be a Whole Number or (so to speak) a Broken Number; a positive number or a negative one. For, as the Analysts write a^2 and a^3 &c. for aa and aaa, so for $\sqrt{a}$, $\sqrt{a^3}$, $\sqrt{c}.a^5$, &c. I write $a^{\frac{1}{2}}$, $a^{\frac{3}{2}}$, $a^{\frac{5}{3}}$, &c.; for $\frac{1}{a}$, $\frac{1}{aa}$, $\frac{1}{aaa}$, a^{-1}, a^{-2}, a^{-3}; for $\dfrac{aa}{\sqrt{c}.a^3 + bbx}$, $aa \times \overline{a^3 + bbx}\,|^{-\frac{1}{2}}$; and for $\dfrac{aab}{\sqrt{c:a^3 + bbx \times a^3 + bbx}:}$, I write $aab \times \overline{a^3 + bbx}\,|^{-\frac{3}{2}}$. In this last case, if $\overline{a^3 + bbx}\,|^{-\frac{3}{2}}$ be taken to mean $P + PQ$ in the Formula, then will $P = a^3$, $Q = bbx/a^3$, $m = -2$, $n = 3$. Finally, in place of the terms that occur in the course of the work in the Quotient, I shall use A, B, C, D, &c. Thus A stands for the first term $P^{\frac{m}{n}}$; B for the second term $\frac{m}{n}AQ$; and so on. The use of this Formula will become clear through Examples."[2]

. . . .

Letter of October 24, 1676[3]

One of my own [methods of deriving infinite series] I described before; and now I shall add another, namely the way in which I discovered these Series, for I found them before I knew the Divisions and Extractions of Roots which I now use. The explanation of this method will give the basis of the Theorem given at the beginning of my former Letter which Dr. Leibniz desires of me.

---

[1] [Evidently a misprint for $3n$.]

[2] [The examples show the application of the formula in cases in which the exponents are ½, ⅓, −⅓, ⅔, 5, −1, −⅜.]

[3] [*Commercium Epistolicum* (1712; 1725 edition, pp. 142–145). This letter begins with a note of appreciation of the work in series done by Leibniz.]

"Towards the beginning of my study of Mathematics, I happened on the works of our most Celebrated Wallis[1] and his considerations of the Series by whose intercalation he himself shows the values of the Area of a Circle and Hyperbola, and of that series of curves that have a common Base or Axis x and whose Ordinates are in the Form $\overline{1 - xx}|^{\frac{0}{2}} . \overline{1 - xx}|^{\frac{1}{2}} . \overline{1 - xx}|^{\frac{2}{2}} . \overline{1 - xx}|^{\frac{3}{2}}$ $.\overline{1 - xx}|^{\frac{4}{2}} . \overline{1 - xx}|^{\frac{5}{2}}$. &c. Then if the Areas of the alternate ones which are x, $x - \frac{1}{3}x^3$, $x - \frac{2}{3}x^3 + \frac{1}{5}x^5$, $x - \frac{3}{3}x^3 + \frac{3}{5}x^5 - \frac{1}{7}x^7$, &c. could have values interpolated between these terms, we should have the Areas of the intermediates, the first of which $\overline{1 - xx}|^{\frac{1}{2}}$ is the Circle. For these interpolations, I noticed that the first term in each is x and that the second term $\frac{0}{3}x^3$, $\frac{1}{3}x^3$, $\frac{2}{3}x^3$, $\frac{3}{3}x^3$, &c., are in Arithmetic progression. Thus the two first terms of the Series to be intercalated should be $x - \frac{\frac{1}{2}x^3}{3}$, $x - \frac{\frac{3}{2}x^3}{3}$, $x - \frac{\frac{5}{2}x^3}{5}$. &c.

For intercalcating the rest, I considered that the Denominators 1, 3, 5, 7, &c. were in Arithmetic progression and so only the Numerical Coefficients of the Numerators would require investigation. Moreover, in the alternate Areas given, these were the figures of the powers of the eleventh number, namely, 11^0, 11^1, 11^2, 11^3, 11^4. That is, first 1, then 1, 1, thirdly 1, 2, 1, fourth, 1, 3, 3, 1, fifth 1, 4, 6, 4, 1, &c. Therefore, I sought a method of deriving the remaining elements in these Series, having given the two first figures. I found that when the second figure m was supplied, the rest would be produced by continuous multiplication of the terms of this Series:

$$\frac{m - 0}{1} \times \frac{m - 1}{2} \times \frac{m - 2}{3} \times \frac{m - 3}{4} \times \frac{m - 4}{5} \text{ &c.}$$

For Example: Let (second term) $m = 4$, then the third term will be $4 \times \frac{m - 1}{2}$, that is 6; and $6 \times \frac{m - 2}{3}$, that is 4, the fourth; and $4 \times \frac{m - 3}{4}$ that is 1, the fifth; and $1 \times \frac{m - 4}{5}$, that is 0, the sixth at which the series ended in this case.

I therefore, applied this Rule to the Series to be inserted. Thus

---

[1] [John Wallis (1616–1703) Savilian professor at Oxford, whose *Arithmetica Infinitorum* appeared in 1655. At a later date, Newton wrote an appendix to Wallis's *Algebra*.]

for a Circle, the second term would be $\frac{\frac{1}{2}x^3}{3}$, I then let $m = \frac{1}{2}$,

and the terms which resulted were $\frac{1}{2} \times \frac{\frac{1}{2} - 1}{2}$ or $-\frac{1}{8}$, $-\frac{1}{8} \times \frac{\frac{1}{2} - 2}{3}$

or $+\frac{1}{16}$, $+\frac{1}{16} \times \frac{\frac{1}{2} - 3}{4}$ or $-\frac{5}{128}$, and so infinity. From this I

learned that the desired Area of a segment of a Circle is

$$x - \frac{\frac{1}{2}x^3}{3} - \frac{\frac{1}{8}x^5}{5} - \frac{\frac{1}{16}x^7}{7} - \frac{\frac{5}{128}x^9}{9} \&c.$$

By the same process the areas of the remaining Curves to be inserted were found, as the area of a Hyperbola, and of the other alternates in this Series $\overline{1 + xx}|^{\frac{0}{2}}$, $\overline{1 + xx}|^{\frac{1}{2}}$, $\overline{1 + xx}|^{\frac{2}{2}}$, $\overline{1 + xx}|^{\frac{3}{2}}$, &c.

The same method may be used for intercalating other Series, even with intervals of two or more terms lacking at once.

This was my first entry into these studies; which would surely have slipped from my memory had I not referred to certain notes a few weeks ago.

But when I had learned this, I soon considered that the terms $\overline{1 - xx}|^{\frac{0}{2}}$, $\overline{1 - xx}|^{\frac{2}{2}}$, $\overline{1 - xx}|^{\frac{4}{2}}$, $\overline{1 - xx}|^{\frac{6}{2}}$, &c. that is 1, $1 - xx$, $1 - 2xx + x^4$, $1 - 3xx + 3x^4 - x^6$, &c. could be interpolated in the same way and areas could be derived from them; and that for this nothing more is required than the omission of the denominators 1, 3, 5, 7, &c. in the terms expressing the areas, that is, the coefficients of the terms of the quantity to be intercalated $\overline{1 - xx}|^{\frac{1}{2}}$, or $\overline{1 - xx}|^{\frac{3}{2}}$, or more generally $\overline{1 - xx}|^{m}$ could be produced by continuous multiplication of the terms of this Series $m \times \frac{m - 1}{2} \times \frac{m - 2}{3} \times \frac{m - 3}{4}$ &c.

Thus, (for example), $\overline{1 - xx}|^{\frac{1}{2}}$ would amount to $1 - \frac{1}{2}x^2 - \frac{1}{8}x^4 - \frac{1}{16}x^6$ &c. And $\overline{1 - xx}|^{\frac{3}{2}}$ would come to $1 - \frac{1}{2}x^2 + \frac{1}{8}x^4 + \frac{1}{16}x^6$ &c. And $\overline{1 - xx}|^{\frac{1}{3}}$ would be $1 - \frac{1}{3}xx - \frac{1}{9}x^4 - \frac{1}{81}x^6$ &c.

Thus the general Reduction of Radicals into infinite Series became known to me through the Rule which I set at the beginning of the former Letter, before I knew the Extractions of Roots.

But, having learned this, the other could not long remain hidden from me. To prove these operations, I multiplied $1 - \frac{1}{2}x^2 -$

$\frac{1}{8}x^4 - \frac{1}{16}x^6$ &c. by itself, and $1 - xx$ resulted, the remaining terms vanishing into infinity by the continuance of the series. Similarly $1 - \frac{1}{3}xx - \frac{1}{9}x^4 - \frac{5}{81}x^6$ &c. twice multiplied by itself produced $1 - xx$. Which, that these might be a Demonstration of these conclusions, led me naturally to try the converse, to see whether these Series which it was certain were Roots of the quantity $1 - xx$ could not be extracted by Arithmetical means. The attempt succeeded well...[1]

Having discovered this, I gave up entirely the interpolation of Series, and used these operations alone as a more genuine basis, nor did I fail to discover Reduction by Division, a method certainly easier.

---

[1] [The algebraic work is given here.]

LEIBNIZ AND THE BERNOULLIS

On the Polynomial Theorem

(Translated from the Latin by Professor Jekuthiel Ginsburg, Yeshiva College, New York City.)

In a letter to Jean (I) Bernoulli, dated May 16, 1695, Leibniz speaks of a rule invented by him for finding the coefficients of a polynomial raised to any power whatsoever. This led to some correspondence between them, which appears in the *Commercium Philosophicum et Mathematicum* (Lausanne and Geneva, 1745). Extracts from this correspondence are given here in translation, the footnotes explaining their origin. Jacques (I) Bernoulli discussed the matter in his *Ars Conjectandi* (posthumously printed at Basel in 1713), and his method is given after the extracts from the correspondence of Leibniz with Jean I, his brother.

Jacques (1) Bernoulli returned to the same problem in a note published posthumously in his *Opera* (Vol. 2, Geneva 1744, pp. 995–6). It represents an attempt to apply the polynomial theorem to the solution of the related but more complicated problem of finding the power of an infinite series of terms arranged according to the ascending power of x. The attempt was inspired by one of the two articles on the subject of the "infinitonome" published by De Moivre in the *Philosophical Transactions* for the years 1697 and 1698. Bernoulli's plan apparently was to apply the previously-found theorem, first to the case of an infinite number of terms and then to an infinite series arranged according to ascending powers of x. This plan was not carried beyond a few theoretical remarks which are of little practical applicability.

The special problem of finding any power of an infinite power series has been the subject of a large number of ingenious memoirs, first among which are those by De Moivre.

[Leibniz to Jean Bernoulli, May 16, 1695]

I have conceived then of a wonderful rule for the coefficients of powers not only of the binomial $x + y$, but also of the trinomial $x + y + z$, in fact, of any polynomial; so that when given the power of any degree say the tenth, and any term contained in it, as $x^5 y^3 z^2$,[1] it should be possible to assign the coefficient (numerum coefficientem) which it must have...

---

[1] [*Commercium Philosophicum...*, I, p. 47. The term $x^5 y^1 z^1$ there given is evidently a misprint.]

[Jean Bernoulli to Leibniz, June 8, 1695[1]]

Let it be required to raise any polynomial $s + x + y + z$ etc. to an arbitrary power r, and let it be required to find the coefficient of the term $s^a x^b y^c z^e$ etc. I say that that coefficient will be

$$\frac{r \cdot r - 1 \cdot r - 2 \cdot r - 3 \cdot r - 4 \ldots a + 1}{1 \cdot 2 \cdot 3 \ldots b \times 1 \cdot 2 \cdot 3 \ldots c \times 1 \cdot 2 \cdot 3 \ldots e \text{ etc.}};$$

that is, the required coefficient will be given by the product of all terms of the arithmetic progression which begins with the number of the power of the multinomial and decreases by 1 until the number is reached which is greater by one than the power of the first character, this product to be divided by the product of all terms of all the arithmetic progressions ascending from 1 up to the respective numbers of powers of all the letters except the first. Note that the tedious division and a considerable part of the multiplication could be eliminated by cancelling before the operation those multiplicative parts [Bernoulli's terms for factors] that the numerator has in common with the denominator. As an example we will take what you proposed: It is required to find the coefficient of the term $s^5 x^3 y^2$ comprehended in the value of the trinomial $s + x + y$ raised to the tenth power. Substituting in the general formula the values $r = 10$, $b = 3$, $c = 2$. We will have for the required coefficient $\dfrac{10 \cdot 9 \cdot 8 \cdot 7 \cdot 6}{1 \cdot 2 \cdot 3 \times 1 \cdot 2} = 10 \cdot 9 \cdot 4 \cdot 7 = 2520$. If the coefficient of $s^8 x^6 y^4 z^2$ in the expansion of the quadrinomial $s + x + y + z$ to the 20th power be required, it will be $=$

$$\frac{20 \cdot 19 \cdot 18 \cdot 17 \cdot 16 \cdot 15 \cdot 15 \cdot 13 \cdot 12 \cdot 11 \cdot 10 \cdot 9}{1 \cdot 2 \cdot 3 \cdot 4 \cdot 5 \cdot 6 \times 1 \cdot 2 \cdot 3 \cdot 4 \times 1 \cdot 2} =$$

$$19 \cdot 17 \cdot 5 \cdot 7 \cdot 13 \cdot 12 \cdot 11 \cdot 10 \cdot 9 = 1745944200.$$

It would be a pleasure to see your rule and it would be well to test whether they agree [experiri liceret, ut inter se consentiant]; yours is possibly simpler:

[Jacques(I) Bernoulli, in the *Ars Conjectandi*[2]]

It is proper here to note the peculiar συμπάθειαν between combinations and powers of multinomials. At the beginning of the

---

[1] [*Ibid.*, p. 55. In this Jean Bernoulli derives the *regula mirabilis* referred to above by Leibniz.]

[2] [The formula is found at the end of Chapter VIII of the second part of his classical work. Having disposed of the problem to find the number of arrangements of many various things when each one may also be combined with itself according to one exponent, he proceeds as in the above translation.]

chapter it has been shown that in order to find the "binions" of all the letters a, b, c, d, each of the letters must be put before every other one (including itself); and in order to get the "ternions," every one of the "binions" must be written before every one of the letters. But the same must take place when the literal quantity [*quantitas literalis*] $a + b + c + d$ is raised to the second, third, and higher powers. It follows from this that when the same symbols are regarded as parts of any multinomial, the "binions" will represent all the terms of the square; the "ternions," the terms of the cube; and the "quaternions," the terms of the fourth power. The terms of the power will be expressed by the addition of the combinations of the parts of the base to the order indicated by the index of the power. Since, however, all the terms containing the same letters, arranged in different ways, represent the same quantity, they should be combined in one term for the sake of brevity. To this terms should be prefixed the number of such equivalent terms, which number is called the coefficient of the term. It is evident that the coefficient of any term is equal to the number of permutations of its characters. The total number of terms is equal to the number of combinations of the order of the index of the power that can be formed of the elements of the base (when the order of terms is disregarded). This number can be found by the rule explained in Chapter V.

The great value of this observation may be seen from the fact that by its means, it is possible to promptly determine both the number of terms in a power and the coefficient of any term. Thus, for example, the tenth power of the trinomial $(a + b + c)$, consists of $\dfrac{11.12}{1.2} \backsim 66$ terms, by the rule of chapter V; and the coefficient of the term a^5b^3cc [1] by the second rule of chapter I, is

$$\frac{1.2.3.4.5.6.7.8.9.10}{1.2.3.4 \text{ in } 1.2.3 \text{ in } 1.2} \backsim 2520.$$

Similarly the cube of the quadrinomial $a + b + c + d$ will be composed of $\dfrac{4.5.6}{1.2.3} \backsim 20$ terms, and the terms aab and abc will have as coefficients the numbers 3 and 6.

---

[1] [It is interesting that Jacques (I) Bernoulli used the example discussed in the correspondence between Leibniz and Jean (I) Bernoulli.]

HORNER'S METHOD

(Selected and Edited by Margaret McGuire, A.M., Teachers College, Columbia University, New York City.)

William George Horner (1786–1837) was educated at Kingswood School, near Bristol, but had no university training and was not a noted mathematician. In 1809, he established a school at Bath, where he remained until his death. It was there that he discovered the method of approximating roots of higher numerical equations which is his sole claim for fame. His method closely resembles that which seems to have been developed during the thirteenth century by the Chinese and perfected by Chin Kiu-shao about 1250.[1] It is also very similar to the approximation process effected in 1804 by Paolo Ruffini (1765–1822).[2] The probability is, however, that neither Horner nor Ruffini knew of the work of the other and that neither was aware of the ancient Chinese method. Apparently Horner knew very little of any previous work in approximation, as he did not mention in his article the contributions of Vieta, Harriot, Oughtred, or Wallis.

The paper here reproduced, the first written by Horner on approximations, was read before the Royal Society July 1, 1819 and was published in the *Philosophical Transactions of the Royal Society of London*, 1819, pp. 308–335. The modern student of mathematics will notice at once the length and difficulty of Horner's treatment when comparing it with the simple, elementary explanation in modern texts. In speaking of the publication of the article in the *Transactions*, T. S. Davies said: "The elementary character of the subject was the professed objection; his recondite mode of treating it was the professed passport for its admission." The paper was reprinted in the *Ladies' Diary* of 1838 and two revisions were published,—the first in Leybourn's *Repository*, (1830) and the second (posthumously) in the first volume (1845) of *The Mathematician*. In his original article, Horner made use of Taylor's Theorem, obtaining his transformations by methods of the calculus, but in his revisions he used ordinary algebra and gave a more simple explanation of the process.

XXI. *A new method of solving numerical equations of all orders, by continuous approximation.*[3] *By* W. G. Horner, *Esq. Communicated by* Davies Gilbert, *Esq. F. R. S.*

Read July 1, 1819.

1. THE process which it is the object of this Essay to establish, being nothing else than the leading theorem in the Calculus of

---

[1] Smith, D. E., *History of Mathematics* (New York, 1925) Vol. II, p. 381.

[2] Cajori, F. "Horner's Method of Approximation Anticipated by Ruffini" *Bulletin of American Mathematical Society*, XVII (1911), pp. 409–414.

[3] The only object proposed by the author in offering this Essay to the acceptance of the Royal Society, for admission into the Philosophical Transactions, is to secure beyond the hazard of controversy, an Englishman's property

Derivations, presented under a new aspect, may be regarded as a universal instrument of calculation, extending to the composition as well as analysis of functions of every kind. But it comes into most useful application in the numerical solution of equations.

2. ARBOGAST's developement of

$$\varphi(\alpha+\beta x+\gamma x^2+\delta x^3+\epsilon x^4+\ldots)$$

(See *Calc. des Der.* § 33) supposes all the coefficients within the parenthesis to be known previously to the operation of φ. To the important cases in which the discovery of γ, δ, &c. depends on the previous developement of the partial functions

$$\varphi(\alpha+\beta x), \quad \varphi(\alpha+\beta x+\gamma x^2), \quad \text{&c.}$$

it is totally inapplicable. A theorem which should meet this deficiency, without sacrificing the great facilitating principle of attaching the functional symbols to α alone, does not appear to have engaged the attention of mathematicians, in any degree proportionate to the utility of the research. This desideratum it has been my object to supply. The train of considerations pursued is sufficiently simple; and as they have been regulated by a particular regard to the genius of arithmetic, and have been carried to the utmost extent, the result seems to possess all the harmony and simplicity that can be desired; and to unite to continuity and perfect accuracy, a degree of facility superior even to that of the best popular methods.

Investigation of the Method.

3. In the general equation

$$\varphi x = 0$$

I assume $x = \text{R} + r + r' + r'' + \ldots\ldots$
and preserve the binomial and continuous character of the operations, by making successively

$$
\begin{aligned}
x = \text{R} \ &+ z \ \ = \text{R} \ + r \ + z' \\
&= \text{R}' \ + z' \ = \text{R}' + r' + z'' \\
&= \text{R}'' + z'' = \text{&c.}
\end{aligned}
$$

in a useful discovery. Useful he may certainly be allowed to call it, though the produce of a purely mathematical speculation; for of all the investigations of pure mathematics, the subject of *approximation* is that which comes most directly, and most frequently into contact with the practical wants of the calculator.

How far the manner in which he has been so fortunate as to contemplate it has conduced, by the result, to satisfy those wants, it is not for him to determine; but his belief is, that both Arithmetic and Algebra have received some degree of improvement, and a more intimate union. The abruptness of transition has been broken down into a gentle and uniform acclivity.

Where R^n represents the whole portion of x which has already been subjected to φ, and $z_x = r^x + z^{x'}$ the portion still excluded; but of which the part r^x is immediately ready for use, and is to be transferred from the side of z to that of R, so as to change φR^x to $\varphi R^{x'}$ without suspending the corrective process.

4. By TAYLOR's theorem, expressed in the more convenient manner of ARBOGAST, we have

$$\varphi x = \varphi(R + z) =$$
$$\varphi R + D\varphi R \cdot z + D^2\varphi R \cdot z^2 + D^3\varphi R \cdot z^3 + \ldots\ldots$$

Where by $D^n\varphi R$ is to be understood $\dfrac{d^n\varphi R}{1.2\ldots\ldots n.dR^{n'}}$, viz. the nth derivee with its proper denominator; or, that function which ARBOGAST calls the *derivée divisée*, and distinguishes by a c subscribed. Having no occasion to refer to any other form of the derivative functions, I drop the distinctive symbol for the sake of convenience. Occasionally these derivees will be represented by a, b, c, &c.

5. Supposing φR and its derivees to be known, the mode of valuing $\varphi R'$ or $\varphi(R + r)$ is obvious. We have only to say in the manner of LAGRANGE, when preparing to develope his Theory of Functions,

$$\varphi R' = \varphi R + Ar$$
$$A = D\varphi R + Br$$
$$B = D^2\varphi R + Cr$$
$$C = D^3\varphi R + Dr$$
$$\cdot \quad \cdot \quad \cdot \quad \cdot \quad \cdot \quad \cdot \quad \cdot \quad \cdot$$
$$V = D^{n-2}\varphi R + Ur$$
$$U = D^{n-1}\varphi R + r \quad \cdot \quad \cdot \quad \cdot \quad \cdot \quad [\text{I.}]$$

Taking these operations in reverse order, we ascend with rapidity to the value of $\varphi(R + r)$ or $\varphi R'$.

6. The next point is, to apply a similar principle to discover the value of $\varphi(R + r + r') = \varphi(R' + r') = \varphi R''$. We here have

$$\varphi R'' = \varphi R' + A'r'$$
$$A' = D\varphi R' + B'r'$$
$$B' = D^2\varphi R' + C'r'$$
$$C' = D^3\varphi R' + D'r'$$
$$\cdot \quad \cdot \quad \cdot \quad \cdot \quad \cdot \quad \cdot \quad \cdot \quad \cdot \quad \cdot$$
$$V' = D^{n-2}\varphi R' + U'r'$$
$$U' = D^{n-1}\varphi R' + r'$$

But the former operation determined $\varphi R'$ only, without giving the value of any of the derived functions. The very simple scale of known quantities, therefore, by which we advance so rapidly in the first process, fails in those which follow.

7. Still we can reduce these formulæ to known terms; for since we have in general

$$D^r D^s \varphi \alpha = \frac{r+1 \cdot r+2 \ldots\ldots r+s}{1 \quad 2 \quad\quad s} D^{r+s} \varphi \alpha$$

(See ARBOGAST, § 137); by applying a similar reduction to the successive terms in the developement of $D^m \varphi R' = D^m \varphi (R+r)$, we obtain [1]

$$D^m \varphi R' = D^m \varphi R + \frac{m+1}{1} D^{m+1} \varphi R \cdot r + \frac{m+1}{1} \cdot \frac{m+2}{2} D^{m+2} \varphi R \cdot r^2$$

$$+ \frac{m+1 \ldots\ldots m+3}{1 \quad\quad\quad 3} D^{m+3} \varphi R \cdot r^3 + \&c.$$

And it is manifest that this expression may be reduced to a form somewhat more simple, and at the same time be accommodated to our principle of successive derivation, by introducing the letters A, B, C, &c. instead of the functional expressions.

8. As a general example, let

$$M = D^m \quad \varphi R + Nr$$
$$N = D^{m+1} \varphi R + Pr$$
$$P = D^{m+2} \varphi R + Qr$$
$$\cdots\cdots\cdots$$

represent any successive steps in the series in Art. 5; then are

$$D^m \quad \varphi R = M - Nr$$
$$D^{m+1} \varphi R = N - Pr$$
$$D^{m+2} \varphi R = P - Qr$$
$$\cdots\cdots\cdots$$

---

[1] This theorem, of which that in Art. 4 is a particular case [$m = o$], has been long in use under a more or less restricted enunciation, in aid of the transformation of equations. HALLEY's *Speculum Analyticum*, NEWTON's limiting equations, and the formulæ in SIMPSON's Algebra (ed. 5, p. 166, *circa fin.*) are instances. In a form still more circumscribed [$r = 1$, $R = o$, 1, 2, &c.] it constitutes the *Nouvelle Metbode* of BUDAN; which has been deservedly characterized by LAGRANGE as simple and elegant. To a purpose which will be noticed hereafter, it applies very happily; but regarded as an instrument of approximation, its extremely slow operation renders it perfectly nugatory: and as LEGENDRE justly reported, and these remarks prove, it has not the merit of originality.

And by substituting these equivalents in the developement just enounced, it becomes

$$D^m\varphi R' = M + mNr + \frac{m \cdot m+1}{1 \quad 2}Pr^2 + \frac{m...m+2}{1....3}Qr^3 + \&c.$$

9. With this advantage, we may now return to the process of Art. 6, which becomes

$$\varphi R'' = \varphi R' + A'r'$$
$$A' = (A + Br + Cr^2 + Dr^3 + Er^4 + \&c.) + B'r'$$
$$B' = (B + 2Cr + 3Dr^2 + 4Er^3 + \&c.) + C'r'$$
$$C' = (C + 3Dr + 6Er^2 + \&c.) + D'r'$$

$$\cdot \quad \cdot \quad \cdot \quad \cdot \quad \cdot \quad \cdot \quad \cdot \quad \cdot$$

$$V' = (V + \frac{n-2}{1}Ur + \frac{n-2 \cdot n-1}{1 \cdot 2}r^2) + U'r'$$

$$U' = (U + \frac{n-1}{1}r) + r' \quad \cdot \quad \quad \cdot \quad \cdot \qquad \text{[II.]}$$

Taking these operations in reverse order as before, by determining U', V'....C', B', A', we ascend to the value of $\varphi R''$.

10. In this theorem, the principle of successive derivation already discovers all its efficacy; for it is obvious that the next functions U'', V''.....C'', B'', A'', $\varphi R'''$, flow from the substitution of A', B', C',....V', U', $\varphi R''$, r', r'', for A, B, C....V, U, $\varphi R'$, r, r', in these formulæ; and from these U''', V'''', &c.; and so on to any desirable extent. In this respect, Theorem II, algebraically considered, perfectly answers the end proposed in Art. 2.

11. We perceive also, that some advance has been made toward arithmetical facility; for all the figurate coefficients here employed are lower by one order than those which naturally occur in transforming an equation of the nth degree. But it is much to be wished, that these coefficients could be entirely dispensed with. Were this object effected, no multipliers would remain, except the successive corrections of the root, and the operations would thus arrange themselves, in point of simplicity, in the same class as those of division and the square root.

12. Nor will this end appear unattainable, if we recur to the known properties of figurate numbers; which present to our view, as *equivalent to the nth term of the mth series:*

1. *The difference of the nth and $n-1^{th}$ term of the $m+1^{th}$ series.*

2. *The sum of the first n terms of the $m-1^{th}$ series.*

3. *The sum of the nth term of the $m-1^{th}$, and the $n-1^{th}$ term of the mth series.*

The depression already attained has resulted from the first of these properties, and a slight effort of reflection will convince us that the second may immediately be called to our aid.

13. For this purpose, let the results of Art. 9 be expressed by the following notation:

$$\varphi R'' = \varphi R' + A'r'$$
$$A' = A_1 + B'r'$$
$$B' = B_2 + C'r'$$
$$C' = C_3 + D'r'$$
$$\cdot \quad \cdot \quad \cdot \quad \cdot \quad \cdot \quad \cdot \quad \cdot$$
$$V' = V_{n-2} + U'r'$$
$$U' = U_{n-1} + r'$$

the exponents subjoined to any letter indicating the degree of the figurate coefficients in that formula of the theorem, of which such letter is the first term.

14. Although this statement appears only to have returned to us the conditions of Art. 6, with all their disadvantages, and to have merely substituted

$$A_1 \text{ for } D\varphi R' \text{ or } a'$$
$$B_2 \text{ for } D^2\varphi R' \text{ or } b'$$
$$C_3 \text{ for } D^3\varphi R' \text{ or } c'$$

&c. yet, by means of the property just alluded to, the essential data A, B, C, &c. which have disappeared, will again be extricated. For the developement of $D^m\varphi R'$, found in Art. 8, undergoes thereby the following analysis:

$$M + mNr + \frac{m \cdot m+1}{1 \cdot 2}Pr^2 + \frac{m \cdot m+1 \cdot m+2}{1 \cdot 2 \cdot 3}Qr^3 + \ldots$$
$$= M + Nr + \quad Pr^2 + \quad Qr^3 + \ldots$$
$$\quad\quad + Nr + 2Pr^2 + 3Qr^3 + \ldots$$
$$\quad\quad + Nr + 3Pr^2 + 6Qr^3 + \ldots$$
$$\cdot \quad\quad \cdot \quad\quad \cdot \quad\quad \cdot \quad\quad \cdot \quad\quad \cdot$$
$$\quad\quad + Nr + mPr^3 + \frac{m \cdot m+1}{1 \cdot 2}Qr^3 + \ldots$$

which equivalence will be thus expressed:

$$M_m = M + N_1 r + N_2 r + N_3 r + \ldots + N_m r$$

Returning therefore once more to our theorem, we now have

$$\varphi R'' = \varphi R' + A'r'$$
$$A = (A + B_1r) + B'r'$$
$$B' = (B + C_1r + C_2r) + C'r'$$
$$C' = (C + D_1r + D_2r + D_3r) + D'r'$$
$$\cdot \quad \cdot \quad \cdot \quad \cdot \quad \cdot \quad \cdot \quad \cdot \quad \cdot$$
$$V' = (V + U_1r + U_2r + U_3r + \ldots\ldots U_{n-1}r) + U'r'$$
$$U' = (U + \overline{n-1} \cdot r) + r'$$

15. This theorem employs exactly the same total number of addends as Theorem II, but with the important improvement, that the number of addends to each derivee is inversely as their magnitude, contrary to what happened before. Figurate multipliers are also excluded. And it is easy to convince ourselves that no embarrassment will arise from the newly introduced functions. For if we expand any of the addends N_kr in the general formula equivalent to M_m, and analyze it by means of the *third property* of figurate series, we shall find

$$M_kr = N_{k-1}r + P_krr.$$

And since we take the scale in our Theorem in a reverse or ascending order, this formula merely instructs us to multiply an addend already determined by r, and to add the product to another known addend; and if we trace its effect through all the descending scale, to the first operations, we observe that the addends to the last derivee, from which the work begins, are simply r repeated $n-1$ times.

16. Because $N_o = N$, the addend exterior to the parenthesis, might for the sake of uniformity be written $N_o'r'$. The harmony of the whole scheme would then be more completely displayed. To render the simplicity of it equally perfect, we may reflect that as the factors r, r', &c. are engaged in no other manner than has just been stated, viz. in effecting the subordinate derivations, their appearance among the principal ones is superfluous, and tends to create embarrassment. Assume therefore

$$_kN = N_kr,$$

and we have

$$\varphi R'' = \varphi R' + {}_0A'$$
$$A' = (A + {}_1B) + {}_0B''$$

$$B' = (B + {}_1C + {}_2C) + {}_0C'$$
$$C' = (C + {}_1D + {}_2D + {}_3D) + {}_0D'$$

. . . .

$$V' = (V + {}_1U + {}_2U + {}_3U + \ldots\ldots {}_{n-2}U) + {}_0U'$$
$$U' = (U + \overline{n-1} \cdot r) + r' \qquad . \qquad . \qquad . \qquad \text{[III]}$$

the subordinate derivations being understood.

17. The Theorems hitherto give only the synthesis of φx, when $x = R + r + r' + \&c.$ is known. To adapt them to the inverse or analytical process, we have only to subtract each side of the first equation from the value of φx; then assuming $\varphi x - \varphi R^x = \Delta^x$, we have

$$\Delta' = \Delta - {}_0A$$
$$A = a + {}_0B$$

&c. as in Theorem I.

$$\Delta'' = \Delta' - {}_0A'$$
$$A' = (A + {}_1B) + {}_0B'$$

&c. as in Theorem II. or III.

The successive invention of R, r, r', &c. will be explained among the numerical details. In the mean time, let it be observed that these results equally apply to the popular formula $\varphi x = $ constant, as to $\varphi x = 0$.

18. I shall close this investigation, by exhibiting the whole chain of derivation in a tabular form. The calculator will then perceive, that the algebraic composition of the addends no longer requires his attention. He is at liberty to regard the characters by which they are represented, in the light of mere corresponding symbols, whose origin is fully explained at their first occurrence in the table, and their ultimate application at the second. The operations included in the parentheses may be mentally effected, whenever r is a simple digit. And lastly, the vertical arrangement of the addends adapts them at once to the purposes of arithmetic, on every scale of notation.

General Synopsis.

n—1th Der.	n—2th Derivee.	n—3th Derivee.	3rd. Derivee.	2nd. Derivee.	1st. Derivee.	Synthesis.	Anal: Root. R+r.....
u	*v*	*t*	*c*	*b*	*a*	φR	Δ
$r\,(Ur=)\ _0U$	$(rV=)\ _0V$	&c.	$Dr=)\ _0D$	$(Cr=)\ _0C$	$(Br=)\ _0B$	$(Ar=)\ _0A$	$-_0A$
U	V	T	C	B	A		
$\overline{n-1}.r$ $(_0U+r^2=)\ _1U$	$(_0V+_1Ur=)_1V$	&c. to $_{n-3}V$	$(_0D+_1Er=)_1D$	$(_0C+_1Dr=)_1C$	$(_0B+_1Cr=)_1B$		
$(_1U+r^2=)\ _2U$	$(_1V+_2Ur=)_2V$		$(_1D+_2Er=)_2D$	$(_1C+_2Dr=)_2C$			
&c. to $_{n-2}U$	&c. to $_{n-3}V$		$(_2D+_3Er=)_3D$				
$r'\,(U'r'=)\ _0U'$	$(V'r'=)\ _0V'$		$(D'r'=)\ _0D'$	$(C'r'=)\ _0C'$	$(B'r'=)\ _0B'$	$(A'r'=)\ _0A'$	$-_0A'$
U'	V'		C'	B'	A'	$\varphi R''$	Δ'
$\overline{n-1}.r'$ $(_0U'+r'^2=)_1U$	$(_0V+_1U'r'=)_1V'$	&c.	$C'\,(_0D'+_1E'r'=)_1D'$	$C'\,(_0C'+_1D'r'=)_1C'$	$(_0B'+_1C'r'=)_1B'$	$(A''r''=)\ _0A''$	$-_0A''$
&c.	&c.		&c.	&c.	&c.	$\varphi R''$ Δ''	
					&c.	&c.	

Illustrations.

19. The remarks which are yet to be adduced will bear almost exclusively on the Analytic portion of the Theorem, from which the Synthetic differs only in the less intricate management of the first derivee; this function having no concern with the discovery of the root, and its multiple being additive like all the rest, instead of subtractive.

From the unrestricted nature of the notation employed, it is evident that no class of equations, whether finite, irrational or transcendental, is excluded from our design. In this respect indeed, the new method agrees with the established popular methods of approximation; a circumstance in favour of the latter, which is overlooked by many algebraists, both in employing those methods, and in comparing them with processes pretending to superior accuracy. The radical feature which distinguishes them from ours is this: they forego the influence of all the derivees, excepting the first and perhaps the second; ours provides for the effectual action of all.

20. Concerning these *derivées* little need be said, as their nature and properties are well known. It is sufficient to state that they may be contemplated either as differential coefficients, as the limiting equations of NEWTON, or as the numerical coefficients of the transformed equation in $R+z$. This last elementary view will suffice for determining them, in most of the cases to which the popular solutions are adequate; viz. in finite equations where R, an unambiguous limiting value of x, is readily to be conjectured. When perplexity arises in consequence of some roots being imaginary, or differing by small quantities,[1] the second notation must be called in aid. The first, in general, when φx is irrational or transcendental.

21. The fact just stated, namely, that our theorem contains within itself the requisite conditions for investigating the limits, or presumptive impossibility, of the roots, demonstrates its sufficiency for effecting the developement of the real roots, independently of any previous knowledge of R. For this purpose, we might assume $R=0$; r, r, &c. $=1$ or $.1$ &c. and adopt, as most suitable to these conditions, the algorithm of Theorem II, until we had arrived at R^z, an unambiguous limiting value of x. But

---

[1] [Horner did not show how to separate two nearly equal roots. He elaborated this discussion in his second paper published in Leybourn's *Repositorv.* Vol. **V**, part II, London, 1830, pp. 21–75.]

since these initiatory researches seem more naturally to depend on the simple derivees, a, b, &c. than on A, B, &c. their aggregates; and since, in fact, as long as r is assumptive or independent of R, our system of derivation offers no peculiar advantage; I should prefer applying the limiting formulæ in the usual way; passing however from column to column (WOOD, § 318.) of the results, at first by means of the neat algorithm suggested in the note on Art. 7, and afterwards by differencing, &c. as recommended by LAGRANGE, (*Res. des Eq. Num.* § 13), when the number of columns has exceeded the dimensions of the equation. (Vide Addendum.)

If, during this process the observation of DE GUA be kept in view, that whenever all the roots of φx are real, $D^{m-1}\varphi x$ and $D^{m+1}\varphi x$ will have contrary signs when $D^m\phi x$ is made to vanish, we shall seldom be under the necessity of resorting to more recondite criteria of impossibility. Every column in which o appears between results affected with like signs, will apprize us of a distinct pair of imaginary roots; and even a horizontal change of signs, occurring between two horizontal permanences of an identical sign, will induce a suspicion, which it will in general be easy, in regard of the existing case, either to confirm or to overthrow.

22. The facilities here brought into a focus, constitute, I believe, a perfectly novel combination; and which, on that account, as well as on account of its natural affinity to our own principles, and still more on account of the extreme degree of simplicity it confers on the practical investigation of limits, appears to merit the illustration of one or two familiar examples.

Ex. 1. Has the equation $x^4-4x^3+8x^2-16x+20=0$ any real root?—See EULER, C. D. p. 678.

$x =$	0	1	2
	20	9	4
	-16	-8	0
	8	2	8
	-4	0	4
	.1	1	1

Here the first column consists of the given co-efficients taken in reverse order. In the second, 9 is = the sum of the first column, -8 is $=-16+2(8)+3(-4)+4(1)$, 2 is $=8+3(-4)+6(1)$, &c. The third column is formed from the second, by the same easy process. We need proceed no farther; for the sequences 2, 0, 1 in the second column, and 4, 0, 8 in the third, show that the equation has two pairs of imaginary roots. Consequently it has no real root.

Ex. 2. To determine the nearest distinct limits of the positive roots of $x^3 - 7x + 7 = 0$. See LAGRANGE, *Res. des E. N.* § 27, and note 4. § 8.

Operating as in the former example, we have

$x =$	0	1	2
	7	1	1
	-7	-4	5
	0	3	6
	1	1	1

Since all the signs are now positive, 2 is greater than any of the positive roots. Again, between -4 and $+5$, it is manifest, that o will occur as a value of the first derivee, and that the simultaneous value of the second derivee will be affirmative. But as the principal result has evidently converged and subsequently diverged again in this interval, no conclusion relative to the simultaneous sign of that result can be immediately drawn. We will return to complete the transformations.

For $x =$	1.0	1.1	1.2	1.3	1.4	1.5	1.6	1.7
	1000	631	328	97	-56	-125	-104	13
	-400	-337	-268					
	30	33	36					
	1	1	1					

Here the first column was formed from that under $x=1$, by annexing ciphers according to the dimensions of the functions; the 2nd and 3rd columns and the number 97 were found as in the former Example; the remaining numbers by differencing and extending the series 1000,631,328,97. We have no need to continue the work, since the changes of signs in the principal results indicate the first digits of the roots in question to be 1.3 and 1.6. But if we proceed by farther differencing to complete all the lines, the columns standing under these numbers will give the co-efficients of $\varphi(1.3 + z)$ and $\varphi(1.6 + z)$ without farther trouble.

23. Assuming, then, that R has been determined, and R+z substituted for x in the proposed equation, thereby transforming it to

$$\Delta = az + bz^2 + cz^3 + dz^4 + \ldots\ldots\ldots$$

it is to this latter equation that the analytical part of our theorem is more immediately adapted. Now the slightest degree of reflection will evince, that our method is absolutely identical for all equations of the same order, whether they be binomial or adfected, as soon as the transformation in R has been accomplished. The following description, therefore, of a familiar process in arithmetic, will convey an accurate general idea of our more extensive calculus, and obviate the necessity of any formal precepts.

In Evolution, the first step is unique, and if not assisted by an effort of memory, could only be tentative. The whole subsequent process may be defined, *division by a variable divisor.* ·For an accurate illustration of this idea, as discoverable in the existing practice of arithmeticians, we cannot however refer to the mode of extracting any root, except that of the square; and to this, only in its most recently improved state. Here, in passing from one divisor to another, *two additive corrections* are introduced; the first depending on the last correction of the root, the second on the correction actually making. And this *new quotient correction* of the root, since it must exist previously to the completion of the divisor by which it is to be verified, *is required to be found by means of the incomplete divisor*; and may be taken out, either to one digit only, as is most usual, or to a number of digits equal to that which the complete and incomplete divisors possess in common. And farther, as these *divisors* may not, *in the first* instance, agree accurately even in a single digit, it is necessary at that stage of the operation, mentally to anticipate the effect of the new quotient, so as to obtain a sufficiently correct idea of the magnitude of the new divisor.

24. This is an accurate statement of the relation which the column headed by the first derivee bears to the analysis. The remaining columns contribute their aid, as successively subsidiary to each other; the contributions commencing with the last or $n-1^{th}$ derivee, and being conveyed to the first through a regular system of *preparatory addends* dependent on the last quotient-correction, and of *closing addends* dependent on the new one. The *overt and registered* manner of conducting the whole calculation, enables us to derive important advantage from *anticipated corrections* of the divisors, not only at the first step, but, if requisite, through the whole performance, and also, without the necessity of a minute's bye-calculation, communicates, with the result, its *verification.*

25. Let us trace the operation of the theorem as far as may be requisite, through the ascending scale of equations.

1. In *Simple equations*, the reduced equation may be represented by $\Delta = az$; whence $z = \dfrac{\Delta}{a}$. Now the theorem directs us to proceed thus:

$$
\begin{array}{ll}
a & \Delta(r + r' + \ldots \\
& \underline{-ar} \\
& \Delta' \\
& \quad \underline{-ar'} \\
& \quad \Delta'' \\
& \qquad \underline{-ar'} \\
& \qquad \Delta''' \\
& \qquad \&c.
\end{array}
$$

precisely the common arithmetical process of division.

2. In *Quadratics*, we have $\Delta = az + z^2$, and proceed in this manner:

$$
\begin{array}{lll}
1 & a & \Delta(r + r' + \ldots \\
& \dfrac{r}{A} & \dfrac{-Ar}{\Delta'} \\
& r & \dfrac{-A'r'}{\Delta''} \\
& \dfrac{r'}{A'} & \&c. \\
& \&c. &
\end{array}
$$

the known arithmetical process for extracting the square root.

3. At *Cubic equations*, the aberration of the old practice of evolution commences, and our theorem places us at once on new ground. We have here

$$\Delta = az + bz^2 + z^3$$

and must proceed thus:

$$
\begin{array}{llll}
1 & b & a & \Delta(r + r + \ldots \\
& \dfrac{r}{B} & \dfrac{Br = {}_0B}{A} & \dfrac{-Ar}{\Delta'} \\
& 2r & {}_0B + r^2 = {}_1B & \dfrac{-A'r'}{\Delta''} \\
& \dfrac{r'}{B'} & \dfrac{B'r'}{A'} & \&c. \\
& \&c. & \&c. &
\end{array}
$$

This *ought to be* the arithmetical practice of the cube root, as an example will prove.

. . .

Ex. I. *Extract the cube root of* 48228544.

Having distributed the number into tridigital periods as usual, we immediately perceive that the first figure of the root is $3 = R$. Consequently, the first subtrahend is $R^3 = 27$, the first derivee $3R^2 = 27$, the second $3R = 9$; the third $(= 1,)$ need not be written. Hence

. . .

```
                                          48228544(364
   9.             27..                     27
   6    ⌐··········· 576                    ──
   ─    ⌐··········· ──                     21228
  96··· ┘           3276·················· 19656
  12.               612..                   ──
   4    ⌐···········4336                   1572544
  ──    ⌐···········──            ⌐········1572544
1084···┘           393136··········┘
```

In this example the reader will perceive that no supplementary operations are concealed. The work before him is complete, and may be verified mentally. I need not intimate *how much more concise it is than even the abbreviated statement of the old process.* (See HUTTON's *Course.*)

The station of 1, 2, &c. numeral places respectively, which the closing addends occupy in advance of the preparatory ones, is an obvious consequence of combining the numeral relation of the successive root-figures with the potential relation of the successive derivees. In fact, as is usual in arithmetic, we tacitly regard the last root-figure as units, and the new one as a decimal fraction; then the common rules of decimal addition and multiplication regulate the vertical alineation of the addends.

26. The advantage of mental verification is common to the solution of equations of every order, provided the successive corrections of the root be simple digits: for the parenthetic derivations will, in that case, consist of multiplying a given number by a digit, and adding the successive digital products to the corresponding digits of another given number; all which may readily be done without writing a figure intermediate to these given numbers and the combined result. For this reason the procedure by single digits appears generally preferable.

Nevertheless, to assist the reader in forming his own option, and at the same time to institute a comparison with known methods on their own grounds, I introduce one example illustrative of the advantage which arises from the anticipatory correction of the divisors spoken of in Art. 24, when the object is to secure a high degree of convergency by as few approximations as possible. The example is that by which NEWTON elucidates his method. I premise as the depreciators of NEWTON do, that it is an extremely easy problem; and I say this to invite comparison, not so much with his mode of treating it, as with theirs.

Ex. II. What is the value of x in the equation $x^3 - 2x = 5$.[1]

The root is manifestly a very little greater than 2. Make it $x = 2+z$, and the equation becomes

$$1 = 10z + 6z^2 + z^3.$$

Hence, arranging the derivees,

$$6. \qquad\qquad 10.. \qquad\qquad \overset{.\quad.}{1.000(}$$
$$6$$

The first digit will obviously be so nearly 1, that by anticipating its effect on the divisor, we are sure this will be very nearly 106. Hence

$$10.6)1.000(.094 \text{ first correction}$$

The square is $94^2 = 8836$.
Hence we have

$$6... \qquad\qquad 10...... \qquad\qquad \overset{.\quad.\quad.\quad.}{1.000000000(.094}$$
$$094 \qquad\qquad\quad 572836 \qquad\qquad\quad 993846584$$
$$\overline{6094 \times 94 =} \qquad \overline{10572836} \qquad\qquad \overline{6153416}$$
$$188 \qquad\qquad\quad 581672$$
$$\qquad\qquad\quad 3$$

The first digit of the next correction will evidently be 5; the effect of which we have as before anticipated as far as one digit. The divisor will therefore be 11158 correct to the last figure. Hence

$$11158)6153416(55148, \text{ second correction.}$$

The square is 30413, &c. to 10 digits.

---

[1] [The equation $x^3 - 2x - 5 = 0$ is Newton's classic example, also used by Ruffini.]

Hence,

6094	10572836
18855148	581672

628255148×5 &c. = ⸺ 34647014901904   6153416

110296.   11157972701490120́4 ⸺ 615339878541781019

34650056   1721458218981

1

Consequently,

1116143772)1721458218979(1542326590,22

This third correction is carried two places beyond the extent of the divisor, for the sake of ascertaining rigidly the degree of accuracy now attained. For this purpose, we proceed thus: 628 &c. × 154 &c. = ,968, &c. is the true correction of the last divisor. Our anticipated correction was 1,000. For which if we substitute 968 &c. it will appear that our divisor should have ended in 1,678, &c. instead of 2. The error is, ,322 &c. which induces an ultimate error of (111 &c. : 154 &c. ::, 322 &c. &c. :),44 &c.

Consequently, our third correction should be.... 1542326590,66, &c. agreeing to 10 figures with the value previously determined. And the root is

$$x = 2.094551481542326590, \text{ &c.}$$

correct in the 18th decimal place at three approximations.

So rapid an advance is to be expected only under very favorable data. Yet this example clearly affixes to the new method, a character of unusual boldness and certainty; advantages derived from the overt manner of conducting the work, which thus contains its own proof.

The abbreviations used in the close of this example, are of a description sufficiently obvious and inartificial; but in order to perfect the algorithm of our method in its application to higher equations, and to the progress by simple digits, attention must be given to the following general principles of

Compendious Operation.[1]

....

28. From these principles we form the following conclusions, demonstrative of the facilities introduced by this improvement on the original process:

1. Whatever be the dimensions (n) of the proposed equation, whose root is to be determined to a certain number of places, only

---

[1] [These principles are stated in Article 27.]

$\frac{1}{n}$th part of that number (reckoning from the point at which the highest place of the closing addend begins to advance to the right of that of the first derivee) needs to be found by means of the process peculiar to the complete order of the equation; after which, $\frac{1}{n \cdot n-1}$ may be found by the process of the $n-1^{th}$ order, $\frac{1}{n-1 \cdot n-2}$ by that of the $n-2^{th}$ order, &c.

2. Several of these inferior processes will often be passed over *per saltum;* and when this advantage ceases, or does not occur, the higher the order of the process, the fewer will be the places determinable by it. And in every case, the latter half of the root will be found by division simply. Meantime, the number of figures employed in verification of each successive root-digit, instead of increasing, is rapidly diminishing.

3. The process with which we commence, need not be of a higher order than is indicated by the number of places to which we would extend the root; and may be even reduced to an order as much lower as we please, by means of an introductory approximation.

Ex. III. Let the root of the equation in Ex. II. be determined to the tenth place of decimals.

Arranging the derivees as before, we proceeded thus: [1]

---

[1] [Horner's arrangement differs from that of Ruffini in that the coefficients of the transformed equation appear in a diagonal line, while Ruffini arranges them in the extreme right hand column. The modern arrangement would begin as follows:

```
1    0    −2   −5 |2
    +2   +4   +4
1   +2   +2  |−1
    +2   +8  |
1   +4  |+10
    +2  |
1   +6       +10        −1         |.09
    + .09   + .5481    + .949329
1   +6.09  +10.5481   |− .050671
    + .09  + .5562    |
1   +6.18 |+11.1043
    + .09 |
1   +6.27
```

etc.]

```
                                          ·  · ·  ·
  6..           10....                  1.000000(.0945514815
  ---             5481                    949329
  609           ------                  --------
   184          105481                  50671000
  ---             5562..                44517584
  62|74          25096                  --------
    |.8.       --------                  6153416
  --|--        11129396                  5578825
|..|62|82          2511|2                --------
                    314|12                574591
               ----------                 558055
              1115764|92                 --------
                   31|4|1          1|1|1|6|1)16536(14815
                    3|1|4                  11161
              ------|-|-                  -----
              111611|0|4                   5375
                    |3|1                   4465
              ------|-|-                  -----
               11161|4|1                    910
                                            893
                                            ---
                                             17
                                             11
                                             --
                                              6
                                              6
```

Consequently the root is 2.0945514815, correct to the proposed extent, as appears on comparing it with the more enlarged value already found. The work occupied a very few minutes, and may be verified by mere perusal, as not a figure was written besides those which appear. By a similar operation, in less than half an hour, I have verified the root to the whole extent found in Ex. II.[1]

. . . .

Ex. VI. If it were proposed to obtain a very accurate solution of an equation of very high dimensions, or of the irrational or transcendental kind, a plan similar to the following might be adopted. Suppose, for example, the root of

$$x^x = 100, \text{ or } x \log x = 2$$

were required correct to 60 decimal places. By an easy experiment we find $x = 3.6$ nearly; and thence, by a process of the *third* order, $x = 3.597285$ more accurately.

[1] [Examples IV and V, which have been omitted, show the extraction of roots of the equations $x^3 - 7x = -7$ and $x^5 + 2x^4 + 3x^3 + 4x^2 - 5x = 321$.]

Now, $3597286 = 98 \times 71 \times 47 \times 11$, whose logarithms, found to 61 decimals in SHARPE's Tables, give R log R $= 2.00000096658$, &c. correct to 7 figures; whence the subsequent functions need be taken out to 55 figures only. They are

$$a = \text{Mod} + \log \text{R} = .990269449408, \text{\&c.}$$
$$b = \text{Mod} \div 2\text{R} = \ldots \ldots 0^7 60364, \text{\&c.}$$
$$c = -b \div 3\text{R} = \ldots \ldots -.0^{14} 55, \text{\&c.}$$

&c. The significant part disappears after the 8th derivee; consequently, the process will at first be of the *eighth* order. If the root is now made to advance by single digits, the first of these will reduce the process to the *seventh* order; one more reduces it to the *sixth* order; two more, to the *fifth*, &c. The last 27 figures will be found by division alone.

But if the first additional correction is taken to 8 figures, and the second to 16, on the principle of Example II, we pass from the 8th order to the 4th at once, and thence to the 1st or mere division, which will give the remaining 29 figures. This mode appears in description to possess the greater simplicity, but is perhaps the more laborious.

It cannot fail to be observed, that in all these examples a great proportion of the whole labour of solution is expended on the comparatively small portion of the root, which is connected with the leading process. The toil attending this part of the solution, in examples similar in kind to the last, is very considerable; since every derivee is at this stage to receive its utmost digital extent. To obviate an unjust prejudice, I must therefore invite the reader's candid attention to the following particulars:

In all other methods the difficulty increases with the extent of the root, nearly through the whole work; in ours, it is in a great measure surmounted at the first step: in most others, there is a periodical recurrence to first conditions, under circumstances of accumulating inconvenience; in the new method, the given conditions affect the first derivees alone, and the remaining process is *arithmetically direct*, and increasingly easy to the end.

The question of practical facility may be decided by a very simple criterion; by comparing the *times* of calculation which I have specified, with a similar datum by Dr. HALLEY in favor of his own favorite method of approximation. (Philosophical Transactions for 1694.)

Addendum I. (*Vide* Art. 21.) *Note.* But in this case, it will be more elegant to find the differences at once by the theorem

$$\Delta^{t+1}D^m\varphi R' = \frac{m+1}{1}\Delta^t D^{m+1}\varphi R.r + \frac{m+1}{1}\cdot\frac{m+2}{2}\Delta^t D^{m+2}\varphi R.r + \ \&c.$$

which, supposing r to be constant, is a sufficiently obvious corollary to the theorem in Art. 7. All the results may then be derived from the first column by addition. Thus, for the latter transformations in Ex. II. Art. 22, the preparatory operation would be

1st. Terms.	Diff. 1st.	2nd.	3rd.
1000	−369	66	6
−400	63	6	
30	3		
1			

and the succeeding terms would be found by adding these differences in the usual way to the respective first terms.

Addendum II. It is with pleasure that I refer to the Imperial Encyclopædia (Art. Arithmetic) for an improved method of extracting the cube root, which should have been noticed in the proper place, had I been aware of its existence; but it was pointed out to me, for the first time, by the discoverer, Mr. EXLEY, of Bristol, after this Essay was completed. It agrees in substance with the method deduced in Art. 25, from my general principle, and affords an additional illustration of the affinity between that principle and the most improved processes of common arithmetic.

ROLLE'S THEOREM

(Translated from the French by Professor Florian Cajori, University of California, Berkeley, Calif.)

Writers on the history of mathematics of the early part of the present century did not know where in the writings of Michel Rolle the theorem named after him could be found—the theorem according to which $f'(x) = 0$ has at least one real root lying between two consecutive real roots of $f(x) = 0$. One historian went so far as to express the opinion that the theorem is wrongly attributed to Rolle. Finally, in 1910, the theorem was found in a little-known book of Rolle, entitled, *Démonstration d'une Methode pour résoudre les Egalitez de tous les degrez; suivie de deux autres Méthodes, dont la première donne les moyens de resoudre ces mêmes égalitez par la Geometrie, et la seconde, pour resoudre plusieurs questions de Diophante qui n'ont pas encore esté resoluës.* A Paris, Chez Jean Cusson, ruë Saint Jacques, à l'Image de Saint Jean Baptiste. M.DC.XCI. (pp. 128).[1] Copies of this book are in the "Bibliothèque Nationale," in the "Bibliothèque de L'Arsenal," and in the "Bibliothèque de l'Institut de France," in Paris. In this treatise the theorem in question is established only incidentally, in Rolle's demonstration of the "method of cascades" for the approximation to the roots of numerical equations.

Nowhere in his *Démonstration*, nor in his *Traité d'algebre*, a widely read book published at Paris a year earlier (1690), is there given a formal definition of a "cascade." But it is implied in what Rolle states that, if in an equation $f(x) = 0$, $f(x)$ is "multiplied by a progression," the result when simplified and equated to zero is a "cascade." He prefers to use the progression 0, 1, 2, 3, ...Then, after multiplying each term of an equation by the corresponding term of the progression, he divides the resulting expression by x and equates the quotient to zero. Thus, multiplying the terms of $a + bz + cz^2 + ...$ by the respective terms of 0, 1, 2,..., he obtains $bz + 2cz^2 + ...$; dividing this by z and equating to zero, he arrives at the first or proximate "cascade," $b + 2cz + ... = 0$. It will be seen that this result is the first derivative of the initial expression, equated to zero.

Rolle's "method of cascades" is given in his *Traité d'algebre*, without sufficient proof. To meet this criticism leveled against it, Rolle wrote the *Démonstration.* In both treatises Rolle used certain technical terms which we must explain. Complex roots of an equation, as well as all but one root of each multiple root, are called "racines défaillantes." We shall translate this phrase by "imaginary roots and multiple roots." Roots which are not "défaillantes" he calls "racines effectives;" we shall translate this by "real and distinct roots." Another term used by Rolle is "hypotheses" or "limits" of the roots. If two numbers a and b are substituted for z in $f(z)$, and $f(a)$ and

[1] See an historical article on Rolle's theorem in *Bibliotheca Mathematica*, 3rd. S., Vol. 11. pp. 300–313.

$f(b)$ have opposite signs, then between a and b there is a root of $f(z) = 0$, and a and b are called "limits" (hypotheses) of the roots.

In the extracts given below, it will be seen that Rolle's theorem is proved in Article IX for the case when the roots of the equation are all positive, and in Artile XI when the roots may be any real or complex numbers.[1]

Before applying to a given equation his "method of cascades," Rolle transforms the equation so that the coefficient of the highest power of the unknown is unity and all real roots are positive. When this is achieved he calls the equation "prepared." In the reasoning which follows the equations are assumed to be "prepared."

Before making quotations from Rolle's *Démonstration*, it is desirable to give an example of his "method of cascades." To find an upper limit of the real roots, he takes the numerically largest negative coefficient $-g$, divides g by the coefficient of the highest power of the unknown, and then adds 1 to the quotient and enough more to get a positive integer; this result is his upper limit. Given the limits 0, 6, 13 of an equation $f(v) \equiv 6v^2 - 72v + 198 = 0$, Rolle approximates to the root between, say, 6 and 13 in this manner: The mean of 6 and 13 is $9\frac{1}{2}$. By substitution of 6 and 9 in $f(v)$, opposite signs are obtained. Hence 6 and 9 are closer limits. Repeating this process yields the limits 6 and 8, and finally 7 and 8. Take 7 as the approximate root.

The "method of cascades" is illustrated by the following quotation from Rolle's *Traité d'algebre*, 1790, p. 133:

Take the equation $v^4 - 24v^3 + 198vv - 648v + 473 \infty \theta,$[2] and the first rule [rule for finding cascades] gives

$$4v - 24 \infty \theta$$
$$6vv - 72v + 198 \infty \theta$$
$$4v^3 - 72vv + 396v - 648 \infty \theta$$
$$v^4 - 24v^3 + 198vv - 648v + 473 \infty \theta$$

In the first cascade one finds $v \infty 6$; then the second has $\theta \cdot 6 \cdot 13$ for limits; and by the means of these limits one finds 4 and 7 as approximate roots of the second cascade. If one regards these approximate roots as veritable roots, they may be taken as intermediate limits of the next cascade. Accordingly the limits of the third cascade are $\theta \cdot 4 \cdot 7 \cdot 163$, by which one discovers that $3 \cdot 6 \cdot 9$ are three roots of this third cascade. Consequently, the fourth cascade has as limits $\theta \cdot 3 \cdot 6 \cdot 9 \cdot 649$. With the aid of these one finds that unity is an exact root of the proposed equation and that $6 \cdot 8 \cdot 10 \cdot$ are approximate roots."

---

[1] The first occurence of the name "Rolle's Theorem" appears to be in the writings of the Italian Mathematician Giusto Bellavitis. He used the expression "teorema del Rolle" in 1846 in the *Memorie dell' I. R. Istituto Veneto di Scienze, Lettere ed Arte*, Vol. III (reprint), p. 46, and again in 1860 in Vol. 9, § 14, p. 187.

[2] [Rolle uses the small Greek letter θ as the symbol for zero. See F. Cajori, *History of Mathematical Notations* (1928), Vol. I, §82. Rolle expresses equality by the sign ∞ used by Descartes. See F. Cajori, *op. cit.*, §191.]

The first five articles in the *Démonstration* refer to elementary matters which it is not necessary to reproduce here. In our quotation we begin with article VI.

Article VI.—Take in order [of magnitude] any number of roots which are positive and different from one another, such as 3, 7, 12, 20, and form equations containing them, such as[1]

$$z - 3 \cdot z - 7 \cdot z - 12 \cdot z - 20 \cdot \text{etc.}$$

This done, in the order shown here, it is evident, that if one substitutes θ in place of z, or else a number smaller than the first root, the results [the resulting factors] are all negative; that if one substitutes a number greater than the first root and less than the others, the results are all negative except one; if one substitutes a number greater than the first two roots and less than the others, the results are all negative except two; and so on. But if one limits the number of roots, the substitution of a number which surpasses the greatest root will give $+$ everywhere. This is clear. Therefrom it follows that if one multiplies together all the results obtained from the substitution of each number, so that there are as many respective products as there are numbers, these products will be alternatively positive and negative, or negative and positive...

Coroll. I.—It is clear that these numbers thus chosen, give by their substitution, a regular sequence of signs and thereby serve the purpose of limits of the roots.

Coroll. II.—It is evident also that if all the limits, except the first and last, are not placed singly between the roots, so to speak, the regular sequence of the signs will be broken.

Coroll. III.—It is likewise clear that the roots [all positive and distinct] are numbers placed singly between these limits, and consequently, if the roots are substituted in an equation whose roots are these limits, this substitution will yield results alternately positive and negative, or negative and positive. One sees this in the example,

$$y - 6 \cdot y - 21 \cdot y - 30. \quad \text{Roots of the equation,}[2]$$
$$y - \theta \cdot y - 12 \cdot y - 26. \quad \text{Roots of the cascade,}$$

---

[1] [The omission of parentheses as seen in Rolle is not infrequent in books of the seventeenth and eighteenth centuries. Rolle's notation is equivalent to $(z - 3)(z - 7)(z - 12)(z - 20)$ etc. See F. Cajori, *op. cit.*, Vol. I, §354.]

[2] [Rolle uses the term "equation" (*égalité*) even when the polynomial is not equated to zero, or the equality is not indicated symbolically.]

where it appears that 6 substituted for y at the cascade...gives the factors whose product is positive; that 21 gives factors whose product is negative, and that 30 gives factors whose product is positive; and consequently the roots 6, 21, 30, being each substituted for y in the cascade, in turn will give alternately $+$ and $-$...Thus the roots are limits[1] of their own limits [taken as roots]...

Coroll. VI.—If one is able to prove that the *Methode* gives necessarily the limits of all [distinct, positive] roots, it follows that there are imaginary and multiple roots when it does not yield limits. But to establish this truth, other principles are necessary.

Article VII.—If one takes each of the letters y and v to represent any number, all the arithmetical progressions which have only three terms are comprised in the following:

$$y \cdot y + v \cdot y + 2v.$$

This is unquestionable.

If one has any arithmetical progression and if one takes in that progression several successive terms, it is evident that these terms are in arithmetical progression. For example, if one has the progression $\theta . 1 . 2 . 3 . 4 . 5$. etc., and if one takes θ, 1, 2 or 1, 2, 3 or also 2, 3, 4, etc., it is clear that the terms in each are in arithmetical progression.

When I say that an equation is multiplied by a progression, it must be understood that the first term of the equation is multiplied by the first term of the progression; that the second term of the equation is multiplied by the second term of the progression, and so on. When the sum of these products is taken to be equal to θ, one says that this equation is generated by the progression.

Article VIII.—When the product of the two quantities $z - a$, $z - b$, is multiplied by the progression $y + 2v$, $y + v$, y, and b is substituted in place of the unknown in the product of the progression, the result of the substitution is measured by [*i. e.* will have the factor] $b - a$. Here is the proof:

$$\left. \begin{array}{l} ab - az + zz \\ \quad - bz \end{array} \right\} \text{ Product of } z - a \text{ and } z - b.$$

$y \cdot y + v \cdot y + 2v$　The progression.

---

[1] [This is the first reference to what we now call "Rolle's theorem," restricted as yet to the case of equations all of whose roots are real and positive.]

Multiplying,

$$
\left.
\begin{array}{l}
aby - ayz + yzz \\
\quad - byz + 2vzz \\
\quad - avz \\
\quad - bvz
\end{array}
\right\} \text{ Product which the progression gives.}
$$

Upon substituting b in place of z in the last product, one obtains $bbv - abv$, having the factor $b - a$, which was to be proved...

Coroll.—Having as above the quantity

$$
\begin{array}{l}
ab - az + zz: \\
\quad - bz
\end{array}
$$

If one multiplies it by z raised to any arbitrary power and if the product is multiplied by an arithmetical progression, it is clear that on substituting b for $\dot{z}$ in the product of the progression the result has the factor $b - a$...

Article IX.—Having as above, the given quantity,

$$
\begin{array}{l}
ab - az + zz, \\
\quad - bz
\end{array}
$$

if one multiplies it by $f + gz + bzz + rz^3 + nz^4$, and so on, so that the unknown z attains any given degree, I say that the partial products may always be disposed as follows:

$$
A \ldots \left.
\begin{array}{l}
abf - afz + fzz \\
\quad - bfz
\end{array}
\right\} \text{ First product}
$$

$$
B \ldots \left.
\begin{array}{l}
+ gabz - agzz + gz^3 \\
\quad - bgzz
\end{array}
\right\} \text{ Second product}
$$

$$
C \ldots \left.
\begin{array}{l}
+ babzz - baz^3 + bz^4 \\
\quad - bbz^3
\end{array}
\right\} \text{ Third product}
$$

Prog. θ . 1 . 2 . 3 . 4 etc.

And so on to infinity, where one sees that each of the partial products which are marked by $A . B . C$. etc. is always measured by [*i. e.*, has as a factor] the given quantity, since that quantity is one of the generators.

Coroll. I.—If the sum of the partial products is multiplied by the arithmetical progression $\theta . 1 . 2 . 3 . 4$. etc., each of the products $A . B . C$. etc. is also multiplied by the progression: that is to say, the product A by $\theta . 1 . 2$, the product B by $1, 2, 3$, and so on.

Observe for the understanding of what follows, that the product A when altered by the progression by which it is multiplied, is designated D; that the product B thus altered is designated E; that the product C after a similar change is marked F, etc.

Coroll. II.—From this first corollary and Articles VII and VIII, one may conclude that on substituting b for z in each of the products $D . E . F$. etc., each of the results is divisible by $b - a$ without a remainder. But substituting b for z in each of these products amounts to making the substitution in the total product. From this it is evident that after this substitution is made, the total product is measured by $b - a$.

Coroll. III.—If in place of the quantity $f + gz + hzz + rz^3 +$ etc. one takes the product of $z - c, z - d, z - e$, etc., one arrives at all the conclusions which have been reached; that is to say, after substituting b for z in the total product which the progression brings forth, the result is divisible by $b - a$ without a remainder. This is evident, since, as we see, f, g, h, r, etc. stand for any given quantities.

Coroll. IV.—It is also clear from the formation of the total product that all the letters a, b, c, d, etc. are on the same footing and all that has been established for b with respect to a, may be concluded for any of the letters with regard to any of the others. From this it follows that on substituting separately, in the total product of the progression, any of the letters a, b, c, d, e, etc. in place of the unknown z, the result will be divisible by the letter substituted less any of the others that we may wish. So that the result which the substitution of a gives, is divisible by $a - b$, by $a - c$, by $a - d$, etc.

In the same way, the substitution of c for z must yield a result, divisible without a remainder, by c minus any one of the other roots taken separately. Similarly for the others.

Coroll. V.—If one supposes... that the root a is greater than the root b, that b is greater than c, that c is greater than d, etc., it follows from Article V[1] and the preceeding corollary that the results [products] which give [*i. e.*, which limit] the roots of the proximate cascade, are alternately positive and negative or negative and positive.

Coroll. VI.—If an equation is formed as in Article I [all the roots being positive and distinct], its roots are the limits of the roots of the proximate cascade, for this cascade is derived by multiplying by the progression $\theta . 1 . 2$. etc. as in this Article IX. Moreover, these roots have the limitations imposed upon them in the preced-

---

[1] [Article V in the *Démonstration*, which we omitted, states that if the positive roots $a, b, c, d, \ldots$ are so related tht $a > b > c > d > \ldots$, then the products $(b - a)(b - c)(b - d) \ldots$ and $(c - a)(c - b)(c - d) \ldots$ have opposite signs.]

ing Coroll. V. Hence it follows from this same corollary and Coroll. III of Article VI, that the roots are limits of the roots of its cascade.[1]

Coroll. VII.—Since the roots of equations thus formed are limits of the roots of their cascade, it follows from Coroll. VI....that the roots of the proximate cascade are limits of the roots of the equation of which it is the cascade.

Since the progression [in Article IX] gives a cascade which is divisible by the unknown z, one sees that θ is one of the roots [of the cascade] and it is evident from this that θ is the lower limit [of the roots of the given equation], according to our suppositions.

If one substitutes the roots [of an equation] in its cascade before dividing it by z, the results are divisible by the letter substituted. But as this letter represents only some positive number, according to our assumptions, it does not bring about any change in the sequence of signs...

Coroll. VIII.—If the roots are irrational, the limits will give the regular sequence signs, on the supposition that the roots satisfy the conditions specified in Article I [*i. e.*, are positive and distinct], for these roots are determined by the equation which contains them, and the proximate cascade is formed from that equation.

Coroll. IX.—The roots being all positive and distinct, there are as many of them as the number indicating the degree of the equation which contains them...

Article X.—Let all the signs of an equation be alternating as the result of the "preparation" of equations, then it always transpires that the real and distinct roots are all positive; and one may prove this truth as shown in what follows.

Let all the powers of an unknown, such as x, which are arranged in order, have alternately the signs $-$ and $+$, as seen in $-x + xx - x^3 + x^4$ etc. From this it is clear that, if one substitutes a negative unknown in an equation the terms of which are alternating [in sign], such as $+q - pz + nzz - pz^3 +$ etc., it comes about that the signs of the resulting equation are all positive. And if the proposed one should be $-q + pz - nzz + rz^3$ etc., a transposition [of terms] after the substitution, produces the same effect. And reciprocally, a [complete] equation all the signs of which are positive, is changed into another in which all terms are alternating, when one substitutes a negative unknown in place of the unknown

---

[1] [This is another passage containing "Rolle's theorem." See also Coroll. VIII.]

of the equation. This is clear. It is clear also that an equation of which all the terms are positive can not have positive roots, for when such a root is substituted in the equation, the sum of the positive terms should destroy that of the negative ones, when as we suppose, all the terms are in the same member; which is impossible...

Article XI.—If some of the roots are real and distinct, the others imaginary, these imaginary ones do not prevent the limits from giving suitable signs to the real and distinct roots. For, the proposed equation may always be conceived to be formed by the multiplication of two simpler equations, the one having all roots real and distinct, the other having all roots imaginary, and by Article IX the cascade involves limits which agree with the real and distinct roots [of the given equation]. And one can see that the imaginary roots do not give rise to the sequence [of signs] which one finds in real and distinct roots...

Article XII.—There are at least as many imaginary roots in an equation as there are in its proximate cascade. For, if the roots of the equation which correspond to these imaginaries were real, it would follow that upon substituting them in the cascade they would give the regular sequence referred in Coroll. V of Article IX, while according to the definition of imaginary roots, they give when substituted always +. This is contrary to supposition.

If one does not take zero as one of the terms of a progression, and if this θ is not placed beneath the last term or beneath the first term of the equation, the proximate cascade will have the same degree as the equation itself. Thus the Method would suppose what is in question.[1] But taking zero for one of the extremes of the progression and marking this progression in general terms, the letter which serves in this general expression is found only of the first degree in each term of the cascade, and disappears in the ordinary cancellation. From this it follows that this progression produces no other effect on the limits than does $\theta . 1 . 2$. This happens also when θ is placed under the last term, for the reasons just stated.

---

[1] [That is, the solution of the cascade equation presents the same problem as does the original equation.]

ABEL

On the Quintic Equation

(Translated from the French by Dr. W. H. Langdon, with Notes by Professor Oystein Ore, Yale University, New Haven, Conn.)

The Norwegian mathematician, Niels Henrik Abel (1802–1829) very early showed an unusual mathematical ability, and in spite of the fact that his short life was a constant struggle against poverty and illness, he wrote a series of scientific papers that secures him a position among the greatest mathematicians of all time. In his "Mémoire sur les équations algébriques ou l'on démontre l'impossibilité de la resolution de l'équation générale du cinquième degré *Œuvres complètes*, (Vol. I, Christiania (Oslo) 1881, p. 28–33), Abel proves the impossibility of solving general equations of the fifth and higher degrees by means of radicals. The paper was published as a pamphlet at Oslo in 1824 at Abel's own expense. In order to save printing costs, he had to give the paper in a very summary form, which in a few places affects the lucidity of his reasoning.

After the solutions of the third and fourth degrees had been found by Cardano and Ferrari, the problem of solving the equation of the fifth degree had been the object of innumerable futile attempts by the mathematicians of the 17th and 18th centuries. Abel's paper shows clearly why these attempts must fail, and opens the road to the modern theory of equations, including group theory and the solution of equations by means of transcendental functions.

Abel proposed himself the problem of finding all equations solvable by radicals, and succeeded in solving all equations with communtative groups, now called Abelian equations. Among Abel's numerous other achievements are his discovery of the elliptic functions and their fundamental properties, his famous theorem on the integration of algebraic functions, theorems on power series (see p. 286), where further biographical notes appear, etc.

A Memoir on Algebraic Equations, Proving the Impossibility of a Solution of the General Equation of the Fifth Degree

The mathematicians have been very much absorbed with finding the general solution of algebraic equations, and several of them have tried to prove the impossibility of it. However, if I am not mistaken, they have not as yet succeeded. I therefore dare hope that the mathematicians will receive this memoir with good will, for its purpose is to fill this gap in the theory of algebraic equations.

Let

$$y^5 - ay^4 + by^3 - cy^2 + dy - e = 0$$

be the general equation of fifth degree and suppose that it can be solved algebraically,—i. e., that y can be expressed as a function of the quantities a, b, c, d, and e, composed of radicals. In this case, it is clear that y can be written in the form

$$y = p + p_1 R^{\frac{1}{m}} + p_2 R^{\frac{2}{m}} + \ldots + p_{m-1} R^{\frac{m-1}{m}},$$

m being a prime number, and R, p, p_1, p_2, etc. being functions of the same form as y. We can continue in this way until we reach rational functions of a, b, c, d, and e. We may also assume that $R^{\frac{1}{m}}$ cannot be expressed as a rational function of a, b, etc., p, p_1, p_2, etc., and substituting $\dfrac{R}{p_1{}^m}$ for R, it is obvious that we can make $p_1 = 1$.
Then

$$y = p + R^{\frac{1}{m}} + P_2 R^{\frac{2}{m}} + \ldots + p_{m-1} R^{\frac{m-1}{m}}$$

Substituting this value of y in the proposed equation, we obtain, on reducing, a result in the form

$$P = q + q_1 R^{\frac{1}{m}} + q_2 R^{\frac{2}{m}} + \ldots + q_{m-1} R^{\frac{m-1}{m}} = 0,$$

q, q_1, q_2, etc. being integral rational functions of a, b, c, d, e, p, p_2, etc. and R.

For this equation to be satisfied, it is necessary that $q = 0$, $q_1 = 0$, $q_2 = 0, \ldots q_{m-1} = 0$. In fact, letting $z = R^{\frac{1}{m}}$, we have the two equations

$$z^m - R = 0, \text{ and } q + q_1 z + \ldots + q_{m-1} z^{m-1} = 0.$$

If now the quantities q, q_1, etc. are not equal to zero, these equations must necessarily have one or more common roots. If k is the number of these roots, we know that we can find an equation of degree k, whose roots are the k roots mentioned, and whose coefficients are rational functions of R, q, q_1, and q_{m-1}. Let this equation be

$$r + r_1 z + r_2 z^2 + \ldots + r_k z^k = 0.$$

It has all its roots in common with the equation $z^m - R = 0$; now all the roots of this equation are of the form $\alpha_\mu z$, α_μ being one of the roots of the equation $\alpha_\mu^m - 1 = 0$. On substituting, we obtain the following equations

$$r + r_1 z + r_2 z^2 + \ldots + r_k z^k = 0,$$
$$r + \alpha r_1 z + \alpha^2 r_2 z^2 + \ldots + \alpha^k r_k z^k = 0,$$
$$\cdots\cdots\cdots\cdots$$
$$r + \alpha_{k-2} r_1 z + \alpha_{k-2}{}^2 r_2 z^2 + \ldots + \alpha^k{}_{k-2} r_k z^k = 0.$$

From these k equations we can always find the value of z, expressed as a rational function of the quantities $r, r_1, \ldots r_k$; and as these quantities are themselves rational functions of $a, b, c, d, e, R, p, p_2,$ $\ldots$, it follows that z is also a rational function of these latter quantities; but that is contrary to the hypotheses. Thus it is necessary that

$$q = 0, q_1 = 0, \ldots q_{m-1} = 0.$$

If now these equations are satisfied, it is clear that the proposed equation is satisfied by all those values which y assumes when $R^{\frac{1}{m}}$ is assigned the values

$$R^{\frac{1}{m}}, \alpha R^{\frac{1}{m}}, \alpha^2 R^{\frac{1}{m}}, \ldots, \alpha^{m-1} R^{\frac{1}{m}},$$

α being a root of the equation

$$\alpha^{m-1} + \alpha^{m-2} + \ldots + \alpha + 1 = 0.$$

We also note that all the values of y are different; for otherwise we should have an equation of the same form as the equation $P = 0$, and we have just seen that such an equation leads to a contradictory result. The number m cannot exceed 5. Letting $y_1, y_2,$ $y_3, y_4,$ and y_5 be the roots of the proposed equation, we have

$$y_1 = p + R^{\frac{1}{m}} + p_2 R^{\frac{2}{m}} + \ldots + p_{m-1} R^{\frac{m-1}{m}},$$

$$y_2 = p + \alpha R^{\frac{1}{m}} + \alpha^2 p R^{\frac{2}{m}} + \ldots + \alpha^{m-1} p_{m-1} R^{\frac{m-1}{m}},$$

$$\ldots \ldots \ldots$$

$$y_m = p + \alpha^{m-1} R^{\frac{1}{m}} + \alpha^{m-2} p_2 R^{\frac{2}{m}} + \ldots + \alpha p_{m-1} R^{\frac{m-1}{m}}.$$

Whence it is easily seen that

$$p = \frac{1}{m}(y_1 + y_2 + \ldots + y_m),$$

$$R^{\frac{1}{m}} = \frac{1}{m}(y_1 + \alpha^{m-1} y_2 + \ldots + \alpha y_m),$$

$$p_2 R^{\frac{2}{m}} = \frac{1}{m}(y_1 + \alpha^{m-2} y_2 + \ldots + \alpha^2 y_m),$$

$$\ldots \ldots \ldots$$

$$p_{m-1} R^{\frac{1}{m}} = \frac{1}{m}(y_1 + \alpha y_2 + \ldots + \alpha^{m-1} y_m).$$

Thus $p, p_2, \ldots p_{m-1}, R,$ and $R^{\frac{1}{m}}$ are rational functions of the roots of the proposed equation.

Let us now consider any one of these quantities, say R. Let

$$R = S + v^{\frac{1}{n}} + S_2 v^{\frac{2}{n}} + \ldots + S_{n-1} v^{\frac{n-1}{n}}.$$

Treating this quantity as we have just treated y, we obtain the similar result that the quantities S, $S_2, \ldots, S_{n-1}$, v, and $v^{\frac{1}{n}}$ are rational functions of the different values of R; and since these are rational functions of y_1, y_2, etc., the functions $v^{\frac{1}{n}}$, v, S, S_2 etc. have the same property. Reasoning in this way, we conclude that all the irrational functions contained in the expression for y, are rational functions of the roots of the proposed equation.

This being established, it is not difficult to complete the demonstration. Let us first consider irrational functions of the form $R^{\frac{1}{m}}$, R being a rational function of a, b, c, d, and e. Let $R^{\frac{1}{m}} = r$. Then r is a rational function of y_1, y_2, y_3, y_4, and y_5, and R is a symmetric function of these quantities. Now as we are interested in the solution of the general equation of the fifth degree, it is clear that we can consider y_1, y_2, y_3, y_4, and y_5 as independent variables; thus the equation $R^{\frac{1}{m}} = r$ must be satisfied under this supposition. Consequently we can interchange the quantities y_1, y_2, y_3, y_4, and y_5 in the equation $R^{\frac{1}{m}} = r$; and, remarking that R is a symmetric function, $R^{\frac{1}{m}}$ takes on m different values by this interchange. Thus the function r must have the property of assuming m values, when the five variables which it contains are permuted in all possible ways. Thus either $m = 5$, or $m = 2$, since m is a prime number, (see the memoir by M. Cauchy in the *Journal de l'école polytechnique*, vol. 17).[1] Suppose that $m = 5$. Then the function r has five different values, and hence can be put in the form

$$R^{\frac{1}{5}} = r = p + p_1 y_1 + p_2 y_1^2 + p_3 y_1^3 + p_4 y_1^4,$$

---

[1] ["Mémoire sur le nombre des valeurs qu'une fonction peut acquérir," etc. Let p be the greatest prime dividing n. Cauchy then proves (p. 9) that a function of n variables, taking less than p values, either is symmetric or takes only two values. In the latter case the function can be written in the form $A + B\Delta$ where A and B are symmetric, and Δ is the special two-valued function

$$\Delta = (y_1 - y_2)(y_1 - y_3) \ldots (y_{n-1} - y_n).]$$

p, p_1, p_2,...being symmetric functions of y_1, y_2, etc. This equation gives, on interchanging y_1 and y_2,

$$p + p_1y_1 + p_2y_1{}^2 + p_3y_1{}^3 + p_4y_1{}^4 = \alpha p + \alpha p_1y_2 + \alpha p_2y_2{}^2$$
$$+ \alpha p_3y_2{}^3 + \alpha p_4y_2{}^4,$$

where

$$\alpha^4 + \alpha^3 + \alpha^2 + \alpha + 1 = 0.$$

But this equation (is impossible);[1] hence m must equal two. Then

$$R^{1/2} = r,$$

and so r must have two different values, of opposite sign. We then have,[2] (see the memoir of M. Cauchy),

$$R^{1/2} = r = v(y_1 - y_2)(y_1 - y_3)\ldots(y_2 - y_3)\ldots(y_4 - y_5) = vS^{1/2}.$$

v being a symmetric function.

Let us now consider irrational functions of the form

$$(p + p_1R^{\frac{1}{\nu}} + p_2R_1{}^{\frac{1}{\mu}} + \ldots)^{\frac{1}{m}},$$

p, p_1, p_2, etc., R, E_1, etc., being rational functions of a, b, c, d, and e, and consequently symmetric functions of y_1, y_2, y_3, y_4, and y_5. We have seen that it is necessary that $\nu = \mu = \ldots = 2$, $R = v^2S$, $R_1 = v_1{}^2S$, etc. The preceeding function can thus be written in the form

$$(p + p_1S^{\frac{1}{2}})^{\frac{1}{m}},$$

Let

$$r = (p + p_1S^{\frac{1}{2}})^{\frac{1}{m}},$$

$$r_1 = (p^2 - p_1S^{\frac{1}{2}})^{\frac{1}{m}}.$$

Multiplying, we have

$$rr_1 = (p^2 - p_1{}^2S)^{\frac{1}{m}}.$$

---

[1] [In a later paper (*Journal für die reine und angewandte Mathematik* Vol. 1, 1826) Abel gives a more detailed proof of the main theorem, based on the same principles. At the corresponding point he gives the following more elaborate proof. By considering y_1 as a common root of the given equation, the relation defining R, y_1 can be expressed in the form

$$y_1 = s_0 + s_1R^{1/5} + s_2R^{2/5} + s_3R^{3/5} + s_4R^{4/5}.$$

Substituting $\alpha^t R^{1/5}$ for R we obtain the other roots of the equation, and solving the corresponding system of five linear equations gives

$$s_1R^{1/5} = \tfrac{1}{5}(y_1 + \alpha^4y_2 + \alpha^3y_3 + \alpha^2y_4 + \alpha y_5).$$

This identity is impossible, however, since the right-hand side has 120 values, and the left-hand side has only 5.]

[2] [Compare 1.]

If now rr_1 is not a symmetric function, m must equal two; but then r would have four different values, which is impossible; hence rr_1 must be a symmetric function. Let v be this function, then

$$r + r_1 = (p + p_1 S^2)^{\frac{1}{m}} + v(p + p_1 S^2)^{-\frac{1}{m}} = z.$$

This function having m different values, m must equal five, since m is a prime number. We thus have

$$z = q + q_1 y + q_2 y^2 + q_3 y^3 + q_4 y^4 = (p + p_1 S^{\frac{1}{2}})^{\frac{1}{5}} + v(p + p_1 S^{\frac{1}{2}})^{-\frac{1}{5}},$$

q, q_1, q_2, etc. being symmetric functions of y_1, y_2, y_3, etc., and consequently rational functions of a, b, c, d, and e. Combining this equation with the proposed equation, we can find y expressed as a rational function of z, a, b, c, d, and e. Now such a function can always be reduced to the form

$$y = P + R^{\frac{1}{5}} + P_2 R^{\frac{2}{5}} + P_3 R^{\frac{3}{5}} + P_4 R^{\frac{4}{5}},$$

where P, R, P_2, P_3, and P_4 are functions of the form $p + p_1 S^{\frac{1}{2}}$, where p, p_1, and S are rational functions of a, b, c, d, and e. From this value of y we obtain

$$R^{\frac{1}{5}} = \tfrac{1}{5}(y_1 + \alpha^4 y_2 + \alpha^3 y_3 + \alpha^2 y_4 + \alpha y_5) = (p + p_1 S^{\frac{1}{2}})^{\frac{1}{5}},$$

where

$$\alpha^4 + \alpha^3 + \alpha^2 + \alpha + 1 = 0.$$

Now the first member has 120 different values, while the second member has only 10; hence y can not have the form that we have found: but we have proved that y must necessarily have this form, if the proposed equation can be solved: hence we conclude that

It is impossible to solve the general equation of the fifth degree in terms of radicals.

It follows immediately from this theorem, that it is also impossible to solve the general equations of degrees higher than the fifth, in terms of radicals.

LEIBNIZ

On Determinants

(Translated from the French and Latin by Dr. Thomas Freeman Cope, National Research Fellow in Mathematics, Harvard University, Cambridge, Mass.)

The work on determinants of Gottfried Wilhelm Leibniz (1646–1716), who was almost equally distinguished as a philosopher, mathematician, and man-of-affairs, is far less widely known than his work on the calculus. In fact, his contributions to this domain of algebra were entirely overlooked until the publication, in 1850, of the correspondence between him and the Marquis de l'Hospital. The letters to L'Hospital disclose the remarkable fact that, more than fifty years before the time of Cramer, who was the real moving spirit in the development of the theory, the fundamental idea of determinants had been clear to Leibniz and had been expounded by him in considerable detail in one of these letters. His work, however, had little or no influence on succeeding investigators.

A study of the following extracts from the writings of Leibniz shows that his contributions to this phase of algebra are at least two in number: (1) a new notation, numerical in character and appearance; (2) a rule for writing out the resultant of a set of linear equations.

The first of the extracts here given is from a letter of Leibniz to L'Hospital, which was dated April 28, 1693, and published for the first time (1850) at Berlin in *Leibnizens Mathematische Schriften*, herausg. von C. I. Gerhardt, Ie. Abth., Band II, pp. 238–240. The second extract is from a manuscript which was published for the first time (1863) at Halle in a subsequent volume of the above-mentioned work, namely, in the 2e. Abth., Band III, pp. 5–6. The original manuscript bears no date, but it was probably written before 1693 and possibly goes back to 1678. Each of the articles was published in Muir's well-known *Theory of Determinants*, the second edition (Macmillan & Co.) of which appeared in 1906. For an excellent account of Leibniz's life and work, the reader is referred to the *Encyclopaedia Britannica*, 12th ed., and, for an analysis of his contributions to the theory of determinants, to the scholarly treatise of Muir mentioned above. For further biographical notes relating particularly to his work on the calculating machine and on the calculus, see pages 173 and 619.

Leibniz on Determinants

I

Since you say that you have difficulty in believing that it is as general and as convenient to use numbers instead of letters, I must not have explained myself very well. There can be no doubt

267

about the generality if one considers that it is permissible to use 2, 3, etc., like a or b, provided that it is understood that these are not really numbers. Thus 2 . 3 does *not* denote 6 but rather ab. As regards convenience, it is so considerable that I myself often use them,[1] especially in long and difficult computations where it is easy to make mistakes. For besides the convenience of checking by numbers and even by the casting out of nines, I find their use a very great advantage even in the analysis itself. As this is quite an extraordinary discovery, I have not yet spoken to any others about it, but here is what it is. When one has need of many letters, is it not true that these letters do not at all express the relationship among the magnitudes they represent, while by the use of numbers I am able to express this relationship. For example, consider three simple equations in two unknowns, the object being to eliminate the two unknowns and indeed by a general law. I suppose that

$$10 + 11x + 12y = 0 \qquad (1),$$

and

$$20 + 21x + 22y = 0 \qquad (2),$$

and

$$30 + 31x + 32y = 0 \qquad (3),$$

where, in the pseudo number of two digits, the first tells me the equation in which it is found, the second, the letter to which it belongs. Thus on carrying out the computation, we find throughout a harmony which not only serves as a check but even makes us suspect at first glance some rules or theorems. For example, eliminating y first from the first and second equations, we shall have:

$$\frac{10 . 22 + 11 . 22x}{-12 . 20 - 12 . 21 . .} = 0 \qquad (4)^2;$$

and from the first and third:

$$\frac{10 . 32 + 11 . 32x}{-12 . 30 - 12 . 31 . .} = 0 \qquad (5),$$

where it is easy to recognize that these two equations differ only in that the anterior character 2 is changed to the anterior character 3. Moreover, in similar terms of an equation, the anterior

---

[1] [*I. e.* numbers in place of letters.]

[2] [This is an abbreviated form, as Muir points out, for
$$\left.\begin{array}{l} +10.22 + 11.22x = 0 \\ -12.20 - 12.21x = 0 \end{array}\right] .$$

characters are the same and the posterior characters have the same sum. It remains now to eliminate the letter x from the fourth and fifth equations, and, as the result, we shall have:[1]

$$1_0 . 2_1 . 3_2 \quad 1_0 . 2_2 . 3_1$$
$$1_1 . 2_2 . 3_0 = 1_1 . 2_0 . 3_2$$
$$1_2 . 2_0 . 3_1 \quad 1_2 . 2_1 . 3_0,$$

which is the final equation freed from the two unknowns that we wished to eliminate, which carries its own proof along with itself from the harmony observable throughout, and which we should find very troublesome to discover using the letters a, b, c, especially when the number of letters and equations is large. A part of the secret of analysis is the characteristic, rather the art, of using notation well, and you see, Sir, by this little example, that Vieta and Descartes did not even know all of its mysteries. Continuing the calculation in this fashion, one will come to a *general theorem* for any desired numbers of letters and simple equations. Here is what I have found it to be on other occasions:—

Given any number of equations which is sufficient for eliminating the unknown quantities which do not exceed the first degree:—for the final equation are to be taken, first, all possible combinations of coefficients, in which one coefficient only from each equation is to enter; secondly, those combinations, after they are placed on the same side of the final equation, have different signs if they have as many factors alike as is indicated by the number which is less by one than the number of unknown quantities: the rest have the same sign.

II

I have found a rule for eliminating the unknowns in any number of equations of the first degree, provided that the number of equations exceeds by one the number of unknowns. It is as follows:—

Make all possible combinations of the coefficients of the letters, in such a way that more than one coefficient of the same unknown and of the same equation never appear together.[2] These combinations, which are to be given signs in accordance with the law which will soon be stated, are placed together, and the result set equal to zero will give an equation lacking all the unknowns.

---

[1] [The notation here has been slightly changed. What is clearly meant is, as Muir notes,
$10.21.32 + 11.22.30 + 12.20.31 = 10.22.31 + 11.20.32 + 12.21.30.$]

[2] [*I. e.*, in the same combination.]

The law of signs is this:—To one of the combinations a sign will be arbitrarily assigned, and the other combinations which differ from this one with respect to two, four, six, etc. factors will take the opposite sign: those which differ from it with respect to three, five, seven, etc. factors will of course take its own sign. For example, let

$$10 + 11x + 12y = 0, \quad 20 + 21x + 22y = 0, \quad 30 + 31x + 32y = 0;$$

there will result

$$\frac{+10 \cdot 21 \cdot 32 - 10 \cdot 22 \cdot 31 - 11 \cdot 20 \cdot 32}{+11 \cdot 22 \cdot 30 + 12 \cdot 20 \cdot 31 - 12 \cdot 21 \cdot 30} = 0.$$

I consider also as coefficients those characters which do not belong to any of the unknowns, as 10, 20, 30.

THE VERSES OF JACQUES BERNOULLI

On Infinite Series

(Translated from the Latin by Professor Helen M. Walker, Teachers College, Columbia University, New York City.)

Jacques (Jakob, Jacobus, James) Bernoulli (1654–1705), the first of the Bernoulli family of mathematicians, a native of Basel, wrote one of the earliest treatises on probability,—the *Ars Conjectandi*. This was published post-humously in 1713. At the close of a section entitled "Tractatus de Seriebus Infinitis Earumque Summa Finita et Usu in Quadraturis Spatiorum & Rectificationibus Curvarum," following Pars Quarta, these six verses appear. Because they represent one of the clearest of the early statements relating to the limit of an infinite series, they are given place in this symposium. Their brevity permits of inserting both the Latin form and the translation.

Ut non-finitam Seriem finita cöercet,
  Summula, & in nullo limite limes adest:
Sic modico immensi vestigia Numinis haerent
  Corpore, & angusto limite limes abest.
Cernere in immenso parvum, dic, quanta voluptas!
  In parvo immensum cernere, quanta, Deum!

Even as the finite encloses an infinite series
  And in the unlimited limits appear,
So the soul of immensity dwells in minutia
  And in narrowest limits no limits inhere.
What joy to discern the minute in infinity!
  The vast to perceive in the small, what divinity!

JACQUES BERNOULLI

On the Theory of Combinations

(Translated from the Latin by Mary M. Taylor, M. A., University of
Pittsburgh, Pittsburgh, Penn.)

The following translation is taken from Part 2 of Jacques (Jakob, James)
Bernoulli's *Ars Conjectandi*. Although Bernoulli (1654–1705) was also
interested and active in other branches of science, it is for his mathematical works that he is particularly known. The *Ars Conjectandi* was
published eight years after his death, and contains, in addition to the work on
combinations, a treatise on Infinite Series. The first part of the book is
attributed to Huygens, but Part 2 is Bernoulli's own. This selection is part of
Chapter V and is from the first edition, pages 112 to 118, inclusive.

While this is by no means the earliest material published on the subject, it si
among the earliest scientific treatments and is so authoritative as to deserve
a place in a source book of this nature. The subject matter chosen presents
for solution a situation which occurs in various problems of higher mathematics. The method of solution is typical of the rest of the work.

Chapter V. Part 2.

To find the number of combinations, when each of the objects
to be combined, whatever they are, is different from the others,
but may be used more than once in each combination.

In the combinations of the preceding chapters we have assumed
that an object could not be joined with itself, and could not even
be accepted more than once in the same combination; but now we
shall add this condition—that each object can be placed next to
itself, and further that it can occur repeatedly in the same
combination.

Thus let the letters to be combined by this plan be *a, b, c, d,* etc.
Let there be made as many series as there are letters, and let the
individual letters, just as so many units, occupy the first place in
each, as was done in chapter two.

In finding the combinations of two, or binary terms of each
series, the letter which heads that sequence is to be combined not
only with each of the letters preceding it, but also with itself.
Thus we shall have in the first series one binary *aa,* in the second
two binaries *ab, bb,* in the third three, *ac, bc, cc,* in the fourth four,
ad, bd, cd, dd, etc.

So also in forming the ternaries,—each letter must be joined not only with the binaries of all the preceding series, but also with those of its own series. In this way we shall have in the first series one ternary, *aaa*; in the second series three, *aab, abb, bbb*; in the third series six, *aac, abc, bbc, acc, bcc, ccc*; and so on.

This same plan is to be followed in combinations of every other degree, by which plan it is clear that none of the possible selections among the given objects can be overlooked. In tabular form;

$$a.\ aa.\ aaa.$$
$$b.\ ab.\ bb.\ aab.\ abb_{.}\ bbb.$$
$$c.\ ac.\ bc.\ cc.\ aac.\ abc.\ bbc.\ acc.\ bcc.\ ccc.$$
$$d.\ ad.\ bd.\ cd.\ dd.\ aad.\ abd.\ bbd\ acd.\ bcd.\ ccd.\ add\ bdd.\ cdd.\ ddd.$$

From this, with no great difficulty, we infer that the single terms of all the series form a group of ones; the binaries, a series of positive integers (or natural numbers); the ternaries, a series of three-sided figures; and the other combinations of higher degree likewise constitute series of other figures of higher order, just as did the combinations of the preceding chapters, with this one difference, that there the series began with zeros, and here they start directly from the ones. Thence if the series are collected into tabular form, they present this arrangement:

Tabula Combinatoria

Exponentes Combinationum

I	II	III	IV	V	VI	VII	VIII	IX	X	XI	XII
1 1	1	1	1	1	1	1	1	1	1	1	1
2 1	2	3	4	5	6	7	8	9	10	11	12
3 1	3	6	10	15	21	28	36	45	55	66	78
4 1	4	10	20	35	56	84	120	165	220	286	364
5 1	5	15	35	70	126	210	330	495	715	1001	1365
6 1	6	21	56	126	252	462	792	1 287	2002	3003	4368
7 1	7	28	84	210	462	924	1716	3 003	5005	8008	12376
8 1	8	36	120	330	792	1716	3432	6435	11440	19448	31824
9 1	9	45	165	495	1287	3003	6435	12870	24310	43758	75582
10 1	10	55	220	715	2002	5005	11440	24310	48620	92378	167960

Moreover it is worth while to note especially two properties of the table thus formed: 1. That the transverse columns are congruent to the vertical, the first to the first, the second to the second, etc. 2. That if two contiguous columns are chosen, whether vertical or horizontal, with an equal number of terms, the sum of the terms of the first column is equal to the last term of the second column.

From these properties it is easy to find the sum of the terms of any series whatever, and so the number of combinations according to the degree thereof. For if the number of terms, that is of things to be combined, is called n, the sum of the ones, or terms of the first series, will be the last term of the second series, likewise n.

We may suppose the second series to have a zero prefixed, so that the number of terms becomes $n + 1$; if the last term n is multiplied by half of this $n + 1$, the product $\dfrac{n.n+1}{1.2}$ will be the sum of the twos or terms of the second series (according to property 12,[1] chapter 3), and the last term of the third, (by property 2 of this chapter).

We may suppose two ciphers to be prefixed to the third series, and the number of terms will become $n + 2$. If the last term just found, $\dfrac{n.n+1}{1.2}$, be multiplied by one-third of this, it will become $\dfrac{n.n+1.n+2}{1.2.3}$, the sum of the ternaries or terms of the third series, and at the same time, by the same properties, the last term of the fourth series.

In the same way the sum of the terms of the fourth series (quaternaries) is found to be $\dfrac{n.n+1.n+2.n+3}{1.2.3.4}$, of the fifth series $\dfrac{n.n+1.n+2.n+3.n+4}{1.2.3.4.5}$; and in general the sum of the terms of the c series, or combinations of degree c, is found to be
$$\frac{n.n+1.n+2.n+3.n+4 \ldots (n+c-1)}{1.2.3.4.5 \ldots c}.$$
Here it should be noted that if $c > n$ the factors of the fraction can be diminished by dividing numerator and denominator by $n.n+1$. …c, so that we have $\dfrac{c+1.c+2.c+3.c+n-1}{1.2.3.4\ldots n-1}$, and since this fraction, worked out according to the formula, should at the

---

[1] [Property 12, Chapter 3. The sum of any number of terms of any vertical column beginning with the proper number of ciphers has the same ratio to the sum of as many terms equal to the last, as unity has to the number of that series; that is, the sum of any number of the natural numbers, beginning the series with one cipher, is to the sum of as many terms, each equal to the greatest of these, or the last, as 1:2; of the third order series beginning with two ciphers as 1:3, etc. This same is also true of the ratio which the sum of the terms of any series beginning with unity has to the sum of as many terms, equal to the term following the last.]

same time indicate the sum of $c + 1$ terms in the series $n - 1$, it follows that the sum of n terms in the series c is always equal to the sum of $c + 1$ terms in the series $n - 1$, which is another by no means negligible property of this table. Thence results the following

Rule

for finding the number of combinations according to a given degree, when the same objects can enter into the same combination more than once.

Let two increasing arithmetic progressions be formed, the first starting from the number of things to be combined, the other from unity, of both of which the common difference is unity, and let each have as many terms as the degree of the combination has units. Then let the product of the terms of the first progression be divided by the product of the terms of the second progression, and the quotient will be the desired number of the combinations according to the given degree. With this understanding, the number of combinations by four among ten different things is

$$\frac{10 \cdot 11 \cdot 12 \cdot 13}{1 \cdot 2 \cdot 3 \cdot 4} \,\infty\, \frac{17160}{24} \,\infty\, 715.$$

NOTE.—If the degree of the combination is greater than the number of objects, (as is clearly possible under the present hypothesis) it will be shorter to begin the first progression with that degree increased by one, and to make each series of one fewer terms than there are objects. Thus the number of combinations of degree 10 among four objects is

$$\frac{11 \cdot 12 \cdot 13}{1 \cdot 2 \cdot 3} \,\infty\, \frac{1716}{6} \,\infty\, 286.$$

But also we can find with no more difficulty the number of combinations according to several degrees following each other successively from unity up, that is, the sum of as many vertical series. For since, for example, the first 10 terms of the first 4 vertical columns are the same as the first 4 terms of the first 10 transverse columns, and moreover the sums of these terms are equal to eleven terms of the first vertical column, decreased by the first or unity (of course the sums are equal one by one to these terms, as is evident from the second property of the table), it is clear, also, that the 10 first terms of the first four vertical columns, *i. e.*, the sum of all the ones, twos, threes, and fours selected from ten things, is less by one than the eleven first terms of the fourth column, i. e., than the number of quaternaries formed of eleven things, or than number of combinations formed from one more than the given number of objects and of degree equal to the greatest of the given degrees. This same fact may also be shown in this way: Obviously, the eleventh object either does not occur in a particular combination of four from the given eleven objects, or it occurs once, twice, thrice, or four times; but it is evident that those quaternaries in which the eleventh object does not appear are just the ones which the ten remaining objects can form among themselves. And it is no less evident that the number of those into which the eleventh enters only once should equal the number of ternaries to be formed from the remaining ten; so also the number of those in which it occurs twice (should equal) the number of binaries, and of those in which it occurs three times the number of ones, since when joined once to the ternaries, twice to the binaries, and three times to the units, it forms quaternaries; besides it is known that there is one quaternion which is formed by the eleventh object, repeated four times.

From this, we conclude that the number of combinations of four included in eleven objects, that is in one more than the given number of objects, exceeds by one all the combinations by one, two, three, and four, of the given ten objects, unless we wish to add to the latter the zero combination, in which case the two are equal.

Wherefore, since, when the number of objects given is n, and the greatest degree c, the number of combinations of that degree in $n + 1$ things is found by Rule of chapter 4 to be

$$\frac{n + 1 . n + 2 . n + 3 . n + 4 \ldots n + c}{1 . 2 . 3 . 4 \ldots c},$$

the number of combinations of n things according to all degrees from one to c becomes (as it is one less than this)

$$\frac{n + 1 . n + 2 . n + 3 . n + 4 \ldots n + c}{1 . 2 . 3 . 4 \ldots c} - 1.$$

But if c is greater than n itself, i. e., if the greatest of the degrees is higher than the number of objects, the terms of the fraction can in this case be divided by $n + 1 . n + 2 . n + 3 \ldots c$, and hence the quantity can be expressed more briefly as

$$\frac{c + 1 . c + 2 . c + 3 \ldots c + n}{1 . 2 . 3 . 4 \ldots n} - 1.$$

From this comes the

Rule

for finding the number of combinations according to several degrees following successively from unity.

Let two increasing arithmetic progressions be formed, the first starting from one more than the number of objects to be combined, the other from unity, of which the common difference is one, and let each have as many terms as the highest degree has units. (But if the greatest of the degrees is larger than the number of objects, it is easier to begin the first progression with that degree increased by one, and to make each of as many terms as there are given objects.) Then the product of the terms of the first progression is to be divided by the product of the terms of the second progression; and the quotient will be the required number of combinations if, of course, we wish the zero combination included; but if not, the quotient diminished by one will indicate the desired quantity. Thus the number of units, binaries, ternaries, and quaternaries, together with the zero combination, in 10 objects is $\frac{11 \cdot 12 \cdot 13 \cdot 14}{1 \cdot 2 \cdot 3 \cdot 4}$ ∞ $\frac{24024}{24}$ ∞ 1001, among only three things is $\frac{5 \cdot 6 \cdot 7}{1 \cdot 2 \cdot 3}$ ∞ $\frac{210}{6}$ ∞ 35; but if the zero is excluded the number of combinations is 1000 in the first case, 34 in the second.

GALOIS

On Groups and Equations and Abelian Integrals

(Translated from the French by Dr. Louis Weisner, Hunter College of the City of New York.)

Evariste Galois (1811–1832) was born in Paris, was educated at the Lycée Louis-le-Grand and the École Normale, was a rabid republican, was twice imprisoned for his political views, and lost his life in a stupid, boyish duel before he had reached the age of twenty-one. His most important paper, "Mémoire sur les conditions de résolubilité des équations par radicaux" was not published until 1846, when his works appeared in Liouville's *Journal de Mathématiques*.

The night before the duel in which Galois was killed he wrote a letter to his friend Auguste Chevalier in which he set forth briefly his discovery of the connection of the theory of groups with the solution of equations by radicals. In this letter, written apparently under the impression that the result of the duel would be fatal to himself, he asked that it be published in the *Revue encyclopédique*, a wish that was carried out the same year (1832, page 568). His works were republished in 1897 under the auspices of La Société Mathématique de France with an introduction by E. Picard. Further writings of Galois were published by J. Tannery in the *Bulletin des Sciences Mathématiques* (1906–1907) and reprinted the following year in book form. It being impossible to include in a source book of this kind the mémoire above mentioned, the letter to M. Chevalier is here given in translation.

My dear friend,

I have made some new discoveries in analysis.

Some are concerned with the theory of equations; others with integral functions.

In the theory of equations, I have sought to discover the conditions under which equations are solvable by radicals, and this has given me the opportunity to study the theory and to describe all possible transformations on an equation even when it is not solvable by radicals.

It will be possible to make three memoirs of all this.

The first is written, and, despite what Poisson has said of it, I am keeping it, with the corrections I have made.

The second contains some interesting applications of the theory of equations. The following is a summary of the most important of these:

1°. From propositions II and III of the first memoir, we perceive a great difference between adjoining to an equation one of the roots of an auxiliary equation and adjoining all of them.

In both cases the group of the equation breaks up by the adjunction in sets such that one passes from one to the other by the same substitution, but the condition that these sets have the same substitutions holds with certainty only in the second case. This is called the *proper decomposition*.[1]

In other words, when a group G contains another H, the group G can be divided into sets, each of which is obtained by multiplying the permutations of H by the same substitution; so that

$$G = H + HS + HS' + \dots$$

And it can also be divided into sets which contain the same substitutions, so that

$$G = H + TH + T'H + \dots$$

These two methods of decomposition are usually not identical. When they are identical, the decomposition is *proper*.

It is easy to see that when the group of an equation is not susceptible of any proper decomposition, then, however, the equation be transformed, the groups of the transformed equations will always have the same number of permutations.

On the other hand, when the group of an equation admits a proper decomposition, in which it has been separated into M groups of N permutations, then we can solve the given equation by means of two equations, one having a group of M permutations, the other N.

When therefore we have exhausted in the group of an equation all the possible proper decompositions, we shall arrive at groups which can be transformed, but whose permutations will always be the same in number.

If each of these groups has a prime number of permutations, the equation will be solvable by radicals; otherwise not.

The smallest number of permutations which an indecomposable group can have, when this number is not a prime, is 5 . 4 . 3.

2°. The simplest decompositions are those which occur in the method of M. Gauss.

As these decompositions are obvious, even in the actual form of the group of the equation, it is useless to spend time on this matter.

---

[1] [A proper decomposition, in modern parlance, is an arrangement of the permutations of a group into cosets with respect to an invariant subgroup.]

What decompositions are practicable in an equation which is not simplified by the method of M. Gauss?

I have called those equations *primitive* which cannot be simplified by M. Gauss's method; not that the equations are really indecomposable, as they can even be solved by radicals.

As a lemma in the theory of primitive equations solvable by radicals, I made in June 1830, in the *Bulletin de Férussac* an analysis of imaginaries in the theory of numbers.

There will be found herewith[1] the proof of the following theorems:

1°. In order that a primitive equation be solvable by radicals its degree must be p^ν, p being a prime.

2°. All the permutations of such an equation have the form

$$x_{k,l,m,\ldots}|x_{ak+bl+cm+\cdots+h,\ \ a'k+b'l+c'm+\cdots+h',a''k+\cdots}, \quad k,\ l,\ m,\ldots$$

being ν indices, which, taking p values each, denote all the roots. The indices are taken with respect to a modulus p; that is to say, the root will be the same if we add a multiple of p to one of the indices.

The group which is obtained on applying all the substitutions of this linear form contains in all

$$p^\nu(p^\nu - 1)(p^\nu - p)\ldots(p^\nu - p^{\nu-1})$$

permutations.

It happens that in general the equations to which they belong are not solvable by radicals.

The condition which I have stated in the *Bulletin de Férussac* for the solvability of the equation by radicals is too restricted; there are few exceptions, but they exist.[2]

The last application of the theory of equations is relative to the modular equations of elliptic functions.

We know that the group of the equation which has for its roots the sines of the amplitude[3] of the $p^3 - 1$ divisions of a period is the following:

$$x_{k,l}, \ x_{ak+bl,\ ck+dl};$$

---

[1] [Liouville remarks: "Galois speaks of manuscripts, hitherto unpublished, which we shall publish."]

[2] [Galois stated in the *Bulletin des sciences mathématiques de M. Férussac* (1830), p. 271, that the elliptic modular equation of degree $p + 1$ could not be reduced to one of degree p when p exceeds 5; but $p = 7$ and $p = 11$ are exceptions to this statement, as Galois shows in the next page of his letter.]

[3] [Meaning the elliptic *sn*-function.]

consequently the corresponding modular equation has for its group

$$x_k, \quad x_{\frac{ak+bl}{ck+dl}},$$

in which $\frac{k}{l}$ may have the $p + 1$ values

$$\infty, 0, 1, 2, \ldots, p - 1.$$

Thus, by agreeing that k may be infinite, we may write simply

$$x_k, \quad x_{\frac{ak+b}{ck+d}}.$$

By giving to a, b, c, d all the values, we obtain

$$(p + 1)p(p - 1)$$

permutations.

Now this group decomposes *properly* in two sets, whose substitutions are

$$x_k, \quad x_{\frac{ak+b}{ck+d}},$$

$ad - bc$ being a quadratic residue of p.

The group thus simplified has $\dfrac{(p + 1)p(p - 1)}{2}$ permutations.

But it is easy to see that it is not further properly decomposable, unless $p = 2$ or $p = 3$.

Thus, in whatever manner we transform the equation, its group will always have the same number of substitutions.

But it is interesting to know whether the degree can be lowered.

First, it cannot be made less than p, as an equation of degree less than p cannot have p as a factor of the number of permutations of its group.

Let us see then whether the equation of degree $p + 1$, whose roots are denoted by x_k on giving k all its values, including infinity, and has for its group of substitutions

$$x_k, \quad x_{\frac{ak+b}{ck+d}}$$

$ad - bc$ being a square, can be lowered to degree p.

Now this can happen only if the group decomposes (improperly, of course) in p sets of $\dfrac{(p + 1)(p - 1)}{2}$ permutations each.

Let 0 and ∞ be two conjoint letters of one of these groups. The substitutions which do not change 0 and ∞ are of the form

$$x_k, \quad x_{m^2 k}.$$

Therefore if M is the letter conjoint to 1, the letter conjoint to m^2 will be m^2M. When M is a square, we shall have $M^2 = 1$. But this simplification can be effected only for $p = 5$.

For $p = 7$ we find a group of $\dfrac{(p + 1)(p - 1)}{2}$ permutations, where

$$\infty, 1, 2, 4$$

have respectively the conjoints

$$0, 3, 6, 5.$$

The substitutions of this group are of the form

$$x_k, \; x_{a \cdot \frac{(k-b)}{k-c}},$$

b being the letter conjoint to c, and a a letter which is a residue or a non-residue simultaneously with c.

For $p = 11$, the same substitutions will occur with the same notations,

$$\infty, 1, 3, 4, 5, 9,$$

having respectively for conjoints

$$0, 2, 6, 8, 10, 7.$$

Thus for the cases $p = 5, 7, 11$, the modular equation can be reduced to degree p.

In all rigor, this equation is not possible in the higher cases.

The third memoir concerns integrals.

We know that a sum of terms of the same elliptic function[1] always reduces to a single term, plus algebraic or logarithmic quantities.

There are no other functions having this property.

But absolutely analogous properties are furnished by all integrals of algebraic functions.

We treat at one time every integral whose differential is a function of a variable and of the same irrational function of the variable, whether this irrationality is or is not a radical, or whether it is expressible or not expressible by means of radicals.

We find that the number of distinct periods of the most general integral relative to a given irrationality is always an even number.

If $2n$ is this number, we have the following theorem:

Any sum of terms whatever reduces to n terms plus algebraic and logarithmic quantities.

---

[1] [Galois presumably means a sum of elliptic integrals of the same species.]

The functions of the first species are those for which the algebraic and logarithmic parts are zero.

There are n distinct functions of the first species.

The functions of the second species are those for which the complementary part is purely algebraic.

There are n distinct functions of the second species.[1]

We may suppose that the differentials of the other functions are never infinite except once for $x = a$, and moreover, that their complementary part reduces to a single logarithm, $\log P$, P being an algebraic quantity. Denoting these functions by $\pi(x, a)$, we have the theorem

$$\pi(x, a) - \pi(a, x) = \Sigma\varphi a \cdot \psi x,$$

$\varphi(a)$ and $\psi(x)$ being functions of the first and of the second species.

We infer, calling $\pi(a)$ and ψ the periods of $\pi(x, a)$ and ψx relative to the same variation of x,

$$\pi(a) = \Sigma\psi \times \varphi a.$$

Thus the periods of the functions of the third species are always expressible in terms of the first and second species.

We can also deduce theorems analogous to the theorem of Legendre [2]

$$FE' + EF' - FF' = \frac{\pi}{2}.$$

The reduction of functions of the third species to definite integrals, which is the most beautiful discovery of M. Jacobi, is not practicable, except in the case of elliptic functions.

The multiplication of integral functions by a whole number is always possible, as is the addition, by means of an equation of degree n whose roots are the values to substitute in the integral to obtain the reduced terms.[3]

The equation which gives the division of the periods in p equal parts is of degree $p^{2n} - 1$. Its group contains in all

$$(p^{2n} - 1)(p^{2n} - p) \ldots (p^{2n} - p^{2n-1}) \text{ permutations.}$$

---

[1] [Picard comments: "We thus acquire the conviction that he (Galois) had in his possession the most essential results concerning Abelian integrals which Riemann was to obtain twenty-five years later."]

[2] [According to Tannery, who collated Galois's manuscripts with Liouville's publication of Galois's Works, Galois wrote Legendre's theorem in the form: $E'F'' - E''F' = \frac{\pi}{2}\sqrt{-1}$. Liouville made other alterations of a minor character.]

[3] [Obscure.]

The equation which gives the division of a sum of n terms in p equal parts is of degree p^{2n}. It is solvable by radicals.

Concerning the Transformation.—First, by reasoning analogous to that which Abel has indicated in his last memoir, we can show that if, in a given relation among integrals, we have the two functions

$$\int\Phi(x, X)dx, \int\Psi(y, Y)dy,$$

the last integral having $2n$ periods, it will be permissible to suppose that y and Y can be expressed by means of a single equation of degree n in terms of x and X.

Then we may suppose that the transformations are constantly made for two integrals only, since one has evidently, in taking any rational function whatever of y and Y,

$\Sigma\int\int(y, Y)dy = \int F(x, X)dx +$ an algebraic and logarithmic quantity.

There are in this equation obvious reductions in the case where the integrals of the two members do not both have the same number of periods.

Thus we have only to compare those integrals both of which have the same number of periods.

We shall prove that the smallest degree of irrationality of two like integrals cannot be greater for one than for the other.

We shall show subsequenty that one may always transform a given integral into another in which one period of the first is divided by the prime number p, and the other $2n - 1$ remain the same.

It will only remain therefore to compare integrals which have the same periods, and such consequently, for which n terms of the one can be expressed without any other equation than a single one of degree n, by means of two of the others, and reciprocally. We know nothing about this.

You know, my dear Auguste, that these subjects are not the only ones I have explored. My reflections, for some time, have been directed principally to the application of the theory of ambiguity to transcendental analysis.[1] It is desired to see *a priori* in a relation among quantities or transcendental functions, what transformations one may make, what quantities one may

---

[1] [Picard comments: "We could almost guess what he means by this, and in this field, which, as he says, is immense, there still to this day remain discoveries to make."]

substitute for the given quantities, without the relation ceasing to be valid. This enables us to recognize at once the impossibility of many expressions which we might seek. But I have no time, and my ideas are not developed in this field, which is immense.

Print this letter in the *Revue encyclopédique*.

I have often in my life ventured to advance propositions of which I was uncertain; but all that I have written here has been in my head nearly a year, and it is too much to my interest not to deceive myself that I have been suspected of announcing theorems of which I had not the complete demonstration.

Ask Jacobi or Gauss publicly to give their opinion, not as to the truth, but as to the importance of the theorems.

Subsequently there will be, I hope, some people who will find it to their profit to decipher all this mess.

Je t'embrasse avec effusion.

E. Galois.

May 29, 1832.

ABEL

On the Continuity of Functions Defined by Power Series

(Translated from the German by Professor Albert A. Bennett, Brown University, Providence, R. I.)

This article constitutes part of the opening portion of a paper originally written in French entitled "Investigation of the series: $1 + \frac{m}{1}x + \frac{m}{1}\frac{(m-1)}{2}x^2 + \frac{m(m-1)(m-2)}{1 \cdot 2 \cdot 3}x^3 + \ldots$ and so forth." It first appeared, in a faithful German translation, in the *Journal für die reine und angewandte Mathematik* (Crelle) Berlin 1826, pages 311 to 339, and the extract translated below covers pages 312 to 315). It was reprinted with corrections and notes in Ostwald's *Klassiker der Exacten Wissenschaft*, No. 71, Leipzig, 1895. The article in the original French is in Abel, *Œuvres complètes*, Vol. I, Christiania, 1881, pages 219 to 250.

Niels Henrik Abel (Aug. 5, 1802 to April 6, 1829) was born in Findö, Norway. As a youth, his mathematical achievement was phenomenal. He studied some eighteen months in Germany and France under a grant from the Norwegian government and collaborated in founding Crelle's Journal. He returned to Christiania, 1827, and died suddenly at the age of 26 years. The two volumes of the second edition of his collected works bear testimony to his productivity. The classical terms "Abelian group" and "Abelian function" indicate in widely different fields something of his originality, profundity, and still increasing influence.

The theorem (which is fundamental in analytic function theory) may be stated in modern notation as follows. *If a real power series converges for some positive value of the argument, the domain of uniform convergence extends at least up to and including this point, and the continuity of the sum-function extends at least up to and including this point.* The extension to complex values follows readily by the method used previously by Cauchy (noted below) in the special case of the infinite geometric progression, *Cours d'Analyse*, Paris, 1821, p. 275–278.

This theorem is of special interest, in that it was included in the scope of the investigation by Cauchy, referred to above. Cauchy correctly stated and in substance proved the theorem for the trivial case of the infinite geometric progression. Cauchy proceeded at once to state and claimed to prove a much more general theorem of which this would have been a special case. Cauchy's more general theorem is however false. Abel remarks indeed in this paper in a footnote (p. 316):

In the above-mentioned work of Mr. Cauchy (page 131) one finds the following theorem:

"If the different terms of the series

$$u_0 + u_1 + u_2 + u_3 + \ldots \text{etc.}$$

are functions of one and the same variable x, and indeed continuous functions with respect to this variable in the neighborhood of a particular value for which the series converges, then the sum s of the series is also a continuous function of x in the neighborhood of this particular value."

It appears to me that this theorem suffers exceptions. Thus for example the series

$$\sin \phi - \frac{1}{2} \sin 2\phi + \frac{1}{3} \sin 3\phi - \ldots \text{etc.}$$

is discontinuous for each value $(2m + 1)\pi$ of ϕ, where m is a whole number. It is well-known that there are many series with similar properties.

Abel was the first to note that Cauchy's announced theorem is not in general valid, and to prove the correct theorem for general power series.

This paper appeared at a critical time in the theory of infinite series. (For reference, see *Enc. des Sci. Math.* I, 1, 2. (1907) p. 213 to 221.) Archimedes used the infinite series $1 + \frac{1}{4} + (\frac{1}{4})^2 + \ldots$ Prop. 22, 23, Quadrature of the Parabola, *Works of Archimedes*, T. L. Heath, 1897. p. 249–251. N. Mercator, and Lord Brouncker simultaneously in 1668 introduced the infinite logarithmic series. Sir Isaac Newton (*De analysi per aequationes numero terminorum infinitas*, (1669; London, 1711), used infinite series systematically. Leibniz 1673 remarked upon the divergence of the harmonic series in connection with his harmonic triangle. (J. M. Child, *Early mathematical manuscripts of Leibniz*, Chicago, Open Court, 1920, Page 50.) Both Jacques and Jean Bernoulli considered the same problem in 1689. Even Lagrange (1768) was content to establish the fact that the successive terms of a convergent series approach zero, apparently assuming the converse theorem in such use as he made of series in his *Théorie des fonctions analytiques* (Paris, year V, 1797, p. 50; *Oeuvres*, vol. 9, Paris 1881, p. 85).

The outstanding general discussion of convergence of series prior to this paper was the *Cours d'Analyse de l'École Royale Polytechnique*, (Paris, 1821) of Augustin-Louis Cauchy (Part One is "Analyse Algébrique"). Chap. 6 (pages 123–172) deals with convergence of real series; Chap. 9 (pages 274–328), with convergence of series with complex terms. Gauss (*Commentationes Soc. Gottingen. math.*, 1812, Mém. no. 1; *Werke*, Göttingen, Vol. III, 1876, see pages 139–143) had considered rigorously a particular series (the hypergeometric series) but stated however no general theorem on convergence such as given in the extract here translated. Cauchy's completed theorem on the circle of convergence of a Taylor-series expansion for a holomorphic function was not published until 1832, three years after Abel's death.

Abel's own preface suggests the state of the theory of infinite series at Abel's time. Quoting page 312:

One of the most remarkable series of algebraic analysis is the following:

$$1 + \frac{m}{1}x + \frac{m(m-1)}{1 \cdot 2}x^2 + \frac{m(m-1)(m-2)}{1 \cdot 2 \cdot 3}x^3 + \ldots$$
$$+ \frac{m(m-1)\ldots[m-(n-1)]}{1 \cdot 2 \ldots\ldots\ldots n}x^n + \ldots$$

When m is a positive whole number the sum of the series which is then finite can be expressed, as is known, by $(1 + x)^n$. When m is not an integer, the series goes on to infinity, and it will converge or diverge according as the quantities m and x have this or that value. In this case, one writes the same equality

$$(1 + x)^m = 1 + \frac{m}{1}x + \frac{m(m-1)}{1 \cdot 2}x^2 + \ldots\text{etc.,}$$

but then the equation shows nothing more than that the two expressions $(1 + x)^m$, $1 + \frac{m}{1} \cdot x + \frac{m \cdot (m-1)}{1 \cdot 2} \cdot x^2 + \ldots$ have certain common properties, upon which for certain values of m and x, depends the *numerical* equality of the expressions. It is assumed that the numerical equality will always occur whenever the series is convergent, but this has never yet been proved. Not even have all the cases in which the series converges been examined as yet. Even if the existence of the equality mentioned above be *assumed*, it would still remain to find the *value* of $(1 + x)^n$, for this expression has in general infinitely many different values, while the series $1 + mx + \ldots$ has but a single one only.

The following is the translation of the extract referred to above:

We will first establish some necessary theorems on series. The excellent work of Cauchy, *Cours d'analyse de l'École Polytechnique,* which should be read by every analyst who loves rigor in mathematical investigations, will serve to guide us.

Definition.—An arbitrary series

$$v_0 + v_1 + v_2 + \ldots + v_m + \ldots$$

will be called *convergent,* if for constantly increasing values of m, the sum, $v_0 + v_1 + \ldots + v_m$, approaches arbitrarily near a certain limit. This limit will be called the *sum of the series.* In the contrary case the series will be called *divergent,* and then it has no sum. From this definition it follows that if a series is to be convergent, it is necessary and sufficient that for continually increasing values of m, the sum $v_m + v_{m+1} + \ldots + v_{m+n}$ shall approach arbitrarily close to zero, no matter what be the value of n.

In any convergent series, therefore, the general term v_m approaches arbitrarily close to zero.[1]

THEOREM I.—If a series of positive quantities is denoted by ρ_0, ρ_1, ρ_2, ..., and if for continually increasing values of m, the quotient ρ_{m+1}/ρ_m approaches a limit α, which is greater than 1, then the series

$$\epsilon_0 \rho_0 + \epsilon_1 \rho_1 + \epsilon_2 \rho_2 + \ldots + \epsilon_m \rho_m + \ldots,$$

where ϵ_m is a quantity which for continually increasing values of m *does not approach arbitrarily close to zero*, will necessarily *diverge*.

THEOREM II.—If in a series of positive quantities such as $\rho_0 + \rho_1 + \rho_2 + \ldots + \rho_m + \ldots$, the quotient ρ_{m+1}/ρ_m, for continually increasing values of m, approaches arbitrarily close to a limit[2] which *is smaller than* 1,[3] then the series

$$\epsilon_0 \rho_0 + \epsilon_1 \rho_1 + \epsilon_2 \rho_2 + \ldots + \epsilon_m \rho_m + \ldots,$$

where ϵ_0, ϵ_1, ϵ_2, ..., are quantities which *do not exceed* 1, will necessarily converge.

Indeed by hypothesis, m can always be taken sufficiently large so that one shall have $\rho_{m+1} < \alpha \rho_m$, $\rho_{m+2} < \alpha \rho_{m+1} \ldots$, $\rho_{m+n} < \alpha \rho_{m+n-1}$. Thence it follows that $\rho_{m+k} < \alpha^k \rho_m$, and hence

$$\rho_m + \rho_{m+1} + \ldots + \rho_{m+n} < \rho_m(1 + \alpha + \ldots + \alpha^n) < \frac{\rho_m}{(1 - \alpha)},$$

and hence a fortiori

$$\epsilon_m \rho_m + \epsilon_{m+1} \rho_{m+1} + \ldots + \epsilon_{m+n} \rho_{m+n} < \frac{\rho_m}{(1 - \alpha)}.$$

Since however $\rho_{m+k} < a^k \rho_m$ and $\alpha < 1$, it is clear that ρ_m and consequently also the sum

$$\epsilon_m \rho_m + \epsilon_{m+1} \rho_{m+1} + \ldots + \epsilon_{m+n} \rho_{m+n}$$

will have zero as limit.[4]

Hence the series given above is convergent.

---

[1] For brevity, in this article, by ω will be meant a quantity which can be smaller than any given quantity no matter how small.

[2] [The text reads "to a limit α which..." This is somewhat inexact in view of the use made of α.]

[3] [And hence smaller than some constant α itself smaller than 1.]

[4] [The context shows that this somewhat ambiguous statement is to be understood in the required sense of $\lim_{m \to \infty}[\lim_{n \to \infty}(\epsilon_m \rho_m + \epsilon_{m+1} \rho_{m+1} + \ldots + \epsilon_{m+n} \rho_{m+n})] = 0$.]

THEOREM III.—If by $t_0, t_1, t_2, \ldots, t_m, \ldots$ is denoted a series of arbitrary quantities, and if the quantity

$$p_m = t_0 + t_1 + t_2 + \ldots + t_m$$

is always less than a definite quantity, δ, then one has

$$r = \epsilon_0 t_0 + \epsilon_1 t_1 + \epsilon_2 t_2 + \ldots + \epsilon_m t_m < \delta\epsilon_0,$$

where $\epsilon_0, \epsilon_1, \epsilon_2, \ldots$ are positive decreasing quantities.

In fact one has

$$t_0 = p_0, \ t_1 = p_1 - p_0, \ t_2 = p_2 - p_1, \ldots$$

hence

$$r = \epsilon_0 p_0 + \epsilon_1(p_1 - p_0) + \epsilon_2(p_2 - p_1) + \ldots + \epsilon_m(p_m - p_{m-1}),$$

or also

$$r = p_0(\epsilon_0 - \epsilon_1) + p_1(\epsilon_1 - \epsilon_2) + \ldots + p_{m-1}(\epsilon_{m-1} - \epsilon_m) + p_m\epsilon_m.$$

Since however $\epsilon_0 - \epsilon_1, \epsilon_1 - \epsilon_2, \ldots$, are positive, the quantity r is obviously smaller than $\delta . \epsilon_0$.

Definition.—A function $f(x)$ is called a continuous function of x between the limits $x = a$, and $x = b$, if for an arbitrary value of x between these limits, the quantity $f(x - \beta)$ approaches arbitrarily close to the limit $f(x)$ for continually decreasing values of β.

THEOREM IV.—If the series

$$f(\alpha) = v_0 + v_1\alpha + v_2\alpha^2 + \ldots + v_m\alpha^m + \ldots$$

converges for a certain value of δ of α, it will also converge for every *smaller* value of α, and in such a way that $f(\alpha - \beta)$, for continually decreasing values of β, approaches arbitrarily close to the limit $f(\alpha)$, it being understood that α is equal to or smaller than δ.

Let

$$v_0 + v_1\alpha + \ldots + v_{m-1}\alpha^{m-1} = \phi(\alpha),$$
$$v_m\alpha^m + v_{m+1}\alpha^{m+1} + \ldots = \psi(\alpha);$$

then one has

$$\psi(\alpha) = \left(\frac{\alpha}{\delta}\right)^m . v_m\delta^m + \left(\frac{\alpha}{\delta}\right)^{m+1} . v_{m+1}\delta^{m+1} + \ldots;$$

hence by means of Theorem III, $\psi(\alpha) < (\alpha/\delta)^m p$, if p denotes the largest of the quantities $v_m\delta^m, \ v_m\delta^m + v_{m+1}\delta^{m+1}, \ v_m\delta^m + v_{m+1}\delta^{m+1} + v_{m+2}\delta^{m+2}, \ldots$ Then for each value of α which is equal to or smaller than δ, one can take m sufficiently large so that one has

$$\psi(\alpha) = \omega.$$

Now $f(\alpha) = \phi(\alpha) + \psi(\alpha)$ holds, and therefore

$$f(\alpha) - f(\alpha - \beta) = \phi(\alpha) - \phi(\alpha - \beta) + \omega.$$

Since further, $\phi(\alpha)$ is an entire function o. α, one can take β so small that

$$\phi(\alpha) - \phi(\alpha - \beta) = \omega$$

holds, and therefore also

$$f(\alpha) - f(\alpha - \beta) = \omega,$$

proving the theorem.

The paper continues, giving an imperfect discussion of power series with variable coefficients, Theorem V, and in Theorem VI disposes of the product of two convergent series: Parts III and IV which form the main substance of the paper deal strictly with the binomial series.

GAUSS

SECOND PROOF OF THE FUNDAMENTAL THEOREM OF ALGEBRA

(Translated from the Latin by Professor C. Raymond Adams, Brown
University, Providence, R. I.)

Carl Friedrich Gauss was born in Braunschweig, Germany, on April 30,
1777. At an early age he displayed marked abilities which brought him to the
notice of the Duke of Braunschweig and secured for him an education. While
a student at Göttingen from 1795 to 1798 he made numerous important discoveries in several fields of mathematics. From 1807 until his death in 1855
he held the post of professor of astronomy at Göttingen, which allowed him to
devote all his time to scientific investigation. He made contributions of
fundamental significance not only in almost every leading field of pure mathematics, but also in astronomy, geodesy, electricity, and magnetism. No other
mathematician of the nineteenth century exerted so profound an influence on
the development of the science as did Gauss.

Gauss gave four proofs[1] of the fundamental theorem of algebra, which
may be stated in the form: *every algebraic equation of degree m has exactly m
roots.*[2] The significance of his first proof in the development of mathematics is

---

[1] The first was discovered in the autumn of 1797 and constituted his Dissertation; it was
published at Helmstädt in 1799 under the title "Demonstratio nova theorematis omnem
functionem algebraicam rationalem integram unius variabilis in factores reales primi vel
secondi gradus resolvi posse;" *Werke*, vol. 3 (1876), pp. 3–30. The second and third proofs,
"Demonstratio nova altera theorematis..." and "Theorematis de resolubilitate...
demonstratio tertia" appeared in 1816 in *Commentationes Societatis regiae scientiarum
Gottingensis recentiores.* vol. 3, (class. math.) pp. 107–134 and pp. 135–142 respectively;
Werke, vol. 3 (1876), pp. 33–56, 59–64. The fourth proof was published in 1850 as
"Beiträge zur Theorie der algebraichen Gleichungen" (erste Abtheilung), *Abhandlungen
der Könilgiden Gesellschaft der Wissenschaften zu Göttingen.* vol. 4, (math Klasse) pp. 3–15;
Werke, vol. 3 (1876), pp. 73–85.

[2] It is not quite certain to whom the credit belongs for first stating this theorem. That an
algebraic equation of the mth degree may have m roots was recognized by Peter Rothe
(*Arithmetica Philosophica*, Nürnberg, 1608). Albert Girard (*Invention Nouvelle en l'Algebre*,
Amsterdam, 1629) asserted that "every algebraic equation has as many solutions as the
exponent of the highest term indicates;" unfortunately he added the qualification "unless
the equation is incomplete" |i. e., does not contain all powers of x from m down to zero], but
he pointed out that if an equation admits fewer roots than its degree indicates, it is useful
to introduce as many impossible |i. e., complex] solutions as will make the total number of
roots and impossible solutions equal the degree of the equation. The clear-cut statement
of the theorem used by Gauss seems to be due to Euler in a letter dated December 15, 1742
(*Correspondence Mathématique et Physique*, ed. by Fuss, St. Petersburg, 1845, vol. 1, p. 171).
Before Gauss several attempts to prove the theorem had been made, notably by d'Alembert
(1746), whose proof was so widely accepted that the theorem came to be known, at least in
France, as d'Alembert's theorem; by Euler (1749); by Foncenex (1759); by Lagrange (1772);
and by Laplace (lectures given at the École Polytechnique in 1795 but published in its
Journal only in 1812). The term *fundamental theorem of algebra* appears to have been
introduced by Gauss.

made clear by his own words in the introduction to the fourth proof: "[the first proof]... had a double purpose, first to show that all the proofs previously attempted of this most important theorem of the theory of algebraic equations are unsatisfactory and illusory, and secondly to give a newly constructed rigorous proof." In the first three proofs (but not in the fourth) the restriction is made that the coefficients in the equation be real; this, however, is not a serious defect since it is readily shown[1] that the case in which the coefficients are complex can be reduced to that in which they are real. While the first proof is based in part on geometrical considerations, the second is entirely algebraic and has been described[2] as "the most ingenious in conception and the most far-reaching in method" of the four. It is appropriate, therefore, to give here the second proof.

Because of the limitations of space we shall not present the entire paper, but shall pass over the introduction (§1) and give a brief resumé of §§2–6, which contain the proofs of certain theorems, now well known, on the primality of rational integral functions and on symmetric functions. From this point on the translation will be given in full except for one section.

In §2 it is proved that if Y and Y' are any two integral functions[3] of x, a necessary and sufficient condition that they have no common factor other than a constant is that there exist two other integral functions of x, Z and Z', satisfying the identity

$$ZY + Z'Y' \equiv 1.$$

In §3 it is pointed out that if a, b, c,... is any set of m constants and if we define

$$v \equiv (x - a)(x - b)(x - c)... \equiv x^m - \lambda'x^{m-1} + \lambda''x^{m-2} - ...,$$

each λ, or any function of the λ's is a symmetric function of a, b, c,...

§4 is devoted to proving that any integral symmetric function of a, b, c,... is an integral function of the λ's; the uniqueness of this function of the λ's is established in §5.

In §6 the product

$$\pi = (a - b)(a - c)(a - d)... \times (b - a)(b - c)(b - d)... \times$$
$$(c - a)(c - b)(c - d)... \times ...$$

is introduced. By §§4, 5 this is a certain integral function of λ', λ'',...; the same function of l', l'',... is denoted by p and is defined as the discriminant[4] of the function

$$y = x^m - l'x^{m-1} + l''x^{m-2} - ...$$

This is regarded as *any* integral function of x of the mth degree with the leading coefficient 1, without regard to the question of factorability, and the l's are to be thought of as variables. On the other hand the function

$$Y = x^m - L'x^{m-1} + L''x^{m-2} - ...$$

is regarded as a *particular*, though arbitrary, function of the same type, with no restrictions on the coefficients, which are to be thought of as arbitrary

---

[1] Cf. Netto, "Rationale Funktionen einer Veränderlichen; ihre Nullstellen," *Encyklopädie der Mathematischen Wissenschaften*, vol. I, p. 233.

[2] Netto, *Die vier Gauss'schen Beweise*..., Leipzig, 1913, p. 81.

[3] [Throughout the paper Gauss uses the term *integral function* in the sense of *rational integral function*.]

[4] [*Determinant* is the term used by Gauss in common with other writers of the time.]

constants. The value of p for $l' = L'$, $l'' = L''$,...is denoted by P. It is with the factorability of Y that this paper is concerned. On the assumption that Y can be broken up into linear factors,

$$Y = (x - A)(x - B)(x - C)\dots,$$

the following theorems are proved

I. *If P, the discriminant of Y, is zero, Y and $Y' = \dfrac{dY}{dx}$ have a common factor.*

II. *If P, the discriminant of Y, is not zero, Y and Y' have no common factor.*

7.

It is well to observe, however, that the entire strength of this very simple proof rests on the assumption that the function Y can be reduced to linear factors; but this amounts, at least in the present connection, where we are concerned with the general proof of this reducibility, to no less than assuming what is to be proved. Yet not all of those who have attempted analytic proofs of our principal theorem have been on their guard against this sort of deduction. The source of such an obvious error can be perceived in the very title of their investigations, since all have studied only the *form* of the roots of the equation while the *existence* of the roots, rashly taken for granted, should have been the object of the demonstration. But about this sort of procedure which is entirely at odds with rigor and clarity, enough has already been said in the paper referred to above.[1] Therefore we will now establish on a more sure foundation the theorems of the preceding section, of which at least a part is essential to our purpose; with the second, and simpler, we begin.

8.

We will denote by ρ the function

$$\frac{\pi(x - b)(x - c)(x - d)\dots}{(a - b)^2(a - c)^2(a - d)^2\dots} + \frac{\pi(x - a)(x - c)(x - d)\dots}{(b - a)^2(b - c)^2(b - d)^2\dots}$$
$$+ \frac{\pi(x - a)(x - b)(x - d)\dots}{(c - a)^2(c - b)^2(c - d)^2\dots} + \dots,$$

which, since π is divisible by the individual denominators, is an integral function of the unknowns x, a, b, c,...Furthermore we set $dv/dx = v'$, obtaining

$$v' = (x - b)(x - c)(x - d)\dots + (x - a)(x - c)(x - d)\dots$$
$$+ (x - a)(x - b)(x - d)\dots + \dots$$

---

[1] [Gauss's first proof, to which reference is made in the introduction, §1.]

For $x = a$ we clearly have $\rho \cdot v' = \pi$, from which we conclude that the function $\pi - \rho v'$ is exactly divisible[1] by $x - a$, likewise by $x - b$, $x - c$, ... and consequently also by the product v. If then we set

$$\frac{\pi - \rho v'}{v} = \sigma,$$

σ is an integral function of the unknowns x, a, b, c, ... and indeed, like ρ, symmetric in the unknowns a, b, c, ... Accordingly there can be found two integral functions r and s of the unknowns x, l', l'', ... which by the substitutions $l' = \lambda'$, $l'' = \lambda''$, ... go over respectively into ρ and σ. If analogously we denote the function

$$mx^{m-1} - (m - 1)l'x^{m-2} + (m - 2)l''x^{m-3} - \ldots,$$

i. e., the derivative dy/dx, by y', so that y' also goes over by those substitutions into v', then clearly by those same substitutions $p - sy - ry'$ goes over into $\pi - \sigma v - \rho v'$, i. e., into zero, and must therefore vanish identically (§5). Hence we have the identity

$$p = sy + ry'$$

If we assume that by the substitutions $l' = L'$, $l'' = L''$, ... r and s become respectively R and S, we have also the identity

$$P = SY + RY';$$

and since S and R are integral functions of x, and P is a definite quantity or number, it follows at once that Y and Y' can have no common factor if P is not zero. This is exactly the second theorem of §6.

9.

The proof of the first theorem we will construct by showing that if Y and Y' have no common factor, P can certainly not be zero. To this end we determine by the method of §2 two integral functions of the unknown x, say $f(x)$ and $\varphi(x)$, such that the identity

$$f(x) \cdot Y + \varphi(x) \cdot Y' = 1$$

holds; this we can also write as

$$f(x) \cdot v + \varphi(x) \cdot v' = 1 + f(x) \cdot (v - Y) + \varphi(x) \cdot \frac{d(v - Y)}{dx},$$

or, since we have

$$v' = (x - b)(x - c)(x - d) \ldots$$
$$+ (x - a)\frac{d[(x - b)(x - c)(x - d) \ldots]}{dx},$$

---

[1] [An integral function will be said to be exactly divisible by a second integral function of the same variables if the quotient of the first by the second is a third integral function of these variables.]

in the form

$$\varphi(x) \cdot (x - b)(x - c)(x - d) \ldots$$
$$+ \varphi(x) \cdot (x - a)\frac{d[(x - b)(x - c)(x - d) \ldots]}{dx} + f(x) \cdot (x - a)(x - b)$$
$$(x - c) \ldots = 1 + f(x) \cdot (v - Y) + (x) \cdot \frac{d(v - Y)}{dx}.$$

For brevity we will denote the expression

$$f(x) \cdot (y - Y) + \varphi(x) \cdot \frac{d(y - Y)}{dx},$$

which is an integral function of the unknowns x, l', l'', \ldots, by

$$F(x, l', l'', \ldots);$$

hence we have identically

$$1 + f(x) \cdot (v - Y) + \varphi(x) \cdot \frac{d(v - Y)}{dx} = 1 + F(x, \lambda', \lambda'', \ldots),$$

and therefore the identities

(1) $\varphi(a) \cdot (a - b)(a - c)(a - d) \ldots = 1 + F(a, \lambda', \lambda'', \ldots),$
$\varphi(b) \cdot (b - a)(b - c)(b - d) \ldots = 1 + F(b, \lambda', \lambda'', \ldots),$
$\ldots \ldots \ldots \ldots$

If then we assume that the product of all the functions

$$1 + F(a, l', l'', \ldots), 1 + F(b, l', l'', \ldots), \ldots,$$

which is an integral function of the unknowns a, b, c, \ldots, l', l'', \ldots
and indeed a symmetric function of a, b, c, \ldots, is denoted by

$$\psi(\lambda', \lambda'', \ldots, l', l'', \ldots),$$

there follows from the multiplication of all the equations (1)
the new identity

(2) $$\pi\varphi a \cdot \varphi b \cdot \varphi c \ldots = \psi(\lambda', \lambda'', \ldots, \lambda', \lambda'', \ldots).$$

It is furthermore clear that since the product $\varphi a \cdot \varphi b \cdot \varphi c \ldots$
involves the unknowns a, b, c, \ldots symmetrically, an integral
function of the unknowns l', l'', \ldots can be found which by the
substitutions $l' = \lambda'$, $l'' = \lambda''$, \ldots goes over into $\varphi a. \varphi b. \varphi c \ldots$ If
t is this function we have identically

(3) $$pt = \psi(l', l'', \ldots, l', l'', \ldots),$$

for by the substitution $l' = \lambda'$, $l'' = \lambda''$, \ldots this equation becomes
the identity (2).

From the definition of the function F follows immediately the
identity

$$F(x, L', L'', \ldots) = 0.$$

Hence we have successively the following identities.

$$1 + F(a, L', L'', \ldots) = 1, \; 1 + F(b, L', L'', \ldots) = 1, \ldots,$$
$$\psi(\lambda', \lambda'', \ldots, L', L'', \ldots) = 1,$$

and

(4) $$\psi(l', l'', \ldots, L', L'', \ldots) = 1.$$

From equations (3) and (4) jointly, if we set $l' = L'$, $l'' = L'', \ldots$, follows the relation

(5) $$PT = 1,$$

where T denotes the value of the function t that corresponds to those substitutions. Since this value must be finite, P can certainly not be zero.

10.

From the foregoing it is apparent that every integral function Y of an unknown x whose discriminant is zero can be broken up into factors of which none has a vanishing discriminant. In fact if we find the greatest common divisor of the functions Y and $\dfrac{dY}{dx}$, Y is thereby broken into two factors. If one of these factors[1] again has the discriminant zero, it may in the same way be broken into two factors, and so we shall proceed until Y is finally reduced to factors no one of which has the discriminant zero.

Moreover one easily perceives that of those factors into which Y has been broken, at least one has the property that among the factors of its degree index the factor 2 is present no more frequently than it occurs among the factors of m, the degree index of Y; accordingly if we set $m = k \cdot 2^\mu$, where k is odd, there will be among the factors of Y at least one whose degree is $k' \cdot 2^\nu$, k' being odd and $\nu = \mu$ or $\nu < \mu$. The validity of this assertion follows immediately from the fact that m is the sum of the numbers which indicate the degree of the individual factors of Y.

11.

Before proceeding further we will explain an expression whose introduction is of the greatest use in all investigations of symmetric functions and which will be exceedingly convenient also for our

---

[1] [As a matter of fact only that factor which is the greatest common divisor can have a vanishing discriminant. But the proof of this statement would lead us into various digressions; moreover it is not necessary here, since we should be able to treat the other factor, in case its discriminant should vanish, in the same way and reduce it to factors.]

purposes. We assume that M is a function of some of the unknowns a, b, c,...; let μ be the number of those which enter into the expression M, without reference to other unknowns which perhaps are present in M. If these μ unknowns are permuted in all possible ways, not only among themselves but also with the $m - \mu$ remaining unknowns of the set a, b, c,..., there arise from M other expressions similar to M, so that we have in all

$$m(m - 1)(m - 2)\ldots(m - \mu + 1)$$

expressions, including M itself; the set of these we call simply the *set of all M*. From this it is clear what is to be understood by the sum of all M, the product of all M,... Thus, for example, π can be called the product of all $a - b$, v the product of all $x - a$, v' the sum of all $\dfrac{v}{x - a}$, etc.

If perchance M should be a symmetric function of some of the μ unknowns which it contains, the permutations of these among themselves will not alter the function M; hence in the set of all M every term is multiple and in fact is present $1 . 2 \ldots v$ times if v stands for the number of unknowns in which M is symmetric. But if M is symmetric not only in v unknowns but also in v' others, and in v'' still different unknowns, etc., then M is unchanged if any two of the first v unknowns are permuted among themselves, or any two of the following v' among themselves, or any two of the next v'' among themselves, etc., so that identical terms always correspond to

$$1 . 2 \ldots v . 1 . 2 \ldots v' . 1 . 2 \ldots v'' \ldots$$

permutations. If then from these identical terms we retain only one of each, we have in all

$$\frac{m(m - 1)(m - 2)\ldots(m - \mu + 1)}{1 . 2 \ldots v . 1 . 2 \ldots v' . 1 . 2 \ldots v'' \ldots}$$

terms, the set of which we call the *set of all M without repetitions* to distinguish it from the *set of all M with repetitions*. Unless otherwise expressly stated we shall always admit the repetitions.

One further sees easily that the sum of all M, or the product of all M, or more generally any symmetric function whatever of all M is always a symmetric function of the unknowns a, b, c,..., whether repetitions are admitted or excluded.

12.

We will now consider the product of all $u - (a + b)x + ab$ without repetitions, where u and x indicate unknowns, and denote the same by ζ. Then ζ will be the product of the following $\frac{1}{2}m(m-1)$ factors:

$$u - (a + b)x + ab, \; u - (a + c)x + ac, \; u - (a + d)x + ad, \ldots;$$
$$u - (b + c)x + bc, \; u - (b + d)x + bd, \ldots;$$
$$u - (c + d)x + cd, \ldots; \ldots$$

Since this function involves the unknowns $a, b, c, \ldots$ symmetrically, it determines an integral function of the unknowns $u, x, l', l'', \ldots$, which shall be denoted by z, with the property that it goes over into ζ if the unknowns $l', l'', \ldots$ are replaced by $\lambda', \lambda'', \ldots$ Finally we will denote by Z the function of the unknowns u and x alone to which z reduces if we assign to the unknowns $l', l'', \ldots$ the particular values $L', L'', \ldots$

These three functions ζ, z, and Z can be regarded as integral functions of degree $\frac{1}{2}m(m-1)$ of the unknown u with undetermined coefficients; these coefficients are

> for ζ, functions of the unknowns $x, a, b, c, \ldots$
> for z, functions of the unknowns $x, l', l'', \ldots$
> for Z, functions of the single unknown x.

The individual coefficients of z will go over into the coefficients of ζ by the substitutions $l' = \lambda', l'' = \lambda'', \ldots$ and likewise into the coefficients of Z by the substitutions $l' = L', l'' = L'', \ldots$ The statements made here for the coefficients hold also for the discriminants of the functions ζ, z, and Z. These we will examine more closely for the purpose of obtaining a proof of the

THEOREM.—*Whenever P is not zero, the discriminant of the function Z certainly cannot vanish identically.*

14.[1]

The discriminant of the function ζ is the product of all differences between pairs of quantities $(a + b)x - ab$, the total number of which is

$$\tfrac{1}{2}m(m - 1)[\tfrac{1}{2}m(m - 1) - 1] = \tfrac{1}{4}(m + 1)m(m - 1)(m - 2).$$

This number also expresses the degree in x of the discriminant of the function ζ. The discriminant of the function z will be of the same degree, while the discriminant of the function Z can be of lower degree if some of the coefficients of the highest power of x

---

[1] [We omit §13 which, containing a proof of the above theorem for the restricted case in which Y is reducible to linear factors, is not essential to the further developments of the paper.]

vanish. Our problem is to prove that in the discriminant of the function Z certainly not *all* the coefficients can be zero.

If we examine more closely the differences whose product is the discriminant of the function ζ, we notice that a part of them (that is, those differences between two quantities $(a + b)x - ab$ which have a common element) provides the *product of all* $(a - b)(x - c)$; from the others (that is, those differences between two quantities $(a + b)x - ab$ which have no common element) arises *the product of all*

$$(a + b - c - d)x - ab + cd$$

without repetitions. The first product contains each factor $a - b$ clearly $m - 2$ times, whereas each factor $x - c$ is contained $(m - 1)(m - 2)$ times; from this it is easily seen that the value of this product is

$$\pi^{m-2}v^{(m-1)(m-2)}.$$

If we denote the second product by ρ, the discriminant of the function ζ becomes equal to

$$\pi^{m-2}v^{(m-1)(m-2)}\rho.$$

If further we indicate by r that function of the unknowns x, l', l'',... which by the substitutions $l' = \lambda'$, $l'' = \lambda''$,... goes over into ρ, and by R that function of x alone into which r goes over by the substitutions $l' = L'$, $l'' = L''$,..., the discriminant of the function z manifestly will be equal to

$$p^{m-2}v^{(m-1)(m-2)}r,$$

while the discriminant of the function Z will be

$$P^{m-2}Y^{(m-1)(m-2)}R.$$

Since by hypothesis P is not zero, it now remains to be shown that R cannot vanish identically.

15.

To this end we introduce another unknown w and will consider the product of all

$$(a + b - c - d)w + (a - c)(a - d)$$

without repetitions; since this involves the $a, b, c,...$ symmetrically, it can be expressed as an integral function of the unknowns w, λ', λ'',... We denote this function by $f(w, \lambda', \lambda'',...)$. The number of the factors $(a + b - c - d)w + (a - c)(a - d)$ will be

$$\tfrac{1}{2}m(m - 1)(m - 2)(m - 3),$$

from which easily follow in succession the equalities

$$f(0, \lambda', \lambda'', \ldots) = \pi^{(m-2)(m-3)}$$
$$f(0, l', l'', \ldots) = p^{(m-2)(m-3)}$$

and

$$f(0, L', L'', \ldots) = P^{(m-2)(m-3)}.$$

The function $f(w, L', L'', \ldots)$ must in general be of degree

$$\tfrac{1}{2}m(m-1)(m-2)(m-3);$$

only in particular cases can it well reduce to lower degree, if perchance some coefficients of the highest power of w vanish; it is however impossible for it to be identically zero, since as the above equation shows, at least the last term of the function does not vanish. We will assume that the highest term of the function $f(w, L', L'', \ldots)$ to have a non-vanishing coefficient is Nw^ν. If we make the substitution $w = x - a$, it is clear that $f(x - a, L', L'', \ldots)$ is an integral function of the unknowns x and a, or what is the same thing, an integral function of x whose coefficients depend upon the unknown a; its highest term is Nx^ν and it therefore has a coefficient that is independent of a and different from zero. In the same way $f(x - b, L', L'', \ldots), f(x - c, L', L'', \ldots),$ $\ldots$ are integral functions of the unknown x which individually have Nx^ν as highest term, while the coefficients of the remaining terms depend upon $a, b, c, \ldots$ Hence the product of the m factors $f(x - a, L', L'', \ldots), f(x - b, L', L'', \ldots), f(x - c, L', L'', \ldots), \ldots$ will be an integral function of x whose highest term is $N^m x^{m\nu}$, whereas the coefficients of the subsequent terms depend upon $a, b, c, \ldots$

We now consider the product of the m factors

$$f(x - a, l', l'', \ldots), \ f(x - b, l', l'', \ldots), \ f(x - c, l', l'', \ldots), \ldots,$$

which as a function of the unknowns $x, a, b, c, \ldots, l', l'', \ldots$, symmetric in the $a, b, c, \ldots$, can be expressed in terms of the unknowns $x, \lambda', \lambda'', \ldots, l', l'', \ldots$ and denoted by

$$\varphi(x, \lambda', \lambda'', \ldots, l', l'', \ldots).$$

Thus

$$\varphi(x, \lambda', \lambda'', \ldots, \lambda', \lambda'', \ldots)$$

becomes the product of the factors

$$f(x - a, \lambda', \lambda'', \ldots), f(x - b, \lambda', \lambda'', \ldots), f(x - c, \lambda', \lambda'', \ldots), \ldots$$

and is exactly divisible by ρ, since as is easily seen each factor of ρ is contained in one of these factors. We will therefore set

$$\varphi(x, \lambda', \lambda'', \ldots, \lambda', \lambda'', \ldots) = \rho\psi(x, \lambda', \lambda'', \ldots),$$

ψ indicating an integral function.   From this follows at once the identity

$$\varphi(x, L', L'', \ldots, L', L'', \ldots) = R\psi(x, L', L'', \ldots).$$

We have proved above, however, that the product of the factors $f(x - a, L', L'', \ldots), f(x - b, L', L'', \ldots), f(x - c, L', L'', \ldots), \ldots,$ which is $\varphi(x, \lambda', \lambda'', \ldots, L', L'', \ldots)$ has $N^m x^{m\nu}$ as its highest term; hence the function $\varphi(x, L', L'', \ldots, L', L'', \ldots)$ will have the same highest term and accordingly will not be identically zero.   Therefore R, and likewise the discriminant of the function Z, cannot be identically zero.   Q. E. D.

16.

THEOREM.—*If[1] $\varphi(u, x)$ denotes the product of an arbitrary number of factors which are linear in u and x and so of the form*

$$\alpha + \beta u + \gamma x, \ \alpha' + \beta' u + \gamma' x, \ \alpha'' + \beta'' u + \gamma'' x, \ldots,$$

and if w is another unknown, the function[2]

$$\left(u + w\frac{\mathrm{d}\varphi(u, x)}{\mathrm{d}x}, \ x - w\frac{\mathrm{d}\varphi(u, x)}{\mathrm{d}u}\right) = \Omega$$

will be exactly divisible by $\varphi(u, x)$.

Proof.—If we set

$$\varphi(u, x) = (\alpha + \beta u + \gamma x)Q = (\alpha' + \beta' u + \gamma' x)Q' = \ldots,$$

then $Q, Q', \ldots$ will be integral functions of the unknowns u, x, α, β, γ, α', β', γ', \ldots and we shall have

$$\frac{\mathrm{d}\varphi(u, x)}{\mathrm{d}x} = \gamma Q + (\alpha + \beta u + \gamma x)\frac{\mathrm{d}Q}{\mathrm{d}x}$$
$$= \gamma' Q' + (\alpha' + \beta' u + \gamma' x)$$
$$\frac{\mathrm{d}Q'}{\mathrm{d}x} = \ldots,$$

$$\frac{\mathrm{d}\varphi(u, x)}{\mathrm{d}u} = \beta Q + (\alpha + \beta u + \gamma x)\frac{\mathrm{d}Q}{\mathrm{d}u}$$
$$= \beta' Q' + (\alpha' + \beta' u + \gamma x)$$
$$\frac{\mathrm{d}Q'}{\mathrm{d}u} = \ldots$$

---

[1] [It is hardly necessary to state that the symbols introduced in the preceding section are restricted to that section, in particular that the present meaning of φ and w is not to be confused with the former.]

[2] [The usual notation for total derivative is used here and in §19 to designate partial derivatives.]

If we introduce these values into the factors of the product Ω, that is, into

$$\alpha + \beta u + \gamma x + \beta w \frac{d\varphi(u, x)}{dx} - \gamma w \frac{d\varphi(u, x)}{du},$$

$$\alpha' + \beta' u + \gamma' x + \beta' w \frac{d\varphi(u, x)}{dx} + \gamma' w \frac{d\varphi(u, x)}{du}, \ldots,$$

we obtain the expressions

$$(\alpha + \beta u + \gamma x)\left(1 + \beta w \frac{dQ}{dx} - \gamma w \frac{dQ}{du}\right),$$

$$(\alpha' + \beta' u + \gamma' x)\left(1 + \beta' w \frac{dQ'}{dx} - \gamma' w \frac{dQ'}{du}\right), \ldots,$$

so that Ω becomes the product of $\varphi(u, x)$ and the factors

$$1 + \beta w \frac{dQ}{dx} - \gamma w \frac{dQ}{du}, \ 1 + \beta' w \frac{dQ'}{dx} - \gamma' w \frac{dQ'}{du}, \ldots,$$

i. e., of $\varphi(u, x)$ and an integral function of the unknowns $u, x, w,$ $\alpha, \beta, \gamma, \alpha', \beta', \gamma', \ldots$ Q. E. D.

17.

The theorem of the foregoing paragraph is clearly applicable to the function ζ, which from now on we will denote by

$$f(u, x, \lambda', \lambda'', \ldots),$$

so that

$$f\left(u + w \frac{d\zeta}{dx}, x - w \frac{d\zeta}{du}, \lambda', \lambda'', \ldots\right)$$

is exactly divisible by ζ; the quotient, which is an integral function of the unknowns $u, x, w, a, b, c, \ldots$ and is symmetric in $a, b, c, \ldots,$ we will denote by

$$\psi(u, x, w, \lambda', \lambda'', \ldots).$$

From this follow the identities

$$f\left(u + w \frac{dz}{dx}, x - w \frac{dz}{du}, l', l'', \ldots\right) = z\psi(u, x, w, l', l'', \ldots),$$

$$f\left(u + w \frac{dZ}{dx}, x - w \frac{dZ}{du}, L', L'', \ldots\right) = Z\psi(u, x, w, L', L'', \ldots).$$

If then we indicate the function Z simply by $F(u, x)$, i. e., set

$$f(u, x, L', L'', \ldots) = F(u, x),$$

we shall have the identity

$$F\left(u + w \frac{dZ}{dx}, x - w \frac{dZ}{du}\right) = Z\psi(u, x, w, L', L'', \ldots).$$

18.

Assuming that particular values of u and x, say $u = U$ and $x = X$, give

$$\frac{dZ}{dx} = X', \frac{dZ}{du} = U',$$

we have identically

$$F(U + wX', X - wU') = F(U, X)\psi(U, X, w, L', L'', \ldots).$$

Whenever U' does not vanish we can set

$$w = \frac{X - x}{U'}$$

and obtain

$$F\left(U + \frac{XX'}{U'} - \frac{X'x}{U'}, x\right) = F(U, X)\psi\left(U, X, \frac{X - x}{U'}, L', L'', \ldots\right).$$

If we set $u = U + \dfrac{XX'}{U'} - \dfrac{X'x}{U'}$, the function Z therefore becomes

$$F(U, X)\psi\left(U, X, \frac{X - x}{U'}, L', L'', \ldots\right).$$

19.

Since in case P is not zero the discriminant of the function Z is a function of the unknown x that is not identically zero, the number of particular values of x for which this discriminant can vanish is finite; accordingly an infinite number of values of the unknown x can be assigned which give this discriminant a value different from zero. Let X be such a value of x (which moreover we may assume *real*). Then the discriminant of the function $F(u, X)$ will not be zero and it follows by Theorem II, §6 that the functions

$$F(u, X) \text{ and } \frac{dF(u, X)}{du}$$

can have no common divisor. We will further assume that there is a particular value U of u, which may be real or imaginary, *i. e.*, of the form $g + b\sqrt{-1}$, and which makes $F(u, X) = 0$, so that $F(U, X) = 0$. Then $u - U$ will be an undetermined factor of the function $F(u, X)$ and hence the function $\dfrac{dF(u, X)}{du}$ is certainly not divisible by $u - U$. If then we assume that this function $\dfrac{dF(u, X)}{du}$ takes on the value U' for $u = U$, surely U' cannot be zero. Clearly, however, U' is the value of the partial derivative

$\dfrac{dZ}{du}$ for $u = U$, $x = X$; if then we denote by X' the value of the partial derivative $\dfrac{dZ}{dx}$ for the same values of u and x, it is clear from the proof in the foregoing section that by the substitution

$$u = U + \frac{XX'}{U'} - \frac{X'x}{U'}$$

the function Z vanishes identically and so is exactly divisible by the factor

$$u + \frac{X'}{U'}x - \left(U + \frac{XX'}{U'} \right).$$

If we set $u = x^2$, clearly $F(x^2, x)$ is divisible by

$$x^2 + \frac{X'}{U'}x - \left(U + \frac{XX'}{U'} \right)$$

and thus takes on the value zero if for x we take a root of the equation

$$x^2 + \frac{X'}{U'}x - \left(U + \frac{XX'}{U'} \right) = 0,$$

i. e.,

$$x = \frac{-X' \pm \sqrt{(4UU'U' + 4XX'U' + X'X')}}{2U''}$$

These values are manifestly either real or of the form $g + b\sqrt{-1}$.

Now it can be easily shown that for these same values of x the function Y also must vanish. For it is clear that $f(xx, x, \lambda', \lambda'', \ldots)$ is the product of all $(x - a)(x - b)$ without repetitions and so equals v^{m-1}. From this follow immediately

$$f(xx, x, l', l'', \ldots) = y^{m-1},$$
$$f(xx, x, L', L'', \ldots) = Y^{m-1},$$

or $F(xx, x) = Y^{m-1}$; accordingly a particular value of this function F cannot be zero unless at the same time the value of Y is zero.

20.

By the above investigations the solution of the equation $Y = 0$, that is the determination of a particular value of x which satisfies the equation and is either real or of the form $g + b\sqrt{-1}$, is made to depend upon the solution of the equation $F(u, X) = 0$, provided the discriminant of the function Y is not zero. It may be remarked that if all the coefficients in Y, i. e., the numbers

L', L'',..., are real, and if as is permissible we take a real value for X, all the coefficients in $F(u, X)$ are also real. The degree of the auxiliary equation $F(u, X) = 0$ is expressed by the number $\frac{1}{2}m(m - 1)$; if then m is an even number of the form $2^\mu k$, k designating an odd number, the degree of the second equation is expressed by a number of the form $2^{\mu-1}k$.

In case the discriminant of the function Y is zero, it will be possible by §10 to find another function $\mathfrak{Y}$ which is a divisor of Y, whose discriminant is not zero, and whose degree is expressed by a number $2^\nu k$ with $\gamma < \mu$. Every solution of the equation $\mathfrak{Y} = 0$ will also satisfy the equation $Y = 0$; the solution of the equation $\mathfrak{Y} = 0$ is again made to depend upon the solution of another equation whose degree is expressed by a number of the form $2^{\nu-1}k$.

From this we conclude that in general the solution of every equation whose degree is expressed by an even number of the form $2^\mu k$ can be made to depend upon the solution of another equation whose degree is expressed by a number of the form $2^{\mu'}k$ with $\mu' < \mu$. In case this number also is even,—i. e., if μ' is not zero,— this method can be applied again, and so we proceed until we come to an equation whose degree is expressed by an odd number; the coefficients of this equation are all real if all the coefficients of the original equation are real. It is known, however, that such an equation of odd degree is surely solvable and indeed has a real root. Hence each of the preceding equations is solvable, having either real roots or roots of the form $g + b\sqrt{-1}$.

Thus it has been proved that every function Y of the form $x^m - L'x^{m-1} + L''x^{m-2} - \ldots$, in which L', L'',... are particular real numbers, has a factor $x - A$ where A is real or of the form $g + b\sqrt{-1}$. In the second case it is easily seen that Y is also zero for $x = g - b\sqrt{-1}$ and therefore divisible by $x - (g - b\sqrt{-1})$ and so by the product $xx - 2gx + gg + bb$. Consequently every function Y certainly has a real factor of the first or second degree. Since the same is true of the quotient [of Y by this factor], it is clear that Y can be reduced to real factors of the first or second degree. To prove this fact was the object of this paper.

Index for Volume One and Volume Two

Chuquet, N., 217
Circle, division of, 348
Circles of proportion, 156, 160
Clarke, F. M., 326
Clavius, C., 455, 459
Clebsch, R. F. A., 517, 518
Clifford, W. K., 524, 540
Coi, Z. de T. da, 207
Colson, J., 613
Combinations, 272
Complex numbers, 46, 55, 119
Conformal representation, 463
Congruence of numbers, 107
Conics, Pascal on, 326
Continued fractions, 80
Continuity, 36, 42, 286
Cope, T. F., 119, 267
Cosines, laws of, 434
Cotes, R., 451
Courcier, Vve., 588
Court, N. Altshiller-, 331
Craig, John, 627
Cramer, G., 267
Crelle, A. L., 443
Cremona, L., 477
Cubic equation, 203
Czuber, E. 440

D

D'Alembert, J. L., 292
Darboux, J. G., 517
Darkow, M. D., 677
Decimals, 20
Dedekind, J. W. R., 35
Delamain, R., 156
De Moivre, A., 229, 440, 566, 588
De Morgan, A., 631
Derivatives (Cauchy), 635
Desargues, G., 307, 311, 326, 329
Descartes, R., 397, 649
Descriptive geometry, 426
Determinants, 267
Dickson, L. E., x, xii
Differential equations (Euler), 638
Diophantus, 214
Dirichlet, P. G. L., 112, 127, 215, 659
Disme, 20, 22, 23
Dithmarsus, N. R. U., 455, 459
D'Ocagne, P. M., 192

E

$e(2.718 \ldots)$, 95, 99
Einstein, A., 425
Emch, A., 403, 426, 476
Engel, F., 351, 360, 485
Equation, biquadratic, 207
cubic, 203
quintic, 261
Errors, probability of, 588
Euler, L., 91, 95, 115, 130, 214, 215, 292, 344, 638, 657
Evans, G. W., 605
Evans, H. P., 463
Exponents, fractional, 217, 219, 224
general, 217, 219, 224
imaginary, 96, 98
negative, 217, 219, 224

F

Faulhaber, J., 85
Fermat, P. de, 213, 214, 389, 397, 546, 610, 649, 650
Ferrari, L., 207
Ferro, Scipio del, 203
Feuerbach, K. W., 337, 339
Fisk, N. C., 192
Florido, A. M., 204
Fluxions, 613
Foncenex, D. de, 292
Fontana, G., 440
Forster, W., 160
Fourier, J., 656
Four-rayed pencil, 311
Fourth dimension, 524–545
Fractions, continued, 80
decimal, 20
Functions, Bessel's, 663
power series, 286
Fundamental theorem (algebra), 292
Fuss, N. and P. H., 91, 95, 96, 214, 292

G

Gaeta, 440
Galileo Galilei, 186
Galois, E., 278
Gambling problem, 546

CATALOG OF DOVER BOOKS

The more difficult books are indicated by an asterisk (*)

Books Explaining Science and Mathematics

WHAT IS SCIENCE?, N. Campbell. The role of experiment and measurement, the function of mathematics, the nature of scientific laws, the difference between laws and theories, the limitations of science, and many similarly provocative topics are treated clearly and without technicalities by an eminent scientist. "Still an excellent introduction to scientific philosophy," H. Margenau in PHYSICS TODAY. "A first-rate primer . . . deserves a wide audience," SCIENTIFIC AMERICAN. 192pp. 5⅜ x 8.   S43 Paperbound **$1.25**

THE NATURE OF PHYSICAL THEORY, P. W. Bridgman. A Nobel Laureate's clear, non-technical lectures on difficulties and paradoxes connected with frontier research on the physical sciences. Concerned with such central concepts as thought, logic, mathematics, relativity, probability, wave mechanics, etc. he analyzes the contributions of such men as Newton, Einstein, Bohr, Heisenberg, and many others. "Lucid and entertaining . . . recommended to anyone who wants to get some insight into current philosophies of science," THE NEW PHILOSOPHY. Index. xi + 138pp. 5⅜ x 8.   S33 Paperbound **$1.25**

EXPERIMENT AND THEORY IN PHYSICS, Max Born. A Nobel Laureate examines the nature of experiment and theory in theoretical physics and analyzes the advances made by the great physicists of our day: Heisenberg, Einstein, Bohr, Planck, Dirac, and others. The actual process of creation is detailed step-by-step by one who participated. A fine examination of the scientific method at work. 44pp. 5⅜ x 8.   S308 Paperbound **75¢**

THE PSYCHOLOGY OF INVENTION IN THE MATHEMATICAL FIELD, J. Hadamard. The reports of such men as Descartes, Pascal, Einstein, Poincaré, and others are considered in this investigation of the method of idea-creation in mathematics and other sciences and the thinking process in general. How do ideas originate? What is the role of the unconscious? What is Poincaré's forgetting hypothesis? are some of the fascinating questions treated. A penetrating analysis of Einstein's thought processes concludes the book. xiii + 145pp. 5⅜ x 8.
T107 Paperbound **$1.25**

THE NATURE OF LIGHT AND COLOUR IN THE OPEN AIR, M. Minnaert. Why are shadows sometimes blue, sometimes green, or other colors depending on the light and surroundings? What causes mirages? Why do multiple suns and moons appear in the sky? Professor Minnaert explains these unusual phenomena and hundreds of others in simple, easy-to-understand terms based on optical laws and the properties of light and color. No mathematics is required but artists, scientists, students, and everyone fascinated by these "tricks" of nature will find thousands of useful and amazing pieces of information. Hundreds of observational experiments are suggested which require no special equipment. 200 illustrations; 42 photos. xvi + 362pp. 5⅜ x 8.   T196 Paperbound **$1.95**

THE UNIVERSE OF LIGHT, W. Bragg. Sir William Bragg, Nobel Laureate and great modern physicist, is also well known for his powers of clear exposition. Here he analyzes all aspects of light for the layman: lenses, reflection, refraction, the optics of vision, x-rays, the photoelectric effect, etc. He tells you what causes the color of spectra, rainbows, and soap bubbles, how magic mirrors work, and much more. Dozens of simple experiments are described. Preface. Index. 199 line drawings and photographs, including 2 full-page color plates. x + 283pp. 5⅜ x 8.   T538 Paperbound **$1.85**

SOAP-BUBBLES: THEIR COLOURS AND THE FORCES THAT MOULD THEM, C. V. Boys. For continuing popularity and validity as scientific primer, few books can match this volume of easily-followed experiments, explanations. Lucid exposition of complexities of liquid films, surface tension and related phenomena, bubbles' reaction to heat, motion, music, magnetic fields. Experiments with capillary attraction, soap bubbles on frames, composite bubbles, liquid cylinders and jets, bubbles other than soap, etc. Wonderful introduction to scientific method; natural laws that have many ramifications in areas of modern physics. Only complete edition in print. New Introduction by S. Z. Lewin, New York University. 83 illustrations; 1 full-page color plate. xii + 190pp. 5⅜ x 8½.   T542 Paperbound **95¢**

CATALOGUE OF DOVER BOOKS

THE STORY OF X-RAYS FROM RONTGEN TO ISOTOPES, A. R. Bleich, M.D. This book, by a member of the American College of Radiology, gives the scientific explanation of x-rays, their applications in medicine, industry and art, and their danger (and that of atmospheric radiation) to the individual and the species. You learn how radiation therapy is applied against cancer, how x-rays diagnose heart disease and other ailments, how they are used to examine mummies for information on diseases of early societies, and industrial materials for hidden weaknesses. 54 illustrations show x-rays of flowers, bones, stomach, gears with flaws, etc. 1st publication. Index. xix + 186pp. 5⅜ x 8.   T622 Paperbound **$1.35**

SPINNING TOPS AND GYROSCOPIC MOTION, John Perry. A classic elementary text of the dynamics of rotation — the behavior and use of rotating bodies such as gyroscopes and tops. In simple, everyday English you are shown how quasi-rigidity is induced in discs of paper, smoke rings, chains, etc., by rapid motions; why a gyrostat falls and why a top rises; precession; how the earth's motion affects climate; and many other phenomena. Appendix on practical use of gyroscopes. 62 figures. 128pp. 5⅜ x 8.   T416 Paperbound **$1.00**

SNOW CRYSTALS, W. A. Bentley, M. J. Humphreys. For almost 50 years W. A. Bentley photographed snow flakes in his laboratory in Jericho, Vermont; in 1931 the American Meteorological Society gathered together the best of his work, some 2400 photographs of snow flakes, plus a few ice flowers, windowpane frosts, dew, frozen rain, and other ice formations. Pictures were selected for beauty and scientific value. A very valuable work to anyone in meteorology, cryology; most interesting to layman; extremely useful for artist who wants beautiful, crystalline designs. All copyright free. Unabridged reprint of 1931 edition. 2453 illustrations. 227pp. 8 x 10½.   T287 Paperbound **$3.00**

A DOVER SCIENCE SAMPLER, edited by George Barkin. A collection of brief, non-technical passages from 44 Dover Books Explaining Science for the enjoyment of the science-minded browser. Includes work of Bertrand Russell, Poincaré, Laplace, Max Born, Galileo, Newton; material on physics, mathematics, metallurgy, anatomy, astronomy, chemistry, etc. You will be fascinated by Martin Gardner's analysis of the sincere pseudo-scientist, Moritz's account of Newton's absentmindedness, Bernard's examples of human vivisection, etc. Illustrations from the Diderot Pictorial Encyclopedia and De Re Metallica. 64 pages.   **FREE**

THE STORY OF ATOMIC THEORY AND ATOMIC ENERGY, J. G. Feinberg. A broader approach to subject of nuclear energy and its cultural implications than any other similar source. Very readable, informal, completely non-technical text. Begins with first atomic theory, 600 B.C. and carries you through the work of Mendelejeff, Röntgen, Madame Curie, to Einstein's equation and the A-bomb. New chapter goes through thermonuclear fission, binding energy, other events up to 1959. Radioactive decay and radiation hazards, future benefits, work of Bohr, moderns, hundreds more topics. "Deserves special mention . . . not only authoritative but thoroughly popular in the best sense of the word," Saturday Review. Formerly, "The Atom Story." Expanded with new chapter. Three appendixes. Index. 34 illustrations. vii + 243pp. 5⅜ x 8.   T625 Paperbound **$1.45**

THE STRANGE STORY OF THE QUANTUM, AN ACCOUNT FOR THE GENERAL READER OF THE GROWTH OF IDEAS UNDERLYING OUR PRESENT ATOMIC KNOWLEDGE, B. Hoffmann. Presents lucidly and expertly, with barest amount of mathematics, the problems and theories which led to modern quantum physics. Dr. Hoffmann begins with the closing years of the 19th century, when certain trifling discrepancies were noticed, and with illuminating analogies and examples takes you through the brilliant concepts of Planck, Einstein, Pauli, Broglie, Bohr, Schroedinger, Heisenberg, Dirac, Sommerfeld, Feynman, etc. This edition includes a new, long postscript carrying the story through 1958. "Of the books attempting an account of the history and contents of our modern atomic physics which have come to my attention, this is the best," H. Margenau, Yale University, in "American Journal of Physics." 32 tables and line illustrations. Index. 275pp. 5⅜ x 8.   T518 Paperbound **$1.50**

SPACE AND TIME, E. Borel. Written by a versatile mathematician of world renown with his customary lucidity and precision, this introduction to relativity for the layman presents scores of examples, analogies, and illustrations that open up new ways of thinking about space and time. It covers abstract geometry and geographical maps, continuity and topology, the propagation of light, the special theory of relativity, the general theory of relativity, theoretical researches, and much more. Mathematical notes. 2 Indexes. 4 Appendices. 15 figures. xvi + 243pp. 5⅜ x 8.   T592 Paperbound **$1.45**

FROM EUCLID TO EDDINGTON: A STUDY OF THE CONCEPTIONS OF THE EXTERNAL WORLD, Sir Edmund Whittaker. A foremost British scientist traces the development of theories of natural philosophy from the western rediscovery of Euclid to Eddington, Einstein, Dirac, etc. The inadequacy of classical physics is contrasted with present day attempts to understand the physical world through relativity, non-Euclidean geometry, space curvature, wave mechanics, etc. 5 major divisions of examination: Space; Time and Movement; the Concepts of Classical Physics; the Concepts of Quantum Mechanics; the Eddington Universe. 212pp. 5⅜ x 8. T491 Paperbound **$1.35**

CATALOGUE OF DOVER BOOKS

*THE EVOLUTION OF SCIENTIFIC THOUGHT FROM NEWTON TO EINSTEIN, A. d'Abro. A detailed account of the evolution of classical physics into modern relativistic theory and the concommitant changes in scientific methodology. The breakdown of classical physics in the face of non-Euclidean geometry and the electromagnetic equations is carefully discussed and then an exhaustive analysis of Einstein's special and general theories of relativity and their implications is given. Newton, Riemann, Weyl, Lorentz, Planck, Maxwell, and many others are considered. A non-technical explanation of space, time, electromagnetic waves, etc. as understood today. "Model of semi-popular exposition," NEW REPUBLIC. 21 diagrams. 482pp. 5⅜ x 8.
T2 Paperbound **$2.00**

EINSTEIN'S THEORY OF RELATIVITY, Max Born. Nobel Laureate explains Einstein's special and general theories of relativity, beginning with a thorough review of classical physics in simple, non-technical language. Exposition of Einstein's work discusses concept of simultaneity, kinematics, relativity of arbitrary motions, the space-time continuum, geometry of curved surfaces, etc., steering middle course between vague popularizations and complex scientific presentations. 1962 edition revised by author takes into account latest findings, predictions of theory and implications for cosmology, indicates what is being sought in unified field theory. Mathematics very elementary, illustrative diagrams and experiments informative but simple. Revised 1962 edition. Revised by Max Born, assisted by Gunther Leibfried and Walter Biem. Index. 143 illustrations. vii + 376pp. 5⅜ x 8.
S769 Paperbound **$2.00**

PHILOSOPHY AND THE PHYSICISTS, L. Susan Stebbing. A philosopher examines the philosophical aspects of modern science, in terms of a lively critical attack on the ideas of Jeans and Eddington. Such basic questions are treated as the task of science, causality, determinism, probability, consciousness, the relation of the world of physics to the world of everyday experience. The author probes the concepts of man's smallness before an inscrutable universe, the tendency to idealize mathematical construction, unpredictability theorems and human freedom, the supposed opposition between 19th century determinism and modern science, and many others. Introduces many thought-stimulating ideas about the implications of modern physical concepts. xvi + 295pp. 5⅜ x 8.
T480 Paperbound **$1.65**

THE RESTLESS UNIVERSE, Max Born. A remarkably lucid account by a Nobel Laureate of recent theories of wave mechanics, behavior of gases, electrons and ions, waves and particles, electronic structure of the atom, nuclear physics, and similar topics. "Much more thorough and deeper than most attempts . . . easy and delightful," CHEMICAL AND ENGINEERING NEWS. Special feature: 7 animated sequences of 60 figures each showing such phenomena as gas molecules in motion, the scattering of alpha particles, etc. 11 full-page plates of photographs. Total of nearly 600 illustrations. 351pp. 6⅛ x 9¼.
T412 Paperbound **$2.00**

THE COMMON SENSE OF THE EXACT SCIENCES, W. K. Clifford. For 70 years a guide to the basic concepts of scientific and mathematical thought. Acclaimed by scientists and laymen alike, it offers a wonderful insight into concepts such as the extension of meaning of symbols, characteristics of surface boundaries, properties of plane figures, measurement of quantities, vectors, the nature of position, bending of space, motion, mass and force, and many others. Prefaces by Bertrand Russell and Karl Pearson. Critical introduction by James Newman. 130 figures. 249pp. 5⅜ x 8.
T61 Paperbound **$1.60**

MATTER AND LIGHT, THE NEW PHYSICS, Louis de Broglie. Non-technical explanations by a Nobel Laureate of electro-magnetic theory, relativity, matter, light and radiation, wave mechanics, quantum physics, philosophy of science, and similar topics. This is one of the simplest yet most accurate introductions to the work of men like Planck, Einstein, Bohr, and others. Only 2 of the 21 chapters require a knowledge of mathematics. 300pp. 5⅜ x 8.
T35 Paperbound **$1.75**

SCIENCE, THEORY AND MAN, Erwin Schrödinger. This is a complete and unabridged reissue of SCIENCE AND THE HUMAN TEMPERAMENT plus an additional essay: "What Is an Elementary Particle?" Nobel Laureate Schrödinger discusses such topics as nature of scientific method, tne nature of science, chance and determinism, science and society, conceptual models for physical entities, elementary particles and wave mechanics. Presentation is popular and may be followed by most people with little or no scientific training. "Fine practical preparation for a time when laws of nature, human institutions . . . are undergoing a critical examination without parallel," Waldemar Kaempffert, N. Y. TIMES. 192pp. 5⅜ x 8.
T428 Paperbound **$1.35**

CONCERNING THE NATURE OF THINGS, Sir William Bragg. The Nobel Laureate physicist in his Royal Institute Christmas Lectures explains such diverse phenomena as the formation of crystals, how uranium is transmuted to lead, the way X-rays work, why a spinning ball travels in a curved path, the reason why bubbles bounce from each other, and many other scientific topics that are seldom explained in simple terms. No scientific background needed—book is easy enough that any intelligent adult or youngster can understand it. Unabridged. 32pp. of photos; 57 figures. xii + 232pp. 5⅜ x 8.
T31 Paperbound **$1.35**

*THE RISE OF THE NEW PHYSICS (formerly THE DECLINE OF MECHANISM), A. d'Abro. This authoritative and comprehensive 2 volume exposition is unique · in scientific publishing. Written for intelligent readers not familiar with higher mathematics, it is the only thorough explanation in non-technical language of modern mathematical-physical theory. Combining both history and exposition, it ranges from classical Newtonian concepts up through the electronic theories of Dirac and Heisenberg, the statistical mechanics of Fermi, and Einstein's relativity theories. "A must for anyone doing serious study in the physical sciences," J. OF FRANKLIN INST. 97 illustrations. 991pp. 2 volumes.
T3 Vol. 1, Paperbound **$2.00**
T4 Vol. 2, Paperbound **$2.00**

SCIENCE AND HYPOTHESIS, Henri Poincaré. Creative psychology in science. How such concepts as number, magnitude, space, force, classical mechanics were developed and how the modern scientist uses them in his thought. Hypothesis in physics, theories of modern physics. Introduction by Sir James Larmor. "Few mathematicians have had the breadth of vision of Poincaré, and none is his superior in the gift of clear exposition," E. T. Bell. Index. 272pp. 5⅜ x 8.
S221 Paperbound **$1.35**

THE VALUE OF SCIENCE, Henri Poincaré. Many of the most mature ideas of the "last scientific universalist" conveyed with charm and vigor for both the beginning student and the advanced worker. Discusses the nature of scientific truth, whether order is innate in the universe or imposed upon it by man, logical thought versus intuition (relating to mathematics through the works of Weierstrass, Lie, Klein, Riemann), time and space (relativity, psychological time, simultaneity), Hertz's concept of force, interrelationship of mathematical physics to pure math, values within disciplines of Maxwell, Carnot, Mayer, Newton, Lorentz, etc. Index. iii + 147pp. 5⅜ x 8.
S469 Paperbound **$1.35**

THE SKY AND ITS MYSTERIES, E. A. Beet. One of the most lucid books on the mysteries of the universe; covers history of astronomy from earliest observations to modern theories of expanding universe, source of stellar energy, birth of planets, origin of moon craters, possibilities of life on other planets. Discusses effects of sunspots on weather; distance, age of stars; methods and tools of astronomers; much more. Expert and fascinating. "Eminently readable book," London Times. Bibliography. Over 50 diagrams, 12 full-page plates. Fold-out star map. Introduction. Index. 238pp. 5¼ x 7½.
T627 Clothbound **$3.50**

OUT OF THE SKY: AN INTRODUCTION TO METEORITICS, H. H. Nininger. A non-technical yet comprehensive introduction to the young science of meteoritics: all aspects of the arrival of cosmic matter on our planet from outer space and the reaction and alteration of this matter in the terrestrial environment. Essential facts and major theories presented by one of the world's leading experts. Covers ancient reports of meteors; modern systematic investigations; fireball clusters; meteorite showers; tektites; planetoidal encounters; etc. 52 full-page plates with over 175 photographs. 22 figures. Bibliography and references. Index. viii + 336pp. 5⅜ x 8.
T519 Paperbound **$1.85**

THE REALM OF THE NEBULAE, E. Hubble. One of great astronomers of our day records his formulation of concept of "island universes." Covers velocity-distance relationship; classification, nature, distances, general types of nebulae; cosmological theories. A fine introduction to modern theories for layman. No math needed. New introduction by A. Sandage. 55 illustrations, photos. Index. iv + 201pp. 5⅜ x 8.
S455 Paperbound **$1.50**

AN ELEMENTARY SURVEY OF CELESTIAL MECHANICS, Y. Ryabov. Elementary exposition of gravitational theory and celestial mechanics. Historical introduction and coverage of basic principles, including: the ecliptic, the orbital plane, the 2- and 3-body problems, the discovery of Neptune, planetary rotation, the shapes of galaxies, satellites (detailed treatment of Sputnik I), etc. First American reprinting of successful Russian popular exposition. Follow actual methods of astrophysicists with only high school math! Appendix. 58 figures. 165pp. 5⅜ x 8.
T756 Paperbound **$1.25**

GREAT IDEAS AND THEORIES OF MODERN COSMOLOGY, Jagjit Singh. Companion volume to author's popular "Great Ideas of Modern Mathematics" (Dover, $1.55). The best non-technical survey of post-Einstein attempts to answer perhaps unanswerable questions of origin, age of Universe, possibility of life on other worlds, etc. Fundamental theories of cosmology and cosmogony recounted, explained, evaluated in light of most recent data: Einstein's concepts of relativity, space-time; Milne's a priori world-system; astrophysical theories of Jeans, Eddington; Hoyle's "continuous creation;" contributions of dozens more scientists. A faithful, comprehensive critical summary of complex material presented in an extremely well-written text intended for laymen. Original publication. Index. xii + 276pp. 5⅜ x 8½.
T925 Paperbound **$1.85**

BASIC ELECTRICITY, Bureau of Naval Personnel. Very thorough, easily followed course in basic electricity for beginner, layman, or intermediate student. Begins with simplest definitions, presents coordinated, systematic coverage of basic theory and application: conductors, insulators, static electricity, magnetism, production of voltage, Ohm's law, direct current series and parallel circuits, wiring techniques, electromagnetism, alternating current, capacitance and inductance, measuring instruments, etc.; application to electrical machines such as alternating and direct current generators, motors, transformers, magnetic magnifiers, etc. Each chapter contains problems to test progress; answers at rear. No math needed beyond algebra. Appendices on signs, formulas, etc. 345 illustrations. 448pp. 7½ x 10.
S973 Paperbound **$2.95**

ELEMENTARY METALLURGY AND METALLOGRAPHY, A. M. Shrager. An introduction to common metals and alloys; stress is upon steel and iron, but other metals and alloys also covered. All aspects of production, processing, working of metals. Designed for student who wishes to enter metallurgy, for bright high school or college beginner, layman who wants background on extremely important industry. Questions, at ends of chapters, many microphotographs, glossary. Greatly revised 1961 edition. 195 illustrations, tables. ix + 389pp. 5⅜ x 8.
S138 Paperbound **$2.00**

CATALOGUE OF DOVER BOOKS

BRIDGES AND THEIR BUILDERS, D. B. Steinman & S. R. Watson. Engineers, historians, and every person who has ever been fascinated by great spans will find this book an endless source of information and interest. Greek and Roman structures, Medieval bridges, modern classics such as the Brooklyn Bridge, and the latest developments in the science are retold by one of the world's leading authorities on bridge design and construction. BRIDGES AND THEIR BUILDERS is the only comprehensive and accurate semi-popular history of these important measures of progress in print. New, greatly revised, enlarged edition. 23 photos; 26 line-drawings. Index. xvii + 401pp. 5⅜ x 8. **T431 Paperbound $2.00**

FAMOUS BRIDGES OF THE WORLD, D. B. Steinman. An up-to-the-minute new edition of a book that explains the fascinating drama of how the world's great bridges came to be built. The author, designer of the famed Mackinac bridge, discusses bridges from all periods and all parts of the world, explaining their various types of construction, and describing the problems their builders faced. Although primarily for youngsters, this cannot fail to interest readers of all ages. 48 illustrations in the text. 23 photographs. 99pp. 6⅛ x 9¼. **T161 Paperbound $1.00**

HOW DO YOU USE A SLIDE RULE? by A. A. Merrill. A step-by-step explanation of the slide rule that presents the fundamental rules clearly enough for the non-mathematician to understand. Unlike most instruction manuals, this work concentrates on the two most important operations: multiplication and division. 10 easy lessons, each with a clear drawing, for the reader who has difficulty following other expositions. 1st publication. Index. 2 Appendices. 10 illustrations. 78 problems, all with answers. vi + 36 pp. 6⅛ x 9¼. **T62 Paperbound 60¢**

HOW TO CALCULATE QUICKLY, H. Sticker. A tried and true method for increasing your "number sense" — the ability to see relationships between numbers and groups of numbers. Addition, subtraction, multiplication, division, fractions, and other topics are treated through techniques not generally taught in schools: left to right multiplication, division by inspection, etc. This is not a collection of tricks which work only on special numbers, but a detailed well-planned course, consisting of over 9,000 problems that you can work in spare moments. It is excellent for anyone who is inconvenienced by slow computational skills. 5 or 10 minutes of this book daily will double or triple your calculation speed. 9,000 problems, answers. 256pp. 5⅜ x 8. **T295 Paperbound $1.00**

MATHEMATICAL FUN, GAMES AND PUZZLES, Jack Frohlichstein. A valuable service for parents of children who have trouble with math, for teachers in need of a supplement to regular upper elementary and junior high math texts (each section is graded—easy, average, difficult —for ready adaptation to different levels of ability), and for just anyone who would like to develop basic skills in an informal and entertaining manner. The author combines ten years of experience as a junior high school math teacher with a method that uses puzzles and games to introduce the basic ideas and operations of arithmetic. Stress on everyday uses of math: banking, stock market, personal budgets, insurance, taxes. Intellectually stimulating and practical, too. 418 problems and diversions with answers. Bibliography. 120 illustrations. xix + 306pp. 5⅝ x 8½. **T789 Paperbound $1.75**

GREAT IDEAS OF MODERN MATHEMATICS: THEIR NATURE AND USE, Jagjit Singh. Reader with only high school math will understand main mathematical ideas of modern physics, astronomy, genetics, psychology, evolution, etc. better than many who use them as tools, but comprehend little of their basic structure. Author uses his wide knowledge of non-mathematical fields in brilliant exposition of differential equations, matrices, group theory, logic, statistics, problems of mathematical foundations, imaginary numbers, vectors, etc. Original publication. 2 appendixes. 2 indexes. 65 illustr. 322pp. 5⅜ x 8. **S587 Paperbound $1.65**

*MATHEMATICS IN ACTION, O. G. Sutton. Everyone with a command of high school algebra will find this book one of the finest possible introductions to the application of mathematics to physical theory. Ballistics, numerical analysis, waves and wavelike phenomena, Fourier series, group concepts, fluid flow and aerodynamics, statistical measures, and meteorology are discussed with unusual clarity. Some calculus and differential equations theory is developed by the author for the reader's help in the more difficult sections. 88 figures. Index. viii + 236pp. 5⅜ x 8. **T440 Clothbound $3.50**

*INTRODUCTION TO SYMBOLIC LOGIC AND ITS APPLICATIONS, Rudolph Carnap. One of the clearest, most comprehensive, and rigorous introductions to modern symbolic logic, by perhaps its greatest living master. Not merely elementary theory, but demonstrated applications in mathematics, physics, and biology. Symbolic languages of various degrees of complexity are analyzed, and one constructed. "A creation of the rank of a masterpiece," Zentralblatt für Mathematik und Ihre Grenzgebiete. Over 300 exercises. 5 figures. Bibliography. Index. xvi + 241pp. 5⅜ x 8. **S453 Paperbound $1.85**

*HIGHER MATHEMATICS FOR STUDENTS OF CHEMISTRY AND PHYSICS, J. W. Mellor. Not abstract, but practical, drawing its problems from familiar laboratory material, this book covers theory and application of differential calculus, analytic geometry, functions with singularities, integral calculus, infinite series, solution of numerical equations, differential equations, Fourier's theorem and extensions, probability and the theory of errors, calculus of variations, determinants, etc. "If the reader is not familiar with this book, it will repay him to examine it," CHEM. & ENGINEERING NEWS. 800 problems. 189 figures. 2 appendices; 30 tables of integrals, probability functions, etc. Bibliography. xxi + 641pp. 5⅜ x 8. **S193 Paperbound $2.00**

THE FOURTH DIMENSION SIMPLY EXPLAINED, edited by Henry P. Manning. Originally written as entries in contest sponsored by "Scientific American," then published in book form, these 22 essays present easily understood explanations of how the fourth dimension may be studied, the relationship of non-Euclidean geometry to the fourth dimension, analogies to three-dimensional space, some fourth-dimensional absurdities and curiosities, possible measurements and forms in the fourth dimension. In general, a thorough coverage of many of the simpler properties of fourth-dimensional space. Multi-points of view on many of the most important aspects are valuable aid to comprehension. Introduction by Dr. Henry P. Manning gives proper emphasis to points in essays, more advanced account of fourth-dimensional geometry. 82 figures. 251pp. 5⅜ x 8. **T711 Paperbound $1.35**

TRIGONOMETRY REFRESHER FOR TECHNICAL MEN, A. A. Klaf. A modern question and answer text on plane and spherical trigonometry. Part I covers plane trigonometry: angles, quadrants, trigonometrical functions, graphical representation, interpolation, equations, logarithms, solution of triangles, slide rules, etc. Part II discusses applications to navigation, surveying, elasticity, architecture, and engineering. Small angles, periodic functions, vectors, polar coordinates, De Moivre's theorem, fully covered. Part III is devoted to spherical trigonometry and the solution of spherical triangles, with applications to terrestrial and astronomical problems. Special time-savers for numerical calculation. 913 questions answered for you! 1738 problems; answers to odd numbers. 494 figures. 14 pages of functions, formulae. Index. x + 629pp. 5⅜ x 8. **T371 Paperbound $2.00**

CALCULUS REFRESHER FOR TECHNICAL MEN. A. A. Klaf. Not an ordinary textbook but a unique refresher for engineers, technicians, and students. An examination of the most important aspects of differential and integral calculus by means of 756 key questions. Part I covers simple differential calculus: constants, variables, functions, increments, derivatives, logarithms, curvature, etc. Part II treats fundamental concepts of integration: inspection, substitution, transformation, reduction, areas and volumes, mean value, successive and partial integration, double and triple integration. Stresses practical aspects! A 50 page section gives applications to civil and nautical engineering, electricity, stress and strain, elasticity, industrial engineering, and similar fields. 756 questions answered. 556 problems; solutions to odd numbers. 36 pages of constants, formulae. Index. v + 431pp. 5⅜ x 8. **T370 Paperbound $2.00**

PROBABILITIES AND LIFE, Emile Borel. One of the leading French mathematicians of the last 100 years makes use of certain results of mathematics of probabilities and explains a number of problems that for the most part, are related to everyday living or to illness and death: computation of life expectancy tables, chances of recovery from various diseases, probabilities of job accidents, weather predictions, games of chance, and so on. Emphasis on results not processes, though some indication is made of mathematical proofs. Simple in style, free of technical terminology, limited in scope to everyday situations, it is comprehensible to laymen, fine reading for beginning students of probability. New English translation. Index. Appendix. vi + 87pp. 5⅜ x 8½. **T121 Paperbound $1.00**

POPULAR SCIENTIFIC LECTURES, Hermann von Helmholtz. 7 lucid expositions by a preeminent scientific mind: "The Physiological Causes of Harmony in Music," "On the Relation of Optics to Painting," "On the Conservation of Force," "On the Interaction of Natural Forces," "On Goethe's Scientific Researches" into theory of color, "On the Origin and Significance of Geometric Axioms," "On Recent Progress in the Theory of Vision." Written with simplicity of expression, stripped of technicalities, these are easy to understand and delightful reading for anyone interested in science or looking for an introduction to serious study of acoustics or optics. Introduction by Professor Morris Kline, Director, Division of Electromagnetic Research, New York University, contains astute, impartial evaluations. Selected from "Popular Lectures on Scientific Subjects," 1st and 2nd series. xii + 286pp. 5⅜ x 8½. **T799 Paperbound $1.45**

SCIENCE AND METHOD, Henri Poincaré. Procedure of scientific discovery, methodology, experiment, idea-germination—the intellectual processes by which discoveries come into being. Most significant and most interesting aspects of development, application of ideas. Chapters cover selection of facts, chance, mathematical reasoning, mathematics, and logic; Whitehead, Russell, Cantor; the new mechanics, etc. 288pp. 5⅜ x 8. **S222 Paperbound $1.35**

HEAT AND ITS WORKINGS, Morton Mott-Smith, Ph.D. An unusual book; to our knowledge the only middle-level survey of this important area of science. Explains clearly such important concepts as physiological sensation of heat and Weber's law, measurement of heat, evolution of thermometer, nature of heat, expansion and contraction of solids, Boyle's law, specific heat. BTU's and calories, evaporation, Andrews's isothermals, radiation, the relation of heat to light, many more topics inseparable from other aspects of physics. A wide, nonmathematical yet thorough explanation of basic ideas, theories, phenomena for laymen and beginning scientists illustrated by experiences of daily life. Bibliography. 50 illustrations. x + 165pp. 5⅜ x 8½. **T978 Paperbound $1.00**

History of Science and Mathematics

THE STUDY OF THE HISTORY OF MATHEMATICS, THE STUDY OF THE HISTORY OF SCIENCE, G. Sarton. Two books bound as one. Each volume contains a long introduction to the methods and philosophy of each of these historical fields, covering the skills and sympathies of the historian, concepts of history of science, psychology of idea-creation, and the purpose of history of science. Prof. Sarton also provides more than 80 pages of classified bibliography. Complete and unabridged. Indexed. 10 illustrations. 188pp. 5⅜ x 8.   T240 Paperbound **$1.25**

A HISTORY OF PHYSICS, Florian Cajori, Ph.D. First written in 1899, thoroughly revised in 1929, this, is still best entry into antecedents of modern theories. Precise non-mathematical discussion of ideas, theories, techniques, apparatus of each period from Greeks to 1920's, analyzing within each period basic topics of matter, mechanics, light, electricity and magnetism, sound, atomic theory, etc. Stress on modern developments, from early 19th century to present. Written with critical eye on historical development, significance. Provides most of needed historical background for student of physics. Reprint of second (1929) edition. Index. Bibliography in footnotes. 16 figures. xv + 424pp. 5⅜ x 8.   T970 Paperbound **$2.00**

A HISTORY OF ASTRONOMY FROM THALES TO KEPLER, J. L. E. Dreyer. Formerly titled A HISTORY OF PLANETARY SYSTEMS FROM THALES TO KEPLER. This is the only work in English which provides a detailed history of man's cosmological views from prehistoric times up through the Renaissance. It covers Egypt, Babylonia, early Greece, Alexandria, the Middle Ages, Copernicus, Tycho Brahe, Kepler, and many others. Epicycles and other complex theories of positional astronomy are explained in terms nearly everyone will find clear and easy to understand. "Standard reference on Greek astronomy and the Copernican revolution," SKY AND TELESCOPE. Bibliography. 21 diagrams. Index. xvii + 430pp. 5⅜ x 8.   S79 Paperbound **$1.98**

A SHORT HISTORY OF ASTRONOMY, A. Berry. A popular standard work for over 50 years, this thorough and accurate volume covers the science from primitive times to the end of the 19th century. After the Greeks and Middle Ages, individual chapters analyze Copernicus, Brahe, Galileo, Kepler, and Newton, and the mixed reception of their startling discoveries. Post-Newtonian achievements are then discussed in unusual detail: Halley, Bradley, Lagrange, Laplace, Herschel, Bessel, etc. 2 indexes. 104 illustrations, 9 portraits. xxxi + 440pp. 5⅜ x 8.
T210 Paperbound **$2.00**

PIONEERS OF SCIENCE, Sir Oliver Lodge. An authoritative, yet elementary history of science by a leading scientist and expositor. Concentrating on individuals—Copernicus, Brahe, Kepler, Galileo, Descartes, Newton, Laplace, Herschel, Lord Kelvin, and other scientists—the author presents their discoveries in historical order, adding biographical material on each man and full, specific explanations of their achievements. The full, clear discussions of the accomplishments of post-Newtonian astronomers are features seldom found in other books on the subject. Index. 120 illustrations. xv + 404pp. 5⅜ x 8.   T716 Paperbound **$1.65**

THE BIRTH AND DEVELOPMENT OF THE GEOLOGICAL SCIENCES, F. D. Adams. The most complete and thorough history of the earth sciences in print. Geological thought from earliest recorded times to the end of the 19th century—covers over 300 early thinkers and systems: fossils and hypothetical explanations of them, vulcanists vs. neptunists, figured stones and paleontology, generation of stones, and similar topics. 91 illustrations, including medieval, renaissance woodcuts, etc. 632 footnotes and bibliographic notes. Index. 511pp. 5⅜ x 8.
T5 Paperbound **$2.00**

THE STORY OF ALCHEMY AND EARLY CHEMISTRY, J. M. Stillman. "Add the blood of a red-haired man"—a recipe typical of the many quoted in this authoritative and readable history of the strange beliefs and practices of the alchemists. Concise studies of every leading figure in alchemy and early chemistry through Lavoisier, in this curious epic of superstition and true science, constructed from scores of rare and difficult Greek, Latin, German, and French texts. Foreword by S. W. Young. 246-item bibliography. Index. xiii + 566pp. 5⅜ x 8.
S628 Paperbound **$2.45**

HISTORY OF MATHEMATICS, D. E. Smith. Most comprehensive non-technical history of math in English. Discusses the lives and works of over a thousand major and minor figures, from Euclid to Descartes, Gauss, and Riemann. Vol. I: A chronological examination, from primitive concepts through Egypt, Babylonia, Greece, the Orient, Rome, the Middle Ages, the Renaissance, and up to 1900. Vol. 2: The development of ideas in specific fields and problems, up through elementary calculus. Two volumes, total of 510 illustrations, 1355pp. 5⅜ x 8. Set boxed in attractive container.   T429,430 Paperbound the set **$5.00**

History, Political Science

THE POLITICAL THOUGHT OF PLATO AND ARISTOTLE, E. Barker. One of the clearest and most accurate expositions of the corpus of Greek political thought. This standard source contains exhaustive analyses of the "Republic" and other Platonic dialogues and Aristotle's "Politics" and "Ethics," and discusses the origin of these ideas in Greece, contributions of other Greek theorists, and modifications of Greek ideas by thinkers from Aquinas to Hegel. "Must" reading for anyone interested in the history of Western thought. Index. Chronological Table of Events. 2 Appendixes. xxiv + 560pp. 5⅜ x 8.   T521 Paperbound **$1.85**

THE IDEA OF PROGRESS, J. B. Bury. Practically unknown before the Reformation, the idea of progress has since become one of the central concepts of western civilization. Prof. Bury analyzes its evolution in the thought of Greece, Rome, the Middle Ages, the Renaissance, to its flowering in all branches of science, religion, philosophy, industry, art, and literature, during and following the 16th century. Introduction by Charles Beard. Index. xl + 357pp. 5⅜ x 8.   T40 Paperbound **$2.00**

THE ANCIENT GREEK HISTORIANS, J. B. Bury. This well known, easily read work covers the entire field of classical historians from the early writers to Herodotus, Thucydides, Xenophon, through Poseidonius and such Romans as Tacitus, Cato, Caesar, Livy. Scores of writers are studied biographically, in style, sources, accuracy, structure, historical concepts, and influences. Recent discoveries such as the Oxyrhinchus papyri are referred to, as well as such great scholars as Nissen, Gomperz, Cornford, etc. "Totally unblemished by pedantry." Outlook. "The best account in English," Dutcher, A Guide to Historical Lit. Bibliography, Index. x + 281pp. 5⅜ x 8.   T397 Paperbound **$1.50**

HISTORY OF THE LATER ROMAN EMPIRE, J. B. Bury. This standard work by the leading Byzantine scholar of our time discusses the later Roman and early Byzantine empires from 395 A.D. through the death of Justinian in 565, in their political, social, cultural, theological, and military aspects. Contemporary documents are quoted in full, making this the most complete reconstruction of the period and a fit successor to Gibbon's "Decline and Fall." "Most unlikely that it will ever be superseded," Glanville Downey, Dumbarton Oaks Research Lib. Geneological tables. 5 maps. Bibliography. Index. 2 volumes total of 965pp. 5⅜ x 8.
T398, 399 Two volume set, Paperbound **$4.00**

A HISTORY OF ANCIENT GEOGRAPHY, E. H. Bunbury. Standard study, in English, of ancient geography; never equalled for scope, detail. First full account of history of geography from Greeks' first world picture based on mariners, through Ptolemy. Discusses every important map, discovery, figure, travel expedition, war, conjecture, narrative, bearing on subject. Chapters on Homeric geography, Herodotus, Alexander expedition, Strabo, Pliny, Ptolemy, would stand alone as exhaustive monographs. Includes minor geographers, men not usually regarded in this context: Hecataeus, Pytheas, Hipparchus, Artemidorus, Marinus of Tyre, etc. Uses information gleaned from military campaigns such as Punic Wars, Hannibal's passage of Alps, campaigns of Lucullus, Pompey, Caesar's wars, the Trojan War. New introduction by W. H. Stahl, Brooklyn College. Bibliography. Index. 20 maps. 1426pp. 5⅜ x 8.
T570-1, clothbound, 2-volume set **$12.50**

POLITICAL PARTIES, Robert Michels. Classic of social science, reference point for all later work, deals with nature of leadership in social organization on government and trade union levels. Probing tendency of oligarchy to replace democracy, it studies need for leadership, desire for organization, psychological motivations, vested interests, hero worship, reaction of leaders to power, press relations, many other aspects. Trans. by E. & C. Paul. Introduction. 447pp. 5⅜ x 8.   T569 Paperbound **$2.00**

A HISTORY OF HISTORICAL WRITING, Harry Elmer Barnes. Virtually the only adequate survey of the whole course of historical writing in a single volume. Surveys developments from the beginnings of historiographies in the ancient Near East and the Classical World, up through the Cold War. Covers major historians in detail, shows interrelationship with cultural background, makes clear individual contributions, evaluates and estimates importance; also enormously rich upon minor authors and thinkers who are usually passed over. Packed with scholarship and learning, clear, easily written. Indispensable to every student of history. Revised and enlarged up to 1961. Index and bibliography. xv + 442pp. 5⅜ x 8½.
T104 Paperbound **$2.25**

Prices subject to change without notice.

Dover publishes books on art, music, philosophy, literature, languages, history, social sciences, psychology, handcrafts, orientalia, puzzles and entertainments, chess, pets and gardens, books explaining science, intermediate and higher mathematics, mathematical physics, engineering, biological sciences, earth sciences, classics of science, etc. Write to:

Dept. catrr.
Dover Publications, Inc.
180 Varick Street, N. Y. 14, N. Y.

Classics of Science

THE DIDEROT PICTORIAL ENCYCLOPEDIA OF TRADES AND INDUSTRY, MANUFACTURING AND THE TECHNICAL ARTS IN PLATES SELECTED FROM "L'ENCYCLOPEDIE OU DICTIONNAIRE RAISONNE DES SCIENCES, DES ARTS, ET DES METIERS" OF DENIS DIDEROT, edited with text by C. Gillispie. The first modern selection of plates from the high point of 18th century French engraving, Diderot's famous Encyclopedia. Over 2000 illustrations on 485 full page plates, most of them original size, illustrating the trades and industries of one of the most fascinating periods of modern history, 18th century France. These magnificent engravings provide an invaluable glimpse into the past for the student of early technology, a lively and accurate social document to students of cultures, an outstanding find to the lover of fine engravings. The plates teem with life, with men, women, and children performing all of the thousands of operations necessary to the trades before and during the early stages of the industrial revolution. Plates are in sequence, and show general operations, closeups of difficult operations, and details of complex machinery. Such important and interesting trades and industries are illustrated as sowing, harvesting, beekeeping, cheesemaking, operating windmills, milling flour, charcoal burning, tobacco processing, indigo, fishing, arts of war, salt extraction, mining, smelting iron, casting iron, steel, extracting mercury, zinc, sulphur, copper, etc., slating, tinning, silverplating, gilding, making gunpowder, cannons, bells, shoeing horses, tanning, papermaking, printing, dying, and more than 40 other categories. 920pp. 9 x 12. Heavy library cloth. T421 Two volume set **$18.50**

THE PRINCIPLES OF SCIENCE, A TREATISE ON LOGIC AND THE SCIENTIFIC METHOD, W. Stanley Jevons. Treating such topics as Inductive and Deductive Logic, the Theory of Number, Probability, and the Limits of Scientific Method, this milestone in the development of symbolic logic remains a stimulating contribution to the investigation of inferential validity in the natural and social sciences. It significantly advances Boole's logic, and describes a machine which is a foundation of modern electronic calculators. In his introduction, Ernest Nagel of Columbia University says, "(Jevons) . . . continues to be of interest as an attempt to articulate the logic of scientific inquiry." Index. liii + 786pp. 5⅜ x 8. S446 Paperbound **$2.98**

*DIALOGUES CONCERNING TWO NEW SCIENCES, Galileo Galilei. A classic of experimental science which has had a profound and enduring influence on the entire history of mechanics and engineering. Galileo based this, his finest work, on 30 years of experimentation. It offers a fascinating and vivid exposition of dynamics, elasticity, sound, ballistics, strength of materials, and the scientific method. Translated by H. Crew and A. de Salvio. 126 diagrams. Index. xxi + 288pp. 5⅜ x 8. S99 Paperbound **$1.75**

DE MAGNETE, William Gilbert. This classic work on magnetism founded a new science. Gilbert was the first to use the word "electricity," to recognize mass as distinct from weight, to discover the effect of heat on magnetic bodies; invented an electroscope, differentiated between static electricity and magnetism, conceived of the earth as a magnet. Written by the first great experimental scientist, this lively work is valuable not only as an historical landmark, but as the delightfully easy-to-follow record of a perpetually searching, ingenious mind. Translated by P. F. Mottelay. 25 page biographical memoir. 90 fix. lix + 368pp. 5⅜ x 8. S470 Paperbound **$2.00**

*OPTICKS, Sir Isaac Newton. An enormous storehouse of insights and discoveries on light, reflection, color, refraction, theories of wave and corpuscular propagation of light, optical apparatus, and mathematical devices which have recently been reevaluated in terms of modern physics and placed in the top-most ranks of Newton's work! Foreword by Albert Einstein. Preface by I. B. Cohen of Harvard U. 7 pages of portraits, facsimile pages, letters, etc. cxvi + 412pp. 5⅜ x 8. S205 Paperbound **$2.25**

A SURVEY OF PHYSICAL THEORY, M. Planck. Lucid essays on modern physics for the general reader by the Nobel Laureate and creator of the quantum revolution. Planck explains how the new concepts came into being; explores the clash between theories of mechanics, electrodynamics, and thermodynamics; and traces the evolution of the concept of light through Newton, Huygens, Maxwell, and his own quantum theory, providing unparalleled insights into his development of this momentous modern concept. Bibliography. Index. vii + 121pp. 5⅜ x 8. S650 Paperbound **$1.15**

A SOURCE BOOK IN MATHEMATICS, D. E. Smith. English translations of the original papers that announced the great discoveries in mathematics from the Renaissance to the end of the 19th century: succinct selections from 125 different treatises and articles, most of them unavailable elsewhere in English—Newton, Leibniz, Pascal, Riemann, Bernoulli, etc. 24 articles trace developments in the field of number, 18 cover algebra, 36 are on geometry, and 13 on calculus. Biographical-historical introductions to each article. Two volume set. Index in each. Total of 115 illustrations. Total of xxviii + 742pp. 5⅜ x 8. S552 Vol I Paperbound **$1.85**
S553 Vol II Paperbound **$1.85**
The set, boxed **$3.50**

CATALOGUE OF DOVER BOOKS

*THE THIRTEEN BOOKS OF EUCLID'S ELEMENTS, edited by T. L. Heath. This is the complete EUCLID — the definitive edition of one of the greatest classics of the western world. Complete English translation of the Heiberg text with spurious Book XIV. Detailed 150-page introduction discusses aspects of Greek and medieval mathematics: Euclid, texts, commentators, etc. Paralleling the text is an elaborate critical exposition analyzing each definition, proposition, postulate, etc., and covering textual matters, mathematical analyses, refutations, extensions, etc. Unabridged reproduction of the Cambridge 2nd edition. 3 volumes. Total of 995 figures, 1426pp. 5⅜ x 8.   S88, 89, 90 — 3 vol. set, Paperbound **$6.00**

*THE GEOMETRY OF RENE DESCARTES. The great work which founded analytic geometry. The renowned Smith-Latham translation faced with the original French text containing all of Descartes' own diagrams! Contains: Problems the Construction of Which Requires Only Straight Lines and Circles; On the Nature of Curved Lines; On the Construction of Solid or Supersolid Problems. Notes. Diagrams. 258pp.   S68 Paperbound **$1.50**

*A PHILOSOPHICAL ESSAY ON PROBABILITIES, P. Laplace. Without recourse to any mathematics above grammar school, Laplace develops a philosophically, mathematically and historically classical exposition of the nature of probability: its functions and limitations, operations in practical affairs, calculations in games of chance, insurance, government, astronomy, and countless other fields. New introduction by E. T. Bell. viii + 196pp. S166 Paperbound **$1.35**

DE RE METALLICA, Georgius Agricola. Written over 400 years ago, for 200 years the most authoritative first-hand account of the production of metals, translated in 1912 by former President Herbert Hoover and his wife, and today still one of the most beautiful and fascinating volumes ever produced in the history of science! 12 books, exhaustively annotated, give a wonderfully lucid and vivid picture of the history of mining, selection of sites, types of deposits, excavating pits, sinking shafts, ventilating, pumps, crushing machinery, assaying, smelting, refining metals, making salt, alum, nitre, glass, and many other topics. This definitive edition contains all 289 of the 16th century woodcuts which made the original an artistic masterpiece. It makes a superb gift for geologists, engineers, libraries, artists, historians, and everyone interested in science and early illustrative art. Biographical, historical introductions. Bibliography, survey of ancient authors. Indices. 289 illustrations. 672pp. 6¾ x 10¾. Deluxe library edition.   S6 Clothbound **$10.00**

GEOGRAPHICAL ESSAYS, W. M. Davis. Modern geography and geomorphology rest on the fundamental work of this scientist. His new concepts of earth-processes revolutionized science and his broad interpretation of the scope of geography created a deeper understanding of the interrelation of the landscape and the forces that mold it. This first inexpensive unabridged edition covers theory of geography, methods of advanced geographic teaching, descriptions of geographic areas, analyses of land-shaping processes, and much besides. Not only a factual and historical classic, it is still widely read for its reflections of modern scientific thought. Introduction. 130 figures. Index. vi + 777pp. 5⅜ x 8.
S383 Paperbound **$2.95**

CHARLES BABBAGE AND HIS CALCULATING ENGINES, edited by P. Morrison and E. Morrison. Friend of Darwin, Humboldt, and Laplace, Babbage was a leading pioneer in large-scale mathematical machines and a prophetic herald of modern operational research—true father of Harvard's relay computer Mark I. His Difference Engine and Analytical Engine were the first successful machines in the field. This volume contains a valuable introduction on his life and work; major excerpts from his fascinating autobiography, revealing his eccentric and unusual personality; and extensive selections from "Babbage's Calculating Engines," a compilation of hard-to-find journal articles, both by Babbage and by such eminent contributors as the Countess of Lovelace, L. F. Menabrea, and Dionysius Lardner. 11 illustrations. Appendix of miscellaneous papers. Index. Bibliography. xxxviii + 400pp. 5⅜ x 8.   T12 Paperbound **$2.00**

*THE WORKS OF ARCHIMEDES WITH THE METHOD OF ARCHIMEDES, edited by T. L. Heath. All the known works of the greatest mathematician of antiquity including the recently discovered METHOD OF ARCHIMEDES. This last is the only work we have which shows exactly how early mathematicians discovered their proofs before setting them down in their final perfection. A 186 page study by the eminent scholar Heath discusses Archimedes and the history of Greek mathematics. Bibliography. 563pp. 5⅜ x 8.   S9 Paperbound **$2.00**

Nature, Biology, Medicine

NATURE RECREATION: Group Guidance for the Out-of-doors, William Gould Vinal. Intended for both the uninitiated nature instructor and the education student on the college level, this complete "how-to" program surveys the entire area of nature education for the young. Philosophy of nature recreation; requirements, responsibilities, important information for group leaders; nature games; suggested group projects; conducting meetings and getting discussions started; etc. Scores of immediately applicable teaching aids, plus completely updated sources of information, pamphlets, field guides, recordings, etc. Bibliography. 74 photographs. + 310pp. 5⅜ x 8½. **T1015 Paperbound $1.75**

HOW TO KNOW THE WILD FLOWERS, Mrs. William Starr Dana. Classic nature book that has introduced thousands to wonders of American wild flowers. Color-season principle of organization is easy to use, even by those with no botanical training, and the genial, refreshing discussions of history, folklore, uses of over 1,000 native and escape flowers, foliage plants are informative as well as fun to read. Over 170 full-page plates, collected from several editions, may be colored in to make permanent records of finds. Revised to conform with 1950 edition of Gray's Manual of Botany. xlii + 438pp. 5⅜ x 8½. **T332 Paperbound $1.85**

HOW TO KNOW THE FERNS, F. T. Parsons. Ferns, among our most lovely native plants, are all too little known. This classic of nature lore will enable the layman to identify almost any American fern he may come across. After an introduction on the structure and life of ferns, the 57 most important ferns are fully pictured and described (arranged upon a simple identification key). Index of Latin and English names. 61 illustrations and 42 full-page plates. xiv + 215pp. 5⅜ x 8. **T740 Paperbound $1.25**

MANUAL OF THE TREES OF NORTH AMERICA, Charles Sprague Sargent. Still unsurpassed as most comprehensive, reliable study of North American tree characteristics, precise locations and distribution. By dean of American dendrologists. Every tree native to U.S., Canada, Alaska, 185 genera, 717 species, described in detail—leaves, flowers, fruit, winterbuds, bark, wood, growth habits etc. plus discussion of varieties and local variants, immaturity variations. Over 100 keys, including unusual 11-page analytical key to genera, aid in identification. 783 clear illustrations of flowers, fruit, leaves. An unmatched permanent reference work for all nature lovers. Second enlarged (1926) edition. Synopsis of families. Analytical key to genera. Glossary of technical terms. Index. 783 illustrations, 1 map. Two volumes. Total of 982pp. 5⅜ x 8.   **T277 Vol. I Paperbound $2.00**
T278 Vol. II Paperbound $2.00
The set $4.00

TREES OF THE EASTERN AND CENTRAL UNITED STATES AND CANADA, W. M. Harlow. A revised edition of a standard middle-level guide to native trees and important escapes. More than 140 trees are described in detail, and illustrated with more than 600 drawings and photographs. Supplementary keys will enable the careful reader to identify almost any tree he might encounter. xiii + 288pp. 5⅜ x 8. **T395 Paperbound $1.35**

GUIDE TO SOUTHERN TREES, Ellwood S. Harrar and J. George Harrar. All the essential information about trees indigenous to the South, in an extremely handy format. Introductory essay on methods of tree classification and study, nomenclature, chief divisions of Southern trees, etc. Approximately 100 keys and synopses allow for swift, accurate identification of trees. Numerous excellent illustrations, non-technical text make this a useful book for teachers of biology or natural science, nature lovers, amateur naturalists. Revised 1962 edition. Index. Bibliography. Glossary of technical terms. 920 illustrations; 201 full-page plates. ix + 709pp. 4⅝ x 6⅜. **T945 Paperbound $2.25**

FRUIT KEY AND TWIG KEY TO TREES AND SHRUBS, W. M. Harlow. Bound together in one volume for the first time, these handy and accurate keys to fruit and twig identification are the only guides of their sort with photographs (up to 3 times natural size). "Fruit Key": Key to over 120 different deciduous and evergreen fruits. 139 photographs and 11 line drawings. Synoptic summary of fruit types. Bibliography. 2 Indexes (common and scientific names). "Twig Key": Key to over 160 different twigs and buds. 173 photographs. Glossary of technical terms. Bibliography. 2 Indexes (common and scientific names). Two volumes bound as one. Total of xvii + 126pp. 5⅝ x 8⅜. **T511 Paperbound $1.25**

INSECT LIFE AND INSECT NATURAL HISTORY, S. W. Frost. A work emphasizing habits, social life, and ecological relations of insects, rather than more academic aspects of classification and morphology. Prof. Frost's enthusiasm and knowledge are everywhere evident as he discusses insect associations and specialized habits like leaf-rolling, leaf-mining, and case-making, the gall insects, the boring insects, aquatic insects, etc. He examines all sorts of matters not usually covered in general works, such as: insects as human food, insect music and musicians, insect response to electric and radio waves, use of insects in art and literature. The admirably executed purpose of this book, which covers the middle ground between elementary treatment and scholarly monographs, is to excite the reader to observe for himself. Over 700 illustrations. Extensive bibliography. x + 524pp. 5⅜ x 8. **T517 Paperbound $2.45**

AMERICAN WILDLIFE AND PLANTS: A GUIDE TO WILDLIFE FOOD HABITS, Alexander C. Martin, Herbert S. Zim, and Arnold L. Nelson. A tremendous amount of material from 25 years of concentrated researches by U.S. Fish and Wildlife Service is collected, correlated, condensed into this 500-page volume. Learn of food, feeding habits of more than 1,000 species of U.S. mammals, birds, fish, their distribution and migratory habits, the most important plant-animal relationships. Last third of book devoted to all genera of plants that furnish food to American wildlife. ". . . should prove a classic in its field and a must for every naturalist," Harold E. Anthony, NATURAL HISTORY. Republication of first (1951) edition. Index. Hundreds of illustrations, tables, range maps, etc. ix + 500pp. 5⅜ x 8.   T793 Paperbound **$2.25**

RACING PIGEONS, C. Osman. A complete, practical, up-to-date, and authoritative book on racing pigeons by a British expert. Covers the anatomy of the pigeon, the homing instinct, the pigeon's life cycle, food and feeding, lofts and aviaries, breeding winners, preparing for races, winning systems, common diseases, and much more. Indispensable for beginner and expert alike. 24 photographs by the author. 10 line drawings. Index. 192pp. 5⅛ x 7⅛.
T513 Clothbound **$3.00**

ANTONY VAN LEEUWENHOEK AND HIS "LITTLE ANIMALS," selected, translated, and edited from his printed works, unpublished manuscripts, contemporary records by Clifford Dobell. 100-page biographical study of the first microbiologist, bacteriologist, micrologist. 4 chapters of the papers that founded protozoology, bacteriology, with many of Leeuwenhoek's illustrative drawings, observations and letters to Royal Society, discussion of Leeuwenhoek's name, language, dwelling, draughtsmen, method, microscope bring to life an excited, naive, completely self-taught genius. 25 years of research went into its compilation by a Fellow of the Royal Society. More than an important book for students and workers in the sciences, it may also be read with pleasure by anyone interested in meeting one of the most interesting and remarkable men in history of science. 32 illustrations. Bibliography of over 400 items. Index. vii + 435pp. 5⅜ x 8.   S594 Paperbound **$2.25**

MICROGRAPHIA, Robert Hooke. Hooke, 17th-century British universal genius, was a major pioneer in celestial mechanics, optics, gravity, and many other fields, but his greatest contribution was this book, now reprinted in its entirety from the original 1655 edition, which gave microscopy its first great impetus. With all the freshness of discovery, he describes his microscope, and his observations of cork, the edge of a razor, insects' eyes, fabrics, and dozens of other objects. 38 plates, full-size or larger, contain all the original illustrations. A fundamental classic in the fields of combustion and heat theory, light and color theory, botany and zoology, hygrometry, and many others. Contains such farsighted predictions as the famous anticipation of artificial silk. Final section is concerned with Hooke's observations of the moon and stars. 348pp. 5⅜ x 8½.   T8 Paperbound **$2.00**

THE AUTOBIOGRAPHY OF CHARLES DARWIN AND SELECTED LETTERS, edited by Francis Darwin. The personal record of the professional and private life of the author of "Origin of Species," whose ideas have shaped our thinking as have few others. His early life; the historic voyage aboard the "Beagle"; the furor surrounding evolution and his replies; revealing anecdotes; reminiscences by his son; letters to Henslow, Lyell, Hooker, Huxley, Wallace, Kingsley, and others; his thought on religion and vivisection. Appendix. Index. 365pp. 5⅜ x 8.
T479 Paperbound **$1.65**

THE MALAY ARCHIPELAGO, Alfred Russel Wallace. A great classic of natural history and travel. The observations of one of the founders of modern biology whose work also provides foundation for scientific study of botany and zoology in many parts of the world. Based on 8 years' personal exploration. Descriptions of the island groupings and peoples, accounts of abundant, strange animals, startling birds and insects—many previously unknown—on either side of the Wallace line, dividing animal life into Indian on the West and Australian on the East and named for the author. Unrivalled travel experience, packed full of intellectual excitement, infectious enthusiasm, this will arouse the empathy of any lay reader interested in strange places and new theories. 62 drawings and maps. Three appendices on crania, 59 languages, and vocabularies. Index. xvii + 515pp. 5⅜ x 8½.
T187 Paperbound **$2.00**

STUDIES ON THE STRUCTURE AND DEVELOPMENT OF VERTEBRATES, Edwin S. Goodrich. This definitive study by the greatest modern comparative anatomist covers the skeleton, fins and limbs, head region morphology, skull, skeletal visceral arches and labial cartilages, middle ear and ear ossicles, visceral clefts and gills, subdivisions of body cavity, vascular, respiratory, excretory, and peripheral nervous systems of vertebrates from fish to the higher mammals. 754 pictures. 69 page biographical study by C. C. Hardy. Bibliography of 1186 references. "For many a day this will certainly be the standard textbook," Journal of Anatomy. Index. Two volumes total 906pp. 5⅜ x 8.   2 volume set S449-50 Paperbound **$5.00**

FINGER PRINTS, PALMS AND SOLES: AN INTRODUCTION TO DERMATOGLYPHICS, Harold Cummins and Charles Midlo. One of the most fascinating of sciences receives careful, thorough treatment. Primitive knowledge of dermatoglyphics; early investigators; fundamental patterns and pattern types; technical methods of classification, identification. Detailed, unique descriptions of uses: identification of twins; paternity cases; racial variation; genetic process; relation of prints to body measurement, criminality and character, blood groups, handedness. New chapter adds information on identification in action, with accounts of criminal cases in which prints played major role. 2nd enlarged edition. 149 figures. 49 tables. 361-item bibliography. Index. xii + 319pp. 5⅝ x 8⅜.   T778 Paperbound **$1.95**

HEREDITY AND YOUR LIFE, A. M. Winchester. Authoritative, concise explanation of human genetics, in non-technical terms. What factors determine characteristics of future generations, how they may be altered, history of genetics, application of knowledge to control health, intelligence, number of entire populations. Physiology of reproduction, chromosomes, genes, blood types, Rh factor, dominant, recessive traits, birth by proxy, sexual abnormalities, radiation, much more. Index. 75 illus. 345pp. 5⅜ x 8. **T598 Paperbound $1.50**

THE ORIGIN OF LIFE, A. I. Oparin. This is the first modern statement of the theory that life evolved from complex nitro-carbon compounds. A historical introduction covers theories of the origin of life from the Greeks to modern times and then the techniques of biochemistry as applied to the problem by Dr. Oparin. The exposition presupposes a knowledge of chemistry but can be read with profit by everyone interested in this absorbing question. "Easily the most scholarly authority on the question," NEW YORK TIMES. Bibliography. Index. xxv + 270pp. 5⅜ x 8. **T213 Paperbound $1.75**

SOURCE BOOK OF MEDICAL HISTORY, edited by Logan Clendening. Chronological compilation of the most significant medical writings of 4000 years, carefully edited to save reading time, isolate important contributions. 124 selections by 120 authors, each with introduction, short biography. Covers every area of medical thought and practice: Hippocrates, Galen, Vesalius, Malpighi, Pasteur, Florence Nightingale, Walter Reed, Lavoisier, Leeuwenhoek, Parkinson, Beaumont, many more. Includes selections from non-medical literature to show lay view of medicine through the ages. Will give anyone interested in medicine, regardless of reason, an immediate, dramatic view of its growth and development. 124 papers. Classified bibliographies. Index. xiv + 685pp. 5⅜ x 8. **T621 Paperbound $2.75**

CLASSICS OF CARDIOLOGY, F. A. Willius, T. E. Keys. Monumental collection of 52 papers by great researchers, physicians on the anatomy, physiology and pathology of the heart and the circulation, and the diagnosis and therapy of their diseases. These are the original writings of Harvey, Sénac, Auenbrugger, Withering, Stokes, Einthoven, Osler, and 44 others from 1628 to 1912. 27 of the papers are complete, the rest in major excerpts; all are in English. The biographical notes and introductory essays make this a full history of cardiology—with exclusively first-hand material. 103 portraits, diagrams, and facsimiles of title pages. Chronological table. Total of xx + 858pp. 5⅝ x 8⅜. Two volume set. **T912 Vol I Paper bound $2.00**
T913 Vol II Paperbound $2.00
The set $4.00

A WAY OF LIFE, by Sir William Osler. An inspirational classic that has helped countless business and professional men since the beloved physician and philosopher first delivered it at Yale in 1913. In warm human terms Osler tells how he managed to make the most of every day by an edifying mental and physical regimen. Illustrated. **FREE**

INTRODUCTION TO THE STUDY OF EXPERIMENTAL MEDICINE, Claude Bernard. The only major work of Claude Bernard now available in English, this classic records Bernard's efforts to transform physiology into an exact science. He examines the roles of chance and error and incorrect hypothesis in leading to scientific truth and describes many classic experiments on the action of curare, carbon monoxide, and other poisons, the functions of the pancreas, the glycogenic function of the liver, and many others. Introduction. Foreword by I. B. Cohen. xxv + 266pp. 5⅜ x 8. **T400 Paperbound $1.50**

A WAY OF LIFE AND OTHER SELECTED WRITINGS, Sir William Osler. Physician and humanist, Osler writes brilliantly on philosophy, religion, and literature in "The Student Life," "Books and Men," "Creators, Transmuters, and Transmitters," "The Old Humanities and the New Science," and the title essay. His medical history is equally acute in discussions of Thomas Browne, Gui Patin, Robert Burton, Michael Servetus, William Beaumont, Laënnec. 5 more of his best essays. 5 photographs. Introduction by G. L. Keynes, M.D., F.R.C.S. Index. xx + 278pp. 5⅜ x 8. **T488 Paperbound $1.50**

FROM MAGIC TO SCIENCE, Charles Singer. Great historian of science examines aspects of medical science from the Roman Empire through the Renaissance. Especially valuable are the sections on early herbals, probably the best coverage of this subject available, and on "The Visions of Hildegarde of Bingen" which are explained by physiological means. Also covered are Arabian and Galenic influences, astrology, the Sphere of Pythagoras, Leonardo da Vinci, Vesalius, Paracelsus, et al. Frequent quotations and translations. New introduction by the author. New unabridged, corrected edition. 158 unusual illustrations from classical and medieval sources. Index. xxvii + 365pp. 5⅜ x 8. **T390 Paperbound $2.00**

A SHORT HISTORY OF ANATOMY AND PHYSIOLOGY FROM THE GREEKS TO HARVEY, C. Singer. An intermediate history formerly entitled THE EVOLUTION OF ANATOMY, this work conveys the thrill of discovery as the nature of the human body is gradually clarified by hundreds of scientists from the Greeks to the Renaissance. Diogenes, Hippocrates, and other early workers, up to Leonardo da Vinci, Vesalius, Harvey, and others, with 139 illustrations from medieval manuscripts, classical sculpture, etc. Index. 221pp. 5⅜ x 8. **T389 Paperbound $1.75**

Psychology

YOGA: A SCIENTIFIC EVALUATION, Kovoor T. Behanan. A complete reprinting of the book that for the first time gave Western readers a sane, scientific explanation and analysis of yoga. The author draws on controlled laboratory experiments and personal records of a year as a disciple of a yoga, to investigate yoga psychology, concepts of knowledge, physiology, "supernatural" phenomena, and the ability to tap the deepest human powers. In this study under the auspices of Yale University Institute of Human Relations, the strictest principles of physiological and psychological inquiry are followed throughout. Foreword by W. A. Miles, Yale University. 17 photographs. Glossary. Index. xx + 270pp. 5⅜ x 8. T505 Paperbound **$1.75**

CONDITIONED REFLEXES: AN INVESTIGATION OF THE PHYSIOLOGICAL ACTIVITIES OF THE CEREBRAL CORTEX, I. P. Pavlov. Full, authorized translation of Pavlov's own survey of his work in experimental psychology reviews entire course of experiments, summarizes conclusions, outlines psychological system based on famous "conditioned reflex" concept. Details of technical means used in experiments, observations on formation of conditioned reflexes, function of cerebral hemispheres, results of damage, nature of sleep, typology of nervous system, significance of experiments for human psychology. Trans. by Dr. G. V. Anrep, Cambridge Univ. 235-item bibliography. 18 figures. 445pp. 5⅜ x 8.   S614 Paperbound **$2.25**

EXPLANATION OF HUMAN BEHAVIOUR, F. V. Smith. A major intermediate-level introduction to and criticism of 8 complete systems of the psychology of human behavior, with unusual emphasis on theory of investigation and methodology. Part I is an illuminating analysis of the problems involved in the explanation of observed phenomena, and the differing viewpoints on the nature of causality. Parts II and III are a closely detailed survey of the systems of McDougall, Gordon Allport, Lewin, the Gestalt group, Freud, Watson, Hull, and Tolman. Biographical notes. Bibliography of over 800 items. 2 Indexes. 38 figures. xii + 460pp. 5½ x 8¾.
T253 Clothbound **$6.00**

SEX IN PSYCHO-ANALYSIS (formerly CONTRIBUTIONS TO PSYCHO-ANALYSIS), S. Ferenczi. Written by an associate of Freud, this volume presents countless insights on such topics as impotence, transference, analysis and children, dreams, symbols, obscene words, masturbation and male homosexuality, paranoia and psycho-analysis, the sense of reality, hypnotism and therapy, and many others. Also includes full text of THE DEVELOPMENT OF PSYCHO-ANALYSIS by Ferenczi and Otto Rank. Two books bound as one. Total of 406pp. 5⅜ x 8.
T324 Paperbound **$1.85**

BEYOND PSYCHOLOGY, Otto Rank. One of Rank's most mature contributions, focussing on the irrational basis of human behavior as a basic fact of our lives. The psychoanalytic techniques of myth analysis trace to their source the ultimates of human existence: fear of death, personality, the social organization, the need for love and creativity, etc. Dr. Rank finds them stemming from a common irrational source, man's fear of final destruction. A seminal work in modern psychology, this work sheds light on areas ranging from the concept of immortal soul to the sources of state power. 291pp. 5⅜ x 8.   T485 Paperbound **$2.00**

ILLUSIONS AND DELUSIONS OF THE SUPERNATURAL AND THE OCCULT, D. H. Rawcliffe. Holds up to rational examination hundreds of persistent delusions including crystal gazing, automatic writing, table turning, mediumistic trances, mental healing, stigmata, lycanthropy, live burial, the Indian Rope Trick, spiritualism, dowsing, telepathy, clairvoyance, ghosts, ESP, etc. The author explains and exposes the mental and physical deceptions involved, making this not only an exposé of supernatural phenomena, but a valuable exposition of characteristic types of abnormal psychology. Originally titled "The Psychology of the Occult." 14 illustrations. Index. 551pp. 5⅜ x 8.   T503 Paperbound **$2.00**

THE PRINCIPLES OF PSYCHOLOGY, William James. The full long-course, unabridged, of one of the great classics of Western literature and science. Wonderfully lucid descriptions of human mental activity, the stream of thought, consciousness, time perception, memory, imagination, emotions, reason, abnormal phenomena, and similar topics. Original contributions are integrated with the work of such men as Berkeley, Binet, Mills, Darwin, Hume, Kant, Royce, Schopenhauer, Spinoza, Locke, Descartes, Galton, Wundt, Lotze, Herbart, Fechner, and scores of others. All contrasting interpretations of mental phenomena are examined in detail — introspective analysis, philosophical interpretation, and experimental research. "A classic," JOURNAL OF CONSULTING PSYCHOLOGY. "The main lines are as valid as ever," PSYCHO-ANALYTICAL QUARTERLY. "Standard reading . . . a classic of interpretation," PSYCHIATRIC QUARTERLY. 94 illustrations. 1408pp. 2 volumes. 5⅜ x 8.   Vol. 1, T381 Paperbound **$2.50**
Vol. 2, T382 Paperbound **$2.50**

THE DYNAMICS OF THERAPY IN A CONTROLLED RELATIONSHIP, Jessie Taft. One of the most important works in literature of child psychology, out of print for 25 years. Outstanding disciple of Rank describes all aspects of relationship or Rankian therapy through concise, simple elucidation of theory underlying her actual contacts with two seven-year olds. Therapists, social caseworkers, psychologists, counselors, and laymen who work with children will all find this important work an invaluable summation of method, theory of child psychology. xix + 296pp. 5⅜ x 8.   T325 Paperbound **$1.75**

Puzzles, Mathematical Recreations

SYMBOLIC LOGIC and THE GAME OF LOGIC, Lewis Carroll. "Symbolic Logic" is not concerned with modern symbolic logic, but is instead a collection of over 380 problems posed with charm and imagination, using the syllogism, and a fascinating diagrammatic method of drawing conclusions. In "The Game of Logic" Carroll's whimsical imagination devises a logical game played with 2 diagrams and counters (included) to manipulate hundreds of tricky syllogisms. The final section, "Hit or Miss" is a lagniappe of 101 additional puzzles in the delightful Carroll manner. Until this reprint edition, both of these books were rarities costing up to $15 each. Symbolic Logic: Index. xxxi + 199pp. The Game of Logic: 96pp. 2 vols. bound as one. 5⅜ x 8.   **T492 Paperbound $1.50**

PILLOW PROBLEMS and A TANGLED TALE, Lewis Carroll. One of the rarest of all Carroll's works, "Pillow Problems" contains 72 original math puzzles, all typically ingenious. Particularly fascinating are Carroll's answers which remain exactly as he thought them out, reflecting his actual mental process. The problems in "A Tangled Tale" are in story form, originally appearing as a monthly magazine serial. Carroll not only gives the solutions, but uses answers sent in by readers to discuss wrong approaches and misleading paths, and grades them for insight. Both of these books were rarities until this edition, "Pillow Problems" costing up to $25, and "A Tangled Tale" $15. Pillow Problems: Preface and Introduction by Lewis Carroll. xx + 109pp. A Tangled Tale: 6 illustrations. 152pp. Two vols. bound as one. 5⅜ x 8.   **T493 Paperbound $1.50**

AMUSEMENTS IN MATHEMATICS, Henry Ernest Dudeney. The foremost British originator of mathematical puzzles is always intriguing, witty, and paradoxical in this classic, one of the largest collections of mathematical amusements. More than 430 puzzles, problems, and paradoxes. Mazes and games, problems on number manipulation, unicursal and other route problems, puzzles on measuring, weighing, packing, age, kinship, chessboards, joiners', crossing river, plane figure dissection, and many others. Solutions. More than 450 illustrations. vii + 258pp. 5⅜ x 8.   **T473 Paperbound $1.25**

THE CANTERBURY PUZZLES, Henry Dudeney. Chaucer's pilgrims set one another problems in story form. Also Adventures of the Puzzle Club, the Strange Escape of the King's Jester, the Monks of Riddlewell, the Squire's Christmas Puzzle Party, and others. All puzzles are original, based on dissecting plane figures, arithmetic, algebra, elementary calculus and other branches of mathematics, and purely logical ingenuity. "The limit of ingenuity and intricacy," The Observer. Over 110 puzzles. Full Solutions. 150 illustrations. vii + 225pp. 5⅜ x 8.   **T474 Paperbound $1.25**

MATHEMATICAL EXCURSIONS, H. A. Merrill. Even if you hardly remember your high school math, you'll enjoy the 90 stimulating problems contained in this book and you will come to understand a great many mathematical principles with surprisingly little effort. Many useful shortcuts and diversions not generally known are included: division by inspection, Russian peasant multiplication, memory systems for pi, building odd and even magic squares, square roots by geometry, dyadic systems, and many more. Solutions to difficult problems. 50 illustrations. 145pp. 5⅜ x 8.   **T350 Paperbound $1.00**

MAGIC SQUARES AND CUBES, W. S. Andrews. Only book-length treatment in English, a thorough non-technical description and analysis. Here are nasik, overlapping, pandiagonal, serrated squares; magic circles, cubes, spheres, rhombuses. Try your hand at 4-dimensional magical figures! Much unusual folklore and tradition included. High school algebra is sufficient. 754 diagrams and illustrations. viii + 419pp. 5⅜ x 8.   **T658 Paperbound $1.85**

CALIBAN'S PROBLEM BOOK: MATHEMATICAL, INFERENTIAL AND CRYPTOGRAPHIC PUZZLES, H. Phillips (Caliban), S. T. Shovelton, G. S. Marshall. 105 ingenious problems by the greatest living creator of puzzles based on logic and inference. Rigorous, modern, piquant; reflecting their author's unusual personality, these intermediate and advanced puzzles all involve the ability to reason clearly through complex situations; some call for mathematical knowledge, ranging from algebra to number theory. Solutions. xi + 180pp. 5⅜ x 8.   **T736 Paperbound $1.25**

MATHEMATICAL PUZZLES FOR BEGINNERS AND ENTHUSIASTS, G. Mott-Smith. 188 mathematical puzzles based on algebra, dissection of plane figures, permutations, and probability, that will test and improve your powers of inference and interpretation. The Odic Force, The Spider's Cousin, Ellipse Drawing, theory and strategy of card and board games like tit-tat-toe, go moku, salvo, and many others. 100 pages of detailed mathematical explanations. Appendix of primes, square roots, etc. 135 illustrations. 2nd revised edition. 248pp. 5⅜ x 8.   **T198 Paperbound $1.00**

MATHEMAGIC, MAGIC PUZZLES, AND GAMES WITH NUMBERS, R. V. Heath. More than 60 new puzzles and stunts based on the properties of numbers. Easy techniques for multiplying large numbers mentally, revealing hidden numbers magically, finding the date of any day in any year, and dozens more. Over 30 pages devoted to magic squares, triangles, cubes, circles, etc. Edited by J. S. Meyer. 76 illustrations. 128pp. 5⅜ x 8.   **T110 Paperbound $1.00**

MATHEMATICAL RECREATIONS, M. Kraitchik. One of the most thorough compilations of unusual mathematical problems for beginners and advanced mathematicians. Historical problems from Greek, Medieval, Arabic, Hindu sources. 50 pages devoted to pastimes derived from figurate numbers, Mersenne numbers, Fermat numbers, primes and probability. 40 pages of magic, Euler, Latin, panmagic squares. 25 new positional and permutational games of permanent value: fairy chess, latruncles, reversi, jinx, ruma, lasca, tricolor, tetrachrome, etc. Complete rigorous solutions. Revised second edition. 181 illustrations. 333pp. 5⅜ x 8.
T163 Paperbound **$1.75**

MATHEMATICAL PUZZLES OF SAM LOYD, selected and edited by M. Gardner. Choice puzzles by the greatest American puzzle creator and innovator. Selected from his famous collection, "Cyclopedia of Puzzles," they retain the unique style and historical flavor of the originals. There are posers based on arithmetic, algebra, probability, game theory, route tracing, topology, counter, sliding block, operations research, geometrical dissection. Includes the famous "14-15" puzzle which was a national craze, and his "Horse of a Different Color" which sold millions of copies. 117 of his most ingenious puzzles in all, 120 line drawings and diagrams. Solutions. Selected references. xx + 167pp. 5⅜ x 8. T498 Paperbound **$1.00**

MATHEMATICAL PUZZLES OF SAM LOYD, Vol. II, selected and edited by Martin Gardner. The outstanding 2nd selection from the great American innovator's "Cyclopedia of Puzzles": speed and distance problems, clock problems, plane and solid geometry, calculus problems, etc. Analytical table of contents that groups the puzzles according to the type of mathematics necessary to solve them. 166 puzzles, 150 original line drawings and diagrams. Selected references. xiv + 177pp. 5⅜ x 8.
T709 Paperbound **$1.00**

ARITHMETICAL EXCURSIONS: AN ENRICHMENT OF ELEMENTARY MATHEMATICS, H. Bowers and J. Bowers. A lively and lighthearted collection of facts and entertainments for anyone who enjoys manipulating numbers or solving arithmetical puzzles: methods of arithmetic never taught in school, little-known facts about the most simple numbers, and clear explanations of more sophisticated topics; mysteries and folklore of numbers, the "Hin-dog-abic" number system, etc. First publication. Index. 529 numbered problems and diversions, all with answers. Bibliography. 60 figures. xiv + 320pp. 5⅜ x 8.
T770 Paperbound **$1.65**

CRYPTANALYSIS, H. F. Gaines. Formerly entitled ELEMENTARY CRYPTANALYSIS, this introductory-intermediate level text is the best book in print on cryptograms and their solution. It covers all major techniques of the past, and contains much that is not generally known except to experts. Full details about concealment, substitution, and transposition ciphers; periodic mixed alphabets, multafid, Kasiski and Vigenere methods, Ohaver patterns, Playfair, and scores of other topics. 6 language letter and word frequency appendix. 167 problems, now furnished with solutions. Index. 173 figures. vi + 230pp. 5⅜ x 8.
T97 Paperbound **$1.95**

CRYPTOGRAPHY, L. D. Smith. An excellent introductory work on ciphers and their solution, the history of secret writing, and actual methods and problems in such techniques as transposition and substitution. Appendices describe the enciphering of Japanese, the Baconian biliteral cipher, and contain frequency tables and a bibliography for further study. Over 150 problems with solutions. 160pp. 5⅜ x 8. T247 Paperbound **$1.00**

PUZZLE QUIZ AND STUNT FUN, J. Meyer. The solution to party doldrums. 238 challenging puzzles, stunts and tricks. Mathematical puzzles like The Clever Carpenter, Atom Bomb; mysteries and deductions like The Bridge of Sighs, The Nine Pearls, Dog Logic; observation puzzles like Cigarette Smokers, Telephone Dial; over 200 others including magic squares, tongue twisters, puns, anagrams, and many others. All problems solved fully. 250pp. 5⅜ x 8.
T337 Paperbound **$1.00**

101 PUZZLES IN THOUGHT AND LOGIC, C. R. Wylie, Jr. Brand new problems you need no special knowledge to solve! Take the kinks out of your mental "muscles" and enjoy solving murder problems, the detection of lying fishermen, the logical identification of color by a blindman, and dozens more. Introduction with simplified explanation of general scientific method and puzzle solving. 128pp. 5⅜ x 8. T367 Paperbound **$1.00**

MY BEST PROBLEMS IN MATHEMATICS, Hubert Phillips ("Caliban"). Only elementary mathematics needed to solve these 100 witty, catchy problems by a master problem creator. Problems on the odds in cards and dice, problems in geometry, algebra, permutations, even problems that require no math at all—just a logical mind, clear thinking. Solutions completely worked out. If you enjoy mysteries, alerting your perceptive powers and exercising your detective's eye, you'll find these cryptic puzzles a challenging delight. Original 1961 publication. 100 puzzles, solutions. x + 107pp. 5⅝ x 8. T91 Paperbound **$1.00**

MY BEST PUZZLES IN LOGIC AND REASONING, Hubert Phillips ("Caliban"). A new collection of 100 inferential and logical puzzles chosen from the best that have appeared in England, available for first time in U.S. By the most endlessly resourceful puzzle creator now living. All data presented are both necessary and sufficient to allow a single unambiguous answer. No special knowledge is required for problems ranging from relatively simple to completely original one-of-a-kinds. Guaranteed to please beginners and experts of all ages. Original publication. 100 puzzles, full solutions. x + 107pp. 5⅜ x 8. T119 Paperbound **$1.00**